The Elements of Mathematical Logic

PAUL C. ROSENBLOOM

ASSOCIATE PROFESSOR, DEPARTMENT OF MATHEMATICS,
SYRACUSE UNIVERSITY

1950

DOVER PUBLICATIONS, INC.

THE DOVER SERIES IN MATHEMATICS AND PHYSICS

W. PRAGER, *Consulting Editor*

First Edition

Printed & Bound in the United States of America

PREFACE

This book is intended for readers who, while mature mathematically, have no knowledge of mathematical logic. We attempt to introduce the reader to the most important approaches to the subject, and, wherever possible within the limitations of space which we have set for ourselves, to give at least a few nontrivial results illustrating each of the important methods for attacking logical problems. Since Lewis' SURVEY OF SYMBOLIC LOGIC and Jørgensen's TREATISE ON FORMAL LOGIC, both of which are now obsolete, the only work of this nature has been the excellent book of Church, which is not suitable for beginners and which is not easily accessible. Thus the present book differs from those which confine themselves to the detailed development of one particular system of formal logic. We have emphasized instead the modern tendency of analyzing the structure of a system as a whole. We feel that too many authors in this field have overlooked the necessity of exhibiting the power of logical methods in non-trivial problems. Otherwise mathematical logic is a mere shorthand for transcribing results obtained without its aid, not a tool for research and discovery.

Thus in the chapter on the logic of classes we have a section on the structure and representation of Boolean algebras, which is applied in the next chapter to the study of deductive systems. In the third chapter we sketch the methods of Russell, Quine, Zermelo, Curry, and Church for the construction of logics of propositional functions. Finally, we give a brief introduction to the general syntax of language, with applications to undecidability and incompleteness theorems.

We have attempted to make the exposition as elementary as possible throughout. Nevertheless, those who are unfamiliar with modern algebra may find it advisable to skip the proofs in Chapter I, Section 3, on the first reading.

In the last chapter we use the profound and beautiful ideas of Post. We hope that one by-product of this book will be a more widespread recognition and appreciation of his work, which amounts to the creation of a new branch of mathematics of the same fundamental importance as algebra and topology.

The connoisseur may find of some interest (1) the insistence on the demonstrable properties of a formal system as a criterion for its acceptability, (2) the simple proof of the completeness of the theory of combinators,* (3) the simple explicit example of a recursively unsolvable problem in elementary number theory, (4) the first connected exposition of all the essential steps in the proof of Church's theorem on the recursive unsolvability of the decision problem for the restricted function calculus.

Much of the material was presented in a course given by the author at Lund University, Sweden, in the spring of 1948.

It is impossible for me to express adequately my debt to the late Professor H. B. Smith for his constant kindness and generosity. I am grateful to Professors Churchman, Post, Curry, McKinsey, Huntington, and Stone for their friendly encouragement when I was beginning my mathematical career. I cannot refrain from also thanking Professors Cohen and Nagel, since it was a misinterpretation of a footnote in their book which led me to abandon chemistry for mathematics twelve years ago! I thank Dover Publications, Inc. for its unfailing courtesy and helpfulness during the preparation of this book. Finally, I should like to express my gratitude to my beloved wife, Elly, for providing the stimulus and the working conditions without which the book could not have been written.

October 11, 1949

PAUL C. ROSENBLOOM
Syracuse, New York

*Curry has arrived independently at essentially the same simplification of the theory of combinators. This appeared since the above was written in Synthèse, Vol. VII, 1948–49, No. 6-A, p. 391–398.

CONTENTS

INTRODUCTION

In this book we shall study the laws of logic by mathematical methods. This may seem unfair, since logic is used in constructing mathematical proofs, and it might appear that the study of logic should come before the study of mathematics. Such a procedure is, however, typical of science. Our actual knowledge is a narrow band of light flanked on both sides by darkness. We may, on the one hand, go forward and develop further the consequences of known principles. Or else we may press backward the obscurity in which the foundations of science are enveloped. Just by using mathematical methods, i.e. by working with ideograms (symbols for ideas) instead of ordinary words (symbols for sounds), we can throw new and important light on the logical principles used in mathematics. This approach has led to more knowledge about logic in one century than had been obtained from the death of Aristotle up to 1847, when Boole's masterpiece was published.

We begin with the simplest branch of the subject, the logic of classes. After an informal introduction, in which we derive the properties of classes by a free use of naive intuition, we formulate that theory as a deductive science, that is, as a science in which the assumptions are explicitly stated, and in which everything else follows from the assumptions by means of explicitly stated rules. The assumptions are stated in terms of certain notions which are not analyzed further and are taken as undefined. All other concepts of the science are defined in terms of these.

We then proceed to a study of the system as a whole. That is, instead of developing more and more consequences of the assumptions, we try to find general characteristics of the science itself. This is typical of the modern tendency to emphasize the *structure* of a science, to derive theorems *about* the science, rather than to concentrate on the detailed derivation of results within the science. This study of the structure of the logic of classes culminates in Chapter I, Section 3.

We then apply the same methods to the logic of propositions. In doing this, we uncover a striking similarity between this science and the logic of classes. It is precisely through formulating these logics as deductive sciences that we see that both are special examples of a general theory.

The logic of propositions has been the subject of much controversy among logicians and mathematicians. We discuss the various alternative approaches which have been proposed.

We then try to construct general logical theories which are adequate for at least a large part of mathematics. Here we run into difficulties since the unreined use of naive intuitive reasoning leads to devastating paradoxes. Thus we must seek a theory which admits as much as possible of the reasoning intuitively accepted as valid, but includes such restrictions as to evade the paradoxes. But a profound theorem of Gödel shows that no logical theory of a very general type can include methods of reasoning strong enough for the proof of its own consistency. Indeed, in any system of logic of this general type, there are propositions which can be proved by an argument outside the system but which cannot be proved within the system. Thus no formal logical system of this type, which includes all adequate logics so far proposed, can contain all valid modes of reasoning. All that we can hope for is stronger and stronger systems which are adequate for more and more powerful arguments, or else some system radically different from anything so far proposed.

In order to arrive at such results as Gödel's, it is necessary for us to scrutinize our tools more closely. In a deductive science the undefined terms are denoted by certain symbols, which may be blobs of printer's ink, speech sounds, printed marks representing the latter, etc. The propositions of this science are communicated by means of these signs. These signs, together with the rules governing their use and combination, constitute a language for stating relationships within the science. This is called the *object language*. In an exposition of the science the assumptions must be communicated in a language whose meaning is already assumed to be known, say English. This is called the *syntax language.* We use the object language to talk *within* the science and the syntax language to talk *about* the science. In ordinary usage the confusion between the two leads to no difficulty, but when the science under consideration is logic itself we must lean over backwards to avoid unclarity.

The primitive signs of the object language are called its alphabet. Certain combinations of these signs may be assigned meanings. Such combinations are often called words or sentences. If a certain combination of signs denotes an object, then this combination will be a name for that object. In speaking about the object we use a name for it. Thus "Dewey smiled" is a sentence wherein we mention the man Dewey by using his name, the word "Dewey." When we are talking about a name or a symbol, it is convenient to use a specimen enclosed in quotation marks as a name of the name or symbol. Thus, " "Dewey" " is a name of "Dewey," which is, in turn, a name of Dewey, who is a man. Again, on p. 2, 25th line from the bottom, we are speaking about a name of the universal class, while on the next line it is the null class itself which is mentioned. To avoid the use of names of names of names and the like, we shall also use such phrases as "the letter —" or "the sign —" as names of the symbols of which specimens are exhibited. It is often overlooked that while we cannot put a man on the printed page and are thus *forced* to use a name when writing about him, we do have greater resources when we wish to write about symbols.

In particular, a sentence is a name of a proposition. We shall say that the sentence *expresses* the proposition, and we shall often use "statement" as a synonym for "sentence." We shall often use the phrase "the proposition that *p*" to indicate the proposition expressed by "*p*." Careful attention to these matters helps in discussing ticklish questions.

We are thus led, in chapter IV, to the mathematical analysis of language. Whereas in the previous chapters our attention is centered on the relationships expressed by the object language, in the last chapter we focus our attention on the structure of the language apart from its meaning. The former process is sometimes called the semantical study of language, i.e. the study of the meanings expressed by the language, while the latter is often called the syntactical study of the language. The methods we use were developed especially by Post. We find in this chapter that certain classes of languages, which include practically all languages which have been precisely formulated, can be singled out and possess important common properties. It is exactly the mathematical method of abstracting from the special features of particular languages which enables us to prove rigorously a number of profound general truths, where metaphysicians would argue back and forth for centuries without ever reaching a conclusion which could be tested.

Mathematical logic is, then, no mere shorthand for expressing in ideograms what has already been discovered by reasoning in ordinary language. It is, rather, a powerful and versatile tool for solving problems which are inaccessible to other methods.

In the following we shall make references thus:

III2 denotes section 2 of chapter III;
T2 denotes theorem 2 of the present section;
T5.2.3 denotes theorem 3 of section 2 of chapter V;
[27]4 denotes number 4 by author 27 in Church's Bibliography, J. Symbolic Logic, vol. 1, no. 4;
[II]35 denotes the article beginning or reviewed on page 35 of vol. II, J. Symbolic Logic.

Chapter I

THE LOGIC OF CLASSES

SECTION 1 INFORMAL INTRODUCTION

FUNDAMENTAL THEOREMS

Logic is the science of the valid processes of reasoning. In mathematical logic we investigate these processes by mathematical methods. In this first chapter we shall study the simplest branch of this science, the logic of classes.

For the moment we shall not attempt to analyze the concept of "class." Rather we shall take it as undefined but shall assume that its intuitive meaning is known. By a class we shall mean any collection of things, for example, the class of all men or the class of red-headed baboons. The members of the class may be abstractions or may be in some other sense not tangible; thus the class of positive integers and the class of jabberwockies are perfectly good classes. We shall denote classes by small Greek letters.

We shall say that the class α is the same as the class β if and only if they have exactly the same members. Thus the class of even primes is the same as the class whose only member is the number 2. We shall denote the relationship "α is the same as β" by the symbols "$\alpha = \beta$." The following propositions are evident:

T1. $\alpha = \alpha$;
T2. *if* $\alpha = \beta$, *then* $\beta = \alpha$;
T3. *if* $\alpha = \beta$ *and* $\beta = \gamma$, *then* $\alpha = \gamma$.

In most statements, if $\alpha = \beta$, then "α" may be substituted for "β" at any point without changing the truth or falsity of the statement.

We shall symbolize the statement "x is a member of α" by "$x \in \alpha$."

If α and β are classes, we shall denote by "$\alpha \cap \beta$" the class of all objects which are members of both α and β. Similarly, we shall use "$\alpha \cup \beta$" for the class of all things which are either in α or in β or in both. Thus if α is the class of females and β is the class of engineers, then $\alpha \cap \beta$ is the class of female engineers, and $\alpha \cup \beta$ is the class of all objects which are either females or engineers or both. By α' we shall mean the class of all objects which are not in α. The class $\alpha - \beta = \alpha \cap \beta'$, by definition, so that $\alpha - \beta$ is the class of all objects which are in α but not in β. Two special classes are of importance, the universal class, denoted by "1", which is the class containing all things, and the null class, 0, which is the class which has no members.

These symbols have been introduced so that we may construct an algebra of classes. They enjoy the following properties:

T4. $\alpha \cap \beta = \beta \cap \alpha$;
T5. $\alpha \cap (\beta \cap \gamma) = (\alpha \cap \beta) \cap \gamma$;
T6. $\alpha \cup \beta = \beta \cup \alpha$;
T7. $\alpha \cup (\beta \cup \gamma) = (\alpha \cup \beta) \cup \gamma$;
T8. $\alpha \cap \alpha = \alpha \cup \alpha = \alpha$;
T9. $\alpha \cap (\beta \cup \gamma) = (\alpha \cap \beta) \cup (\alpha \cap \gamma)$;
T10. $\alpha \cup (\beta \cap \gamma) = (\alpha \cup \beta) \cap (\alpha \cup \gamma)$;
T11. $\alpha \cup \alpha' = 1$;
T12. $\alpha \cap \alpha' = 0$;
T13. $\alpha \cap 1 = \alpha \cup 0 = \alpha$;
T14. $\alpha \cup 1 = 1$;
T15. $\alpha \cap 0 = 0$;
T16. $(\alpha')' = \alpha$;
T17. $0' = 1$; $1' = 0$;
T18. $(\alpha \cup \beta)' = \alpha' \cap \beta'$;
T19. $(\alpha \cap \beta)' = \alpha' \cup \beta'$;
T20. $\alpha \cup (\alpha \cap \beta) = \alpha \cap (\alpha \cup \beta) = \alpha$.

These propositions are for the most part obvious. Thus T4 says that if x is in $\alpha \cap \beta$, i.e. if x is in both α and β, then x is in $\beta \cap \alpha$, and conversely. Let us check one of the more complicated properties, say T10, as an illustration. We must show that every member of the class on the left-hand side of the equation is also a member of the class on the right, and conversely. If $x \in \alpha \cup (\beta \cap \gamma)$, then either $x \in \alpha$ or $x \in \beta \cap \gamma$ or both. If $x \in \alpha$, then certainly $x \in \alpha \cup \beta$ and also $x \in \alpha \cup \gamma$. Hence $x \in (\alpha \cup \beta) \cap (\alpha \cup \gamma)$. Alternatively, if $x \in \beta \cap \gamma$, then $x \in \beta$ and $x \in \gamma$. From the first, $x \in \alpha \cup \beta$, and from the second, $x \in \alpha \cup \gamma$. Hence $x \in (\alpha \cup \beta) \cap (\alpha \cup \gamma)$. We have thus shown that if $x \in \alpha \cup (\beta \cap \gamma)$, then $x \in (\alpha \cup \beta) \cap (\alpha \cup \gamma)$. The converse may be shown in a similar manner. In view of T5 and T7, we shall write $\alpha \cap \beta \cap \gamma$, for $(\alpha \cap \beta) \cap \gamma$, and $\alpha \cup \beta \cup \gamma$ for $(\alpha \cup \beta) \cup \gamma$, etc.

We say that α is included in β, or that α is a subclass of β, (in symbols, $\alpha \subset \beta$) if every member of α is also a member of β, i.e. $x \in \alpha$ always implies that $x \in \beta$. The following propositions are easy to prove:

T21. $\alpha = \beta$ *if and only if* $\alpha \subset \beta$ *and* $\beta \subset \alpha$;
T22. $\alpha \subset \beta$ *if and only if* $\alpha \cap \beta = \alpha$;
T23. $\alpha \subset \beta$ *if and only if* $\alpha \cup \beta = \beta$;
T24. $\alpha \subset \beta$ *if and only if* $\alpha - \beta = 0$;
T25. $\alpha \subset \beta$ *if and only if* $\alpha' \cup \beta = 1$;
T26. $\alpha \subset \alpha$;
T27. $\alpha \cap \beta \subset \alpha \subset \alpha \cup \beta$;
T28. $0 \subset \alpha \subset 1$;
T29. *if* $\alpha \subset 0$, *then* $\alpha = 0$;
T30. *if* $1 \subset \alpha$, *then* $\alpha = 1$;
T31. *if* $\alpha \subset \beta$ *and* $\beta \subset \gamma$, *then* $\alpha \subset \gamma$;
T32. *if* $\alpha \subset \beta$, *then* $\alpha \cap \gamma \subset \beta \cap \gamma$ *and* $\alpha \cup \gamma \subset \beta \cup \gamma$;
T33. *if* $\alpha \subset \beta$, *then* $\beta' \subset \alpha'$;
T34. *if* $\alpha \subset \beta$ *and* $\alpha \subset \gamma$, *then* $\alpha \subset \beta \cap \gamma$;
T35. *if* $\alpha \subset \gamma$ *and* $\beta \subset \gamma$, *then* $\alpha \cup \beta \subset \gamma$.

We have thus shown that if the operations with classes are symbolized in the above fashion, we obtain an algebra similar to our ordinary algebra of numbers. The similarity becomes more striking if we introduce the "exclusive" either–or. Let $\alpha + \beta = (\alpha - \beta) \cup (\beta - \alpha)$, by definition; i.e. $\alpha + \beta$ is the class of all things which are in one of α and β but not the other. If for the moment we abbreviate "$\alpha \cap \beta$" by "$\alpha\beta$", we obtain the following propositions:

T36. $\alpha\beta = \beta\alpha$; $\alpha(\beta\gamma) = (\alpha\beta)\gamma$;
T37. $\alpha + \beta = \beta + \alpha$; $\alpha + (\beta + \gamma) = (\alpha + \beta) + \gamma$;
T38. $\alpha(\beta + \gamma) = \alpha\beta + \alpha\gamma$;
T39. $\alpha + 0 = \alpha = \alpha 1$;
T40. $\alpha + \alpha = 0$.

It is unnecessary to go back to the original meanings of the symbols in order to prove these statements. We can instead use the properties already stated. Thus

$$\begin{aligned}
\alpha(\beta + \gamma) &= \alpha \cap ((\beta \cap \gamma') \cup (\beta' \cap \gamma)) \\
&= (\alpha \cap \beta \cap \gamma') \cup (\alpha \cap \beta' \cap \gamma) \\
&= \alpha\beta\gamma' \cup \alpha\beta'\gamma,
\end{aligned}$$

$$\begin{aligned}
\text{and } \alpha\beta + \alpha\gamma &= ((\alpha \cap \beta) \cap (\alpha \cap \gamma)') \cup ((\alpha \cap \beta)' \cap (\alpha \cap \gamma)) \\
&= ((\alpha \cap \beta) \cap (\alpha' \cup \gamma')) \cup ((\alpha' \cup \beta') \cap (\alpha \cap \gamma)) \\
&= (((\alpha \cap \beta) \cap \alpha') \cup ((\alpha \cap \beta) \cap \gamma')) \\
&\qquad \cup (((\alpha \cap \gamma) \cap \alpha') \cup ((\alpha \cap \gamma) \cap \beta')) \\
&= \alpha\alpha'\beta \cup \alpha\beta\gamma' \cup \alpha\alpha'\gamma \cup \alpha\beta'\gamma \\
&= 0\beta \cup \alpha\beta\gamma' \cup 0\gamma \cup \alpha\beta'\gamma \\
&= 0 \cup \alpha\beta\gamma' \cup 0 \cup \alpha\beta'\gamma \\
&= \alpha\beta\gamma' \cup \alpha\beta'\gamma.
\end{aligned}$$

Here we have used the definition of $\alpha + \beta$, and equations T9, T4, T5, T19, T12, and T13 above.

By virtue of equations T36 to T40 the algebra of classes is what mathematicians call a ring with respect to the operations $\alpha\beta$ and $\alpha + \beta$. Indeed, this ring is a very special one because of T8 and T40, which show that the algebra of this ring is much simpler than our ordinary algebra since there are no exponents or coefficients.

By virtue of T21, T22, T23, T26, T27, T31, T34, and T35, (or alternatively, by T4, T5, T6, T7, T8, and T20) the algebra of classes is also what mathematicians call a lattice. This is a very special type of lattice because of T10 to T13.

We shall not use the knowledge already accumulated concerning rings and lattices in our present work. In more advanced work, however, these points of view are useful.

The algebra of classes is called Boolean algebra after the man (G. Boole, Irish, 1815–1864) who first studied it intensively.

All the formal laws of Boolean algebra can be obtained from one general principle. We must first define the concept of a "Boolean function" step by step. If $f(\alpha) \equiv \gamma$, where γ is a constant class, for all α, then f is a Boolean function. If $f(\alpha) \equiv \alpha$ for all α, then f is a Boolean function, the so-called identity function. If f is a Boolean function, and if $g(\alpha) = (f(\alpha))'$ for all α, then g is a Boolean function. If f and g are Boolean functions, and if $h(\alpha) = f(\alpha) \cup g(\alpha)$ and $k(\alpha) = f(\alpha) \cap g(\alpha)$ for all α, then h and k are Boolean functions. The class of Boolean functions is the smallest class of functions satisfying these conditions, i.e. it is the class of all functions which can be obtained by starting with constants and the identity function, and applying the operations α', $\alpha \cap \beta$, and $\alpha \cup \beta$ a finite number of times. Thus $f(\alpha) \equiv (\gamma \cap \alpha) \cup (\delta \cap \alpha')$, where γ and δ are constant classes, is a Boolean function.

The fundamental theorem of Boolean algebra is

THEOREM 41. *If f is a Boolean function, then*

$$f(\alpha) = (f(1) \cap \alpha) \cup (f(0) \cap \alpha')$$

Proof. If $f(\alpha) \equiv \gamma$, where γ is a constant, then

$$\begin{aligned}(f(1) \cap \alpha) \cup (f(0) \cap \alpha') &= (\gamma \cap \alpha) \cup (\gamma \cap \alpha') \\ &= \gamma \cap (\alpha \cup \alpha') \quad \text{(by T9)} \\ &= \gamma \cap 1 \quad \text{(by T11)} \\ &= \gamma \quad \text{(by T14)} \\ &= f(\alpha).\end{aligned}$$

If $f(\alpha) \equiv \alpha$, then

$$\begin{aligned}(f(1) \cap \alpha) \cup (f(0) \cap \alpha') &= (1 \cap \alpha) \cup (0 \cap \alpha') \\ &= \alpha \cup 0 \quad \text{(by T13, T15)} \\ &= \alpha \quad \text{(by T13)} \\ &= f(\alpha).\end{aligned}$$

Suppose the theorem is true for f. Let $g(\alpha) = (f(\alpha))'$ for all α. Then

$$\begin{aligned}
(\alpha) &= ((f(1) \cap \alpha) \cup (f(0) \cap \alpha'))' \\
&= (f(1) \cap \alpha)' \cap (f(0) \cap \alpha')' \qquad \text{(by T18)} \\
&= (f(1)' \cup \alpha') \cap (f(0)' \cup (\alpha')') \quad \text{(by T19)} \\
&= (f(1)' \cap f(0)') \cup (f(1)' \cap (\alpha')') \\
&\qquad \cup (\alpha' \cap f(0)') \cup (\alpha' \cap (\alpha')') \\
&\qquad\qquad\qquad\qquad \text{(by T9, applied twice)} \\
&= (f(1)' \cap f(0)') \cup (f(1)' \cap \alpha) \cup (f(0)' \cap \alpha') \\
&\qquad\qquad\qquad\qquad \text{(by T16, T12, T13)} \\
&= ((f(1)' \cap f(0)') \cap (\alpha \cup \alpha')) \cup (f(1)' \cap \alpha) \\
&\qquad \cup (f(0)' \cap \alpha') \qquad \text{(by T11)} \\
&= (f(0)' \cap f(1)' \cap \alpha) \cup (f(1)' \cap f(0)' \cap \alpha') \\
&\qquad \cup (f(1)' \cap \alpha) \cup (f(0)' \cap \alpha') \text{ (by T4, T5, T9)} \\
&= (f(1)' \cap \alpha) \cup (f(0)' \cap \alpha') \qquad \text{(by T20).}
\end{aligned}$$

Suppose the theorem is true for f and g, and let $h(\alpha) = f(\alpha) \cup g(\alpha)$ and $k(\alpha) = f(\alpha) \cap g(\alpha)$ for all α. Then

$$\begin{aligned}
h(\alpha) &= (f(1) \cap \alpha) \cup (f(0) \cap \alpha') \cup (g(1) \cap \alpha) \cup (g(0) \cap \alpha') \\
&= ((f(1) \cup g(1)) \cap \alpha) \cup ((f(0) \cup g(0)) \cap \alpha') \quad \text{(by T9)}
\end{aligned}$$

Also

$$\begin{aligned}
k(\alpha) &= ((f(1) \cap \alpha) \cup (f(0) \cap \alpha')) \cap ((g(1) \cap \alpha) \\
&\qquad \cup (g(0) \cap \alpha')) \\
&= (f(1) \cap g(1) \cap \alpha \cap \alpha) \cup (f(1) \cap g(0) \cap \alpha \cap \alpha') \\
&\qquad \cup (f(0) \cap g(1) \cap \alpha' \cap \alpha) \\
&\qquad \cup (f(0) \cap g(0) \cap \alpha' \cap \alpha') \text{ (by T9, T4, T5)} \\
&= (((f(1) \cap g(1)) \cap \alpha) \cup ((f(0) \cap g(0)) \cap \alpha') \\
&\qquad\qquad\qquad\qquad \text{(by T8, T12, T13, T15).}
\end{aligned}$$

If f is any Boolean function, then it can be built up in a finite number of steps from constants and the identity function by means of the operations α', $\alpha \cap \beta$, and $\alpha \cup \beta$. Therefore, by combining these results, we immediately obtain the theorem.

This theorem shows that in order to prove that two Boolean functions, f and g, are equal for all α, it is sufficient to prove that $f(0) = g(0)$ and $f(1) = g(1)$.

All these considerations can be extended to Boolean functions of several variables. Thus if f is a Boolean function of two variables, then

$$f(\alpha, \beta) = (f(1, 1)\alpha\beta) \cup (f(1, 0)\alpha\beta') \cup (f(0, 1)\alpha'\beta) \cup (f(0, 0)\alpha'\beta').$$

As a corollary we obtain

$$f(\alpha \cup \beta) \cup f(\alpha \cap \beta) = f(\alpha) \cup f(\beta),$$

if f is any Boolean function. For let $g(\alpha, \beta) = f(\alpha \cup \beta) \cup f(\alpha \cap \beta)$, $h(\alpha, \beta) = f(\alpha) \cup f(\beta)$. Then $g(1, 1) = h(1, 1)$, $g(1, 0) = h(1, 0)$, etc. Therefore, $g(\alpha, \beta) = h(\alpha, \beta)$ for all α and β.

EXERCISES

Ex. 1. Verify T4–T40.

Ex. 2. (a). Prove T8 from T27, T34, and T21.
(b). Prove T11 from T26 and T25.
(c). Prove that $\alpha'' \subset \alpha$ from T11, T6, and T25.
(d). Prove T35 from T34, T33, T18, and T16.

Ex. 3. Show that if f is any Boolean function of one variable, then
(a). $f(\alpha) = (f(1) \cup \alpha') \cap (f(0) \cup \alpha)$.
(b). $f(f(0)) = f(0) \cap f(1) \subset f(\alpha) \subset f(0) \cup f(1) = f(f(1))$.
(c). $f(\alpha) = \gamma + \delta\alpha$, where γ and δ are constants.
(d). If $f(0) \cap f(1) \subset \eta \subset f(0) \cup f(1)$, then the equation $f(\alpha) = \eta$ has a solution. Find all solutions.
(e). If the equation $f(\xi) = \eta$ has a unique solution for one value of η, then it has a unique solution, namely $f(\eta)$, for all values of η.
(f). If $f(\xi_1) \subset f(\xi_2)$ whenever $\alpha \subset \xi_1 \subset \xi_2 \subset \beta$, then $\beta \cap f(0) \subset \alpha \cup f(1)$, and conversely.
(g). If $\xi \subset \eta$, then $f(f(\xi)) \subset f(f(\eta))$.
(h). If $\alpha \subset \beta$ and $f(\alpha) \subset f(\beta)$, then $f(\xi_1) \subset f(\xi_2)$ whenever $\alpha \subset \xi_1 \subset \xi_2 \subset \beta$.

SECTION 2 BOOLEAN ALGEBRA AS A DEDUCTIVE SCIENCE

In the previous section we assumed that the concept of a class and the simpler properties of this concept were intuitively known. In the "proofs" of the propositions T1.1.1–T1.1.41 properties of classes were used which were not explicitly stated. This leaves the foundations of our previous work completely in the dark. In the present section we shall remedy the situation by presenting Boolean algebra as a deductive science.

By a deductive science we mean a body of propositions constructed in the following way. We start out with a certain set of undefined ideas which we make no attempt to analyze further, and a set of unproved propositions stated in terms of these undefined ideas. All other propositions in the science must be proved using only the unproved propositions and previously proved propositions. Similarly, all other concepts in the science must be defined in terms of the undefined ideas and previously defined ideas. For in any exposition of the science, i.e. in any setting forth of the science in a sequence of propositions, there must be a first proposition. If this is proved on the basis of other propositions, then its proof depends on propositions whose truth is not known at this time. Similarly, in any exposition there must be undefined terms.

Furthermore, among the assumptions there must be rules telling us how we can obtain one true proposition from others known to be true. These we call rules of inference. These will be perhaps of the form: "if p, q, r are true, then s is true." Here p, q, r, s, . . . are stated in terms of the concepts of the science. The words "if," "are," etc., are in ordinary English and are not part of the language of the system under construction. Otherwise we would not know the meaning of this rule and therefore could not apply it. This shows us that in communicating our science we must use to some extent some language which we already know in order to describe the rules of operating within the science. This "embedding" language we call the *syntax language;* it is used to talk about the system while the undefined terms of the system constitute a basis for a language which we use to talk within the system. The language of the system is called the *object* language. This is analogous to the problem of teaching a new language. We describe the language in terms of a known language before we can communicate within the new language. Of course, it is desirable to use as simple a syntax language as possible in order that as few unanalyzed notions as possible be used. The undefined terms in our science will be a non-empty class of objects C and two operations $\cap$ and $'$. The unproved propositions are:

A1. *If α is in C, then α' and $\alpha \cap \beta$ are uniquely determined members of C.*

A2. *If α and β are in C, then $\alpha \cap \beta = \beta \cap \alpha$.*

A3. *If α, β, and γ are in C, then $(\alpha \cap \beta) \cap \gamma = \alpha \cap (\beta \cap \gamma)$.*

A4. *If α, β, and γ are in C, and $\alpha \cap \beta' = \gamma \cap \gamma'$, then $\alpha \cap \beta = \alpha$.*

A5. *If α, β, and γ are in C, and $\alpha \cap \beta = \alpha$, then $\alpha \cap \beta' = \gamma \cap \gamma'$.*

A6. *If α and β are in C, and $\alpha = \beta$, then $\alpha' = \beta'$.*

A7. *If α, β, and γ are in C, and $\alpha = \beta$, then $\alpha \cap \gamma = \beta \cap \gamma$ and $\gamma \cap \alpha = \gamma \cap \beta$.*

Here the relation "$=$" is taken to be part of the known syntax language. The only properties of this relation which will be used are T1.1.1, T1.1.2, T1.1.3, and their consequences in conjunction with A1–A7. Hence we could alternatively take "$=$" as an undefined term and postulate T1.1.1–T1.1.3. A relation satisfying the latter conditions is called an *equivalence relation.*

We shall show that this is a deductive science whose true propositions are those and only those of the algebra constructed informally in I1.

Note that since the propositions of this science are all consequences of A1–A7 and the primitive terms are undefined, then if C, $\cap$, and $'$ are given any concrete interpretation in which A1–A7 are true propositions, all their consequences are automatically true in this interpretation. Thus this science is, like all deductive sciences, abstract; that is, its concepts have no specific meaning, and its propositions apply whenever specific meanings are assigned to its undefined terms in such a way that the assumptions become true propositions. For example, if C is the class whose only member is the number 1, and $'$ and $\cap$ are defined by the equations $1' = 1 \cap 1 = 1$, then it is obvious that A1–A7 are true with this interpretation. A less trivial example is this: let C be the class of all positive divisors of 210, i.e. C is the class whose members are 1, 2, 3, 5, 6, 7, 10, 14, 15, 21, 30, 35, 42, 70, 105, and 210, $\alpha \cap \beta$ is the least common multiple of α and β, and $\alpha' = 210/\alpha$. It is slightly more laborious but still easy to verify the assumptions in this case. Of course, in formulating these assumptions we had in mind the algebra of I1, and intend that algebra to be one concrete interpretation of our science. Indeed, if C is the class of all classes, and $\alpha \cap \beta$ and α' are interpreted as in I1, then A1–A7 are true.

We shall use throughout this section the convention that small Greek letters denote members of C. This amounts to a hypothesis not explicitly stated in the formulations of the following theorems.

It is convenient to begin with the following definitions:

D1. $\alpha \cap \beta \cap \gamma = (\alpha \cap \beta) \cap \gamma$, $\alpha \cap \beta \cap \gamma \cap \delta = (\alpha \cap \beta \cap \gamma) \cap \delta$, *etc.*

D2. $\alpha \subset \beta$ *for* $\alpha \cap \beta = \alpha$.

We now have the following theorems:

T1. $\alpha \cap \alpha = \alpha$.

Proof. $\alpha \cap \alpha' = \alpha \cap \alpha'$. Now apply A4.

T2. $\alpha \cap \alpha' = \gamma \cap \gamma'$. (T1, A5).

This justifies the definitions:

D3. $0 = \alpha \cap \alpha'$. $1 = 0'$.

T3. $\alpha \subset \beta$ *if and only if* $\alpha \cap \beta' = 0$. (T2, A4, A5).

T4. $\alpha \subset \alpha$.

T5. *If* $\alpha \subset \beta$ *and* $\beta \subset \gamma$, *then* $\alpha \subset \gamma$.

Proof. If $\alpha \cap \beta = \alpha$ and $\beta \cap \gamma = \beta$, then $\alpha \cap \gamma = (\alpha \cap \beta) \cap \gamma = \alpha \cap (\beta \cap \gamma) = \alpha \cap \beta = \alpha$. (A3).

T6. $\alpha \cap \beta \subset \alpha$. (A2, A3, T1).

T7. *If* $\alpha \subset \beta$ *and* $\beta \subset \alpha$, *then* $\alpha = \beta$. (A2).

T8. $\beta \cap 0 = 0$. $0 \subset \beta$.

Proof. $0 = \beta \cap \beta' \subset \beta$. (T2, T6).

T9. $\alpha'' = \alpha$.

Proof. $\alpha'' \cap \alpha' = \alpha' \cap \alpha'' = 0$. (A2, T2).

$\therefore$ $\alpha'' \subset \alpha$, *for any member* α *of C*. (A4).

Hence $\alpha''' \subset \alpha'$ and $\alpha'''' \subset \alpha''$.

$\therefore \alpha'''' \subset \alpha$. (T5).

$\therefore \alpha'''' \cap \alpha' = 0$. (T3).

$\therefore \alpha' \subset \alpha'''$. (A2, T3).

$\therefore \alpha' = \alpha'''$. (T7).

$\therefore \alpha \cap \alpha''' = 0$. (T2).

$\therefore \alpha \subset \alpha''$. (T3).

$\therefore \alpha = \alpha''$. (T7).

D4. $\alpha \cup \beta = (\alpha' \cap \beta')'$.

T10. $\alpha \cap \beta = (\alpha' \cup \beta')'$. (T9).

T11. $\alpha \subset \beta$ *if and only if* $\beta' \subset \alpha'$.

Proof. If $\alpha \subset \beta$, then $\alpha \cap \beta' = 0$; hence $\beta' \cap \alpha'' = 0$ (A2, T9), which implies that $\beta' \subset \alpha'$. If $\beta' \subset \alpha'$, then $\alpha'' \subset \beta''$, by the case just proved, and therefore $\alpha \subset \beta$, by T9.

T12. $\alpha \subset \beta$ *if and only if* $\alpha \cup \beta = \beta$.

Proof. $\alpha \subset \beta$ if and only if $\beta' \subset \alpha'$, which means that $\beta' \cap \alpha' = \beta'$. The latter is true if and only if $\beta = \beta'' = (\beta' \cap \alpha')' = (\alpha' \cap \beta')' = \alpha \cup \beta$.

T13. $\alpha \cup \beta = \beta \cup \alpha$. $(\alpha \cup \beta) \cup \gamma = \alpha \cup (\beta \cup \gamma)$. (A2, A3, D4, T9).

T14. $\alpha \cup \alpha = \alpha$. (T1, D4, T9).

T15. $\alpha \cup \alpha' = 1$. (D4, D3).

T16. $\alpha \subset \alpha \cup \beta$.

Proof. $(\alpha \cup \beta)' = (\alpha' \cap \beta')'' = \alpha' \cap \beta' \subset \alpha'$. (T9, T6, T11).

T17. $\alpha \cup (\alpha \cap \beta) = \alpha \cap (\alpha \cup \beta) = \alpha$.

Proof. $\alpha \cup (\alpha \cap \beta) = \alpha$ (T6, T12).

$\alpha \cap (\alpha \cup \beta) = \alpha$ (D2, T16).

T18. *If* $\alpha \subset \beta$, *then* $\alpha \cap \gamma \subset \beta \cap \gamma$ *and* $\alpha \cup \gamma \subset \beta \cup \gamma$.

Proof. If $\alpha \subset \beta$, then $(\alpha \cap \gamma) \cap (\beta \cap \gamma)$

$= \alpha \cap \beta \cap \gamma$ (A2, A3, T1)

$= \alpha$ (D2).

The rest follows in the same way by T12.

T19. *If* $\alpha \subset \gamma$ *and* $\beta \subset \gamma$, *then* $\alpha \cup \beta \subset \gamma$.

If $\gamma \subset \alpha$ *and* $\gamma \subset \beta$, *then* $\gamma \subset \alpha \cap \beta$.

Proof. If $\gamma \subset \alpha$ and $\gamma \subset \beta$, then $\gamma = \gamma \cap \alpha = \gamma \cap \beta$, so that $\gamma \cap (\alpha \cap \beta) = (\gamma \cap \alpha) \cap \beta = \gamma \cap \beta = \gamma$. The other part is proved similarly.

T20. $\alpha \cap (\alpha' \cup \beta) = \alpha \cap \beta$.

Proof. $\alpha \cap (\alpha' \cup \beta) = \alpha \cap (\alpha'' \cap \beta')' = \alpha \cap (\alpha \cap \beta')'$.

Hence $(\alpha \cap (\alpha' \cup \beta)) \cap \beta' = 0$ (T2, A2, A3).

$\therefore \alpha \cap (\alpha' \cup \beta) = (\alpha \cap (\alpha' \cup \beta)) \cap \beta$

$= \alpha \cap ((\alpha' \cup \beta) \cap \beta) = \alpha \cap \beta$. (A3, T17).

T21. $\alpha \cap (\beta \cup \gamma) = (\alpha \cap \beta) \cup (\alpha \cap \gamma)$.

Proof. $\beta \subset \beta \cup \gamma, \gamma \subset \beta \cup \gamma$. (T13, T16).

$\therefore \alpha \cap \beta \subset \alpha \cap (\beta \cup \gamma), \alpha \cap \gamma \subset \alpha \cap (\beta \cup \gamma)$. (T18).

$\therefore (\alpha \cap \beta) \cup (\alpha \cap \gamma) \subset \alpha \cap (\beta \cup \gamma)$. (T19).

Now $\alpha \cap (\beta \cup \gamma) \cap ((\alpha \cap \beta) \cup (\alpha \cap \gamma))'$

$= \alpha \cap (\beta \cup \gamma) \cap (\alpha \cap \beta)' \cap (\alpha \cap \gamma)'$ (D4, T9)

$= \alpha \cap (\beta \cup \gamma) \cap (\alpha' \cup \beta') \cap (\alpha' \cup \gamma')$ (D4, T9)

$= \beta' \cup \gamma' \cap (\beta \cup \gamma)$ (T20, A2, A3)

$= 0$ (D4, T2).

Hence $\alpha \cap (\beta \cup \gamma) \subset (\alpha \cap \beta) \cup (\alpha \cap \gamma)$.

T22. $\alpha \cup 0 = \alpha, \alpha \cup 1 = 1, \alpha \cap 1 = \alpha$. (T8, T12, T11).

We now have everything necessary for the proof of T1.1.41, with the slight simplification that the combination $f \cap g$ need not be considered separately since it may be expressed in terms of the operations $\cup$ and $'$ by T10. For the sake of completeness, we give also a proof of the analogous theorem for functions of several variables.

THEOREM 23. *If* $f(\alpha_1, \cdots, \alpha_k)$ *is a Boolean function, then*

$$f(\alpha_1, \cdots, \alpha_k) = \sum_{i_1=0}^{1} \sum_{i_2=0}^{1} \cdots \sum_{i_k=0}^{1} f(1^{i_1}, 1^{i_2}, \cdots, 1^{i_k})\alpha_1^{i_1} \cdots \alpha_k^{i_k}.$$

Remark. Here "α^i" means α if $i = 0$ amd α' if $i = 1$;

$$\text{"}\sum_{j=0}^{m} \beta_j\text{" means } \beta_0 \cup \beta_1 \cup \cdots \cup \beta_m .$$

We use juxtaposition for "$\cap$" as on p. 4.

Proof. The theorem is true for $k = 1$. If it is true for $k - 1$, then

$$f(\alpha_1, \alpha_2, \cdots, \alpha_k) = \sum_{i_2=0}^{1} \cdots \sum_{i_k=0}^{1} f(\alpha_1, 1^{i_2}, \cdots, 1^{i_k})\alpha_2^{i_2} \cdots \alpha_k^{i_k}.$$

But $f(\alpha_1, 1^{i_2}, \cdots, 1^{i_k}) = (f(1^0, 1^{i_2}, \cdots, 1^{i_k})\alpha_1^0)$
$\cup (f(1^1, 1^{i_2}, \cdots, 1^{i_k})\alpha_1^1)$,
by T1.1.41; now an application of T21 yields the desired result.

The question arises, are the postulates A1–A7 complete in the sense that all general formal laws in the algebra of classes which can be formulated in terms of $\cap$ and $'$ can be proved from them? The answer is given by Theorem 24 below.

We say that B is a Boolean algebra whenever B is a triple $(C, \cap, ')$ consisting of a class C and two operations $\cap$ and $'$ defined in C and satisfying A1–A7.

A quadruple $(C, \cap, ', =)$ satisfying A1–A7 and T1.1.1–

T1.1.3 will be called a Boolean algebra with respect to the equivalence relation $=$.

Lemma 1. If B is a Boolean algebra in which C has at least two members, then $0 \neq 1$.

Proof. If $0 = 1$, then $\alpha = \alpha \cap 1 = \alpha \cap 0 = 0$, so that C has only the single member 0.

THEOREM 24. *Let B be a Boolean algebra with at least two elements.*

Let $f(\alpha_1, \cdots, \alpha_k)$ and $g(\alpha_1, \cdots, \alpha_k)$ be two Boolean functions containing no constants in their construction. If $f = g$ for all $\alpha_1, \cdots, \alpha_k$ in C, then $f = g$ is provable from A1–A7, and is therefore true in all Boolean algebras.

Proof. By hypothesis $f(\alpha_1, \cdots, \alpha_k) = g(\alpha_1, \cdots, \alpha_k)$ for all $\alpha_1, \cdots, \alpha_k$ in C, in particular when the α's have the values 0 or 1. Now

$$1 \cap 1 = 1, \quad 1 \cap 0 = 0 \cap 1 = 0 \cap 0 = 0, \quad 0' = 1, \quad 1' = 0,$$

and all these equations are consequences of A1–A7. Hence if the α's take on the values 0 or 1, then $f(\alpha_1, \cdots, \alpha_k)$ and $g(\alpha_1, \cdots, \alpha_k)$ have the values 0 or 1, and these values are deducible from A1–A7. By Lemma 1, $0 \neq 1$. Therefore if the α's have the values 0 or 1, then $f(\alpha_1, \cdots, \alpha_k) = g(\alpha_1, \cdots, \alpha_k)$ if and only if this equation follows from A1–A7. By theorem 23, then, the equation "$f(\alpha_1, \cdots, \alpha_k) = g(\alpha_1, \cdots, \alpha_k)$" is valid for all values of $\alpha_1, \cdots, \alpha_k$ in any Boolean algebra and is deducible from A1–A7.

COROLLARY 24a. *Let f and g be Boolean functions as in theorem 24. Suppose that for all $\alpha_1, \cdots, \alpha_k$ in C such that $f(\alpha_1, \cdots, \alpha_k) = 1$, the element $g(\alpha_1, \cdots, \alpha_k) = 1$ also. Then "$f(\alpha_1, \cdots, \alpha_k) \subset g(\alpha_1, \cdots, \alpha_k)$" is provable from* A1–A7, *and is therefore valid in all Boolean algebras.*

Proof. Let $h(\alpha_1, \cdots, \alpha_k) = f(\alpha_1, \cdots, \alpha_k) \cap (g(\alpha_1, \cdots, \alpha_k))'$. If $\alpha_1, \cdots, \alpha_k$ take on only the values 0 or 1, then $f(\alpha_1, \cdots,$

$\alpha_k) = 0$ or 1. If $f(\alpha_1, \cdots, \alpha_k) = 0$, then $h(\alpha_1, \cdots, \alpha_k) = 0$. If $f(\alpha_1, \cdots, \alpha_k) = 1$, then $g(\alpha_1, \cdots, \alpha_k) = 1$, and $h(\alpha_1, \cdots, \alpha_k) = 0$. Hence $h(\alpha_1, \cdots, \alpha_k) = 0$ for all $\alpha_1, \cdots, \alpha_k$ in C by theorem 23, and is therefore deducible from A1–A7 and valid in all Boolean algebras. The inclusion "$f \subset g$" follows by T3.

We now know that all generally true equations between Boolean functions are provable from our assumptions and, by theorem 23, have a simple systematic procedure for proving them or for testing their validity. Before going on to a deeper study of Boolean algebras, we wish to make a few remarks about deductive sciences in general.

First, what is to prevent us from laying down any assumptions we please? From a logical point of view, there is nothing but the requirement of consistency to restrict the possible assumptions; that is, it must be impossible to prove some proposition and also its falsity from the postulates. The simplest way to prove that a system of postulates is consistent is to exhibit a concrete interpretation of the undefined terms in which all the postulates are true. Thus we have given three concrete interpretations of "C", "$\cap$", "$'$" in which A1–A7 hold. If a contradiction could follow from the postulates, this contradiction would be true of the concrete interpretation. But anything actually existing in the real world must be self-consistent; hence the postulates must be consistent. The last sentence might be contested by some philosophers, notably Berkeley, but we shall not enter into any further discussion of such questions. A more serious difficulty is that the real world, so far as we know, contains only a finite number of objects. Therefore it is impossible to give a concrete model of a system of postulates requiring that some class have an infinite number of members. Hilbert has proposed another method of proving consistency whereby on the basis of an analysis of the methods of proof in the deductive science we show that no contradiction can arise. This method requires the machinery of Chapter IV.

While logically we can take any consistent set of assumptions and construct a deductive science from them, actually our choice of postulates is constrained by other considerations.

Usually we have one or more concrete interpretations in mind and we know, roughly speaking, some of the propositions which we wish to be true in the deductive science to be constructed. Aesthetic considerations also play an important role. We want the postulates to be simple and the proofs based on them to be elegant. Here science merges inseparably with art; we wish not only to build up a body of knowledge but also to create a thing of beauty. Finally, the principle first enunciated by E. H. Moore—"The existence of analogies between the central features of various theories implies the existence of a general theory which underlies the particular theories and unifies them with respect to those central features"—also serves as a valuable guide in constructing deductive sciences.

Another desirable, though not essential, requirement of a system of postulates is that they be independent; that is, that none of them be deducible from the rest. If the postulates are not independent then some of them can be omitted without changing the totality of true propositions in the deductive science. For the sake of economy, then, we want the postulates to be independent. To say that a postulate p is independent of the others is equivalent to saying that "p is false" is consistent with the rest. Having thus reduced the problem of independence to that of consistency, we can use the methods described above to prove the independence of a system of postulates. Thus, if in a concrete interpretation of the undefined terms all of the assumptions except p become true propositions, then p is independent of the others.

For example, if we define C as the set whose members are the numbers 0, 1, and 2, and define $\cap$ and $'$ by the following tables:

$\cap$	0	1	2
0	0	0	0
1	0	1	1
2	0	2	2

α	α'
0	1
1	0
2	0

then it is easy to verify that all of A1–A7 except A2 are true. Here we read the table for $\cap$ as follows: $\alpha \cap \beta$ is found in the

α^{th} row and β^{th} column; for example $1 \cap 2 = 1$, $2 \cap 1 = 2$, $2 \cap 0 = 0$, etc. Since $1 \cap 2 \neq 2 \cap 1$, A2 is false. Similarly we can prove the other postulates independent.

The problem of the independence of a system of postulates led to the important discoveries of non-Euclidean geometry and the theory of relativity.

EXERCISES

Ex. 1. Deduce the rest of T1.1.4–T1.1.40 from the postulates.

Ex. 2. Prove that if $(C, \cap, ')$ is a Boolean algebra and if we define $\cup$ as above, then $(C, \cup, ')$ is also a Boolean algebra. For the moment let us denote $\alpha \cup \beta$ by "$\alpha \cap {}^*\beta$", so as to suggest the corresponding operations in the new algebra. Let $T(\alpha) = \alpha'$ for all α in C. Show that

$$T(\alpha') = T(\alpha)',$$
$$T(\alpha \cap \beta) = T(\alpha) \cap^* T(\beta),$$
$$T(\alpha) = T(\beta) \text{ if and only if } \alpha = \beta,$$

and for every β in C there is an α such that $T(\alpha) = \beta$. Hence these algebras have exactly the same structure. This is called the *law of duality*.

Ex. 3. Verify that all the postulates except A3 are valid in the following model:

$\cap$	0	1	2
0	0	2	1
1	2	1	0
2	1	0	2

α	α'
0	0
1	2
2	1

Ex. 4. Construct a model showing the independence of A4.

Ex. 5. Show that the arithmetical interpretation on p. 10 works if 210 is replaced by any square-free number n, i.e. any number n such that no perfect square except 1 divides n. Does it work for any other values of n?

SECTION 3 THE STRUCTURE AND REPRESENTATION OF BOOLEAN ALGEBRAS

We now ask how completely does the deductive science constructed in the last section describe the algebra of classes. In other words, are there Boolean algebras essentially different from the algebra of classes? If so, what is their relation to that algebra?

Let us begin with the case where C has m members, where m is finite and greater than 1. We say that α is an *atom* whenever $\alpha \neq 0$, and $\beta \subset \alpha$ implies that $\beta = 0$ or $\beta = \alpha$. If we think of the relation $\beta \subset \alpha$ as meaning that β is contained in α, then an atom is an element of C which contains no others but itself and 0.

T1. *If $\alpha \neq 0$, then there is an atom β such that $\beta \subset \alpha$.*

Proof. If α is itself an atom, then the conclusion immediately follows. If α is not an atom, then there is an element α_1 such that $\alpha_1 \neq 0$, $\alpha_1 \neq \alpha$, $\alpha_1 \subset \alpha$. If α_1 is not an atom, then there is an element α_2 such that $\alpha_2 \neq 0$, $\alpha_2 \neq \alpha_1$, $\alpha_2 \subset \alpha_1$. Now $\alpha_2 \neq \alpha$, for if $\alpha_2 = \alpha$, then $\alpha \subset \alpha_1$, $\alpha_1 \subset \alpha$, and therefore $\alpha = \alpha_1$. If α_2 is not an atom, there is an element α_3 such that $\alpha_3 \neq 0$, $\alpha_3 \neq \alpha_2$, and $\alpha_3 \subset \alpha_2$. Proceeding in this way we show that there are distinct elements $\alpha_1, \alpha_2, \cdots, \alpha_k$ such that

$$\alpha_k \subset \alpha_{k-1},\ \alpha_{k-1} \subset \alpha_{k-2},\ \cdots,\ \alpha_2 \subset \alpha_1,\ \alpha_1 \subset \alpha,$$

and $\alpha_k \neq 0$. If α_k is not an atom, then we can extend this chain to one more element. But there are only m elements altogether in C. Consequently after at most $m - 1$ steps, the chain must stop and it must be impossible to add another element to it. Hence if α_k is the last element in the chain, then α_k must be an atom contained in α.

Let $R(\alpha)$ denote the class of all atoms β such that $\beta \subset \alpha$. Then $R(1)$ is the set of all atoms in C.

T2. *If γ is an atom, then either $\gamma \subset \alpha$ or $\gamma \cap \alpha = 0$.*

Proof. $\gamma \cap \alpha \subset \gamma$. Therefore $\gamma \cap \alpha = \gamma$ or $\gamma \cap \alpha = 0$.

T3. *$R(\alpha \cap \beta) = R(\alpha) \cap R(\beta)$, $R(\alpha') = R(1) - R(\alpha)$ and $R(\alpha) = R(\beta)$ if and only if $\alpha = \beta$. If $\alpha_1, \cdots, \alpha_k$ are distinct* *atoms, then* $R(\alpha_1 \cup \alpha_2 \cup \cdots \cup \alpha_k)$ *is the class whose members are* $\alpha_1, \cdots, \alpha_k$.

Notice that here $\alpha \cap \beta$ is the combination defined in B, while $R(\alpha) \cap R(\beta)$ is the common part of the two sets $R(\alpha)$ and $R(\beta)$.

Proof. If $\gamma \in R(\alpha \cap \beta)$, then $\gamma \subset \alpha \cap \beta$. But $\alpha \cap \beta \subset \alpha$ and $\alpha \cap \beta \subset \beta$, by T1.1.27. Hence $\gamma \subset \alpha$ and $\gamma \subset \beta$. Therefore $\gamma \in R(\alpha) \cap R(\beta)$. Conversely, if $\gamma \in R(\alpha) \cap R(\beta)$, then $\gamma \subset \alpha$ and $\gamma \subset \beta$. Consequently $\gamma \subset \alpha \cap \beta$ by T1.1.34. Hence $\gamma \in R(\alpha \cap \beta)$.

If $\gamma \in R(\alpha')$ and $\gamma \in R(\alpha)$, then $\gamma \in R(\alpha) \cap R(\alpha') = R(\alpha \cap \alpha') = R(0)$. Therefore $\gamma \subset 0$, and, by T1.1.2, $\gamma = 0$, which is impossible. Hence if $\gamma \in R(\alpha')$, $\gamma \in R(1) - R(\alpha)$. Conversely, if $\gamma \in R(1) - R(\alpha)$, then γ is not in $R(\alpha)$. Hence $\gamma \cap \alpha = \gamma \cap \alpha'' = 0$ by T2, so that $\gamma \subset \alpha'$, and finally, $\gamma \in R(\alpha')$.

If $R(\alpha) = R(\beta)$ and $\alpha \neq \beta$, then either $\alpha \subset \beta$ or $\beta \subset \alpha$ must be false, say the first. Then $\alpha \cap \beta' \neq 0$, so that, by T1, there is an atom $\gamma \subset \alpha \cap \beta'$. But $R(\alpha \cap \beta') = R(\alpha) \cap R(\beta') = R(\alpha) \cap (R(1) - R(\beta)) = R(\alpha) - R(\beta)$. Since $\gamma \in R(\alpha)$ and not in $R(\beta)$, then $R(\alpha) \neq R(\beta)$, contrary to hypothesis.

Finally, $\alpha_1, \cdots, \alpha_k$ are members of $R(\alpha_1 \cup \cdots \cup \alpha_k)$. If $\gamma \in R(\alpha_1 \cup \cdots \cup \alpha_k)$ and $\gamma \neq \alpha_1, \cdots, \gamma \neq \alpha_k$, then, by T2, $\gamma \cap \alpha_1 = \cdots = \gamma \cap \alpha_k = 0$. Hence $\gamma = \gamma \cap (\alpha_1 \cup \cdots \cup \alpha_k) = (\gamma \cap \alpha_1) \cup \cdots \cup (\gamma \cap \alpha_k) = 0$, which is impossible.

By a *one-to-one correspondence* between two classes we mean a relation whereby to each member of one class corresponds a unique member of the other and vice versa. Thus at a dance in which there are no wallflowers, the relation between each girl and her partner is a one-to-one correspondence between the girls and the men. We say that two Boolean algebras B_1 and B_2 are *isomorphic* if there is a one-to-one correspondence between the classes C_1 and C_2 such that whenever α_1 corresponds to α_2 and β_1 to β_2, the subscripts indicating to which algebra the elements belong, then α_1' corresponds to α_2' and $\alpha_1 \cap \beta_1$ corresponds to $\alpha_2 \cap \beta_2$. If B_1 and B_2 are isomorphic, then they have exactly the same structure. We are now in a position to prove

THEOREM 4. *If* B *is a Boolean algebra in which* C *has* m *ele-*

ments, where m is finite and greater than 1, *then B is isomorphic to* B_1, *the Boolean algebra of all subclasses of the class of all atoms in C. If n is the number of atoms in C, then* $m = 2^n$.

Proof. By T3, the relation between α and $R(\alpha)$ is a one-to-one correspondence between C and C_1, and B and B_1 are isomorphic. If $\alpha_1, \cdots, \alpha_n$ are the atoms in C, then to each class $R(\alpha)$ corresponds a sequence $a_1, \cdots, a_n$ of 0's and 1's where $a_k = 1$ or 0 according as α_k is in $R(\alpha)$ or not. There are two possible values for each of the a's; therefore, there are 2^n possible sequences of a's, and hence also 2^n subclasses of $R(1)$.

COROLLARY 4a. *If* B_1 *and* B_2 *are Boolean algebras with the same finite number of elements, then they are isomorphic.*

Proof. If n_1 and n_2 are the numbers of atoms in B_1 and B_2 respectively, then $2^{n_1} = 2^{n_2}$, so that $n_1 = n_2 = n$. Let $\alpha_1, \cdots, \alpha_n$ be the distinct atoms of B_1 and let $\beta_1, \cdots, \beta_n$ be those of B_2. If $\alpha \in C$, then $R(\alpha)$ is some subclass of $R(1)$; say that it has the distinct members $\alpha_{i_1}, \cdots, \alpha_{i_k}$. Then $R(\alpha) = R(\alpha_{i_1} \cup \cdots \cup \alpha_{i_k})$ by T4, so that $\alpha = \alpha_{i_1} \cup \cdots \cup \alpha_{i_k}$. Let $T(\alpha) = \beta_{i_1} \cup \cdots \cup \beta_{i_k}$. Then the relation between α and $T(\alpha)$ is a one-to-one correspondence between B_1 and B_2. By T3, $R(\alpha') = R(1_1) - R(\alpha) =$ the set of all those α_j's different from $\alpha_{i_1}, \cdots, \alpha_{i_k}$. Hence $T(\alpha') = \beta_{j_1} \cup \cdots \cup \beta_{j_{n-k}}$, where the β's are all those β_j's which are not in $R(T(\alpha))$. This shows that $R(T(\alpha')) = R(1_2) - R(T(\alpha)) = R((T(\alpha))')$, so that $T(\alpha') = (T(\alpha))'$. Similarly we can show that $T(\alpha \cap \beta) = T(\alpha) \cap T(\beta)$. Therefore B_1 and B_2 are isomorphic.

In order to handle the more difficult case where C has infinitely many members we need the so-called Zorn's Lemma. The pair (A, R) consisting of a non-empty class A and a relation R defined for the members of A is called an *ordered system* if $a\ R\ b$ and $b\ R\ c$ always imply $a\ R\ c$. (Here "$a\ R\ b$" means "a has the relation R to b.") A non-empty subclass B of A is called a *linear subsystem* if for every pair of distinct members, b_1 and b_2, of B either $b_1\ R\ b_2$ or $b_2\ R\ b_1$ or both. If B is a subclass of A and a is a member of A such that $b\ R\ a$ for all b in B, then a is said to

be an *upper bound* of B. If $a \, R \, b$ implies $b \, R \, a$ for all b in A, then a is said to be a *maximal element* of A.

Zorn's Lemma. An ordered system, each of whose linear subsystems has an upper bound, contains a maximal element.

This will be taken as an axiom in what follows. We shall discuss Zorn's Lemma in greater detail later in III7.

Let B be an arbitrary Boolean algebra. We introduce some concepts of modern algebra which prove to be very useful in the deeper study of Boolean algebras. By an *ideal* we mean a non-empty subclass I of C such that for all α and β in C the element $\alpha \cup \beta \in I$, and for all $\alpha \in I$ and $\gamma \in C$ the element $\alpha \cap \gamma \in I$. A *proper* ideal is one which is not identical with C. The dual concept is the notion of a *sum ideal,* i.e. S is a sum ideal if and only if S is a non-empty subclass of C such that α, $\beta \in S$ implies that $\alpha \cap \beta \in S$, and $\alpha \in S$, $\gamma \in C$ implies that $\alpha \cup \gamma \in S$. This last condition is equivalent to the condition that $\alpha \in S$ and $\alpha \subset \beta$ imply that $\beta \in S$. (T1.1.23, T1.1.27). Similarly a *proper* sum ideal is a sum ideal S different from C. By a *product system* we mean a subclass K of C such that α, $\beta \in K$ implies that $\alpha \cap \beta \in K$. By a *maximal sum ideal* (abbreviated MSI) we mean a proper sum ideal which is contained in no other sum ideal. If B is the algebra of all subclasses of a given class U, then the simplest type of maximal sum ideal is the set of all α's such that $x \in \alpha$, for a fixed element x in U. Note that S is a proper sum ideal if and only if S is a sum ideal and $0 \notin S$. Also $1 \in S$ whenever S is a sum ideal. In the proof of theorem 7 below, the maximal sum ideals play a role similar to that of the atoms in the case where C contains only a finite number of elements. The chief difficulty is the proof of theorem 5, whose corollary corresponds to T1. It will be helpful in following this analysis to refer constantly to the corresponding points in the proof of theorem 4.

THEOREM 5: *If K is a product system, and $0 \notin K$, then there is a maximal sum ideal S containing K.*

Proof. Let A be the class of all product systems K_1 such that

$K \subset K_1$ and $0 \notin K_1$, and let "$K_1\ R\ K_2$" mean that $K_1 \subset K_2$. Then A is non-empty, for K itself is in A. Hence (A, R) is an ordered system. If L is a linear subsystem of A, let K^* be the class of all α's such that there is a product system $K_1 \in L$ such that $\alpha \in K_1$. We claim that K^* is an upper bound of L. For if $\alpha_1, \alpha_2 \in K^*$, then there are product systems, K_1 and K_2 in L such that $\alpha_1 \in K_1$ and $\alpha_2 \in K_2$. Since L is linear, either $K_1 \subset K_2$ or $K_2 \subset K_1$. If, for example, $K_1 \subset K_2$, then $\alpha_1, \alpha_2 \in K_2$, so that $\alpha_1 \cap \alpha_2 \in K_2 \subset K^*$. Thus K^* is a product system. If $0 \in K^*$, then there is a $K_1 \in L$ such that $0 \in K_1$. But this is impossible since $L \subset A$. Hence $K^* \in A$, and is therefore an upper bound of L. Let S be a maximal element of A. Then S is a product system containing K and not containing 0. We wish to prove that S is a sum ideal, for which it now suffices to show that if $\alpha \in S$, $\gamma \in C$, then $\alpha \cup \gamma \in S$. If $\gamma \in C$, let S_1 be the class consisting of all members of S, and all elements of C of the forms $\alpha \cap (\beta \cup \gamma)$ or $\alpha \cup \gamma$, where $\alpha, \beta \in S$. If $0 \in S_1$, then there are elements $\alpha, \beta \in S$ such that $\alpha \cap (\beta \cup \gamma) = 0$. Then $\alpha \cap \beta = \alpha \cap (\beta \cup \gamma) \cap \beta = 0 \in S$, which is impossible. Thus $0 \notin S_1$. Clearly S_1 is a product system containing S, and therefore K, so that $S_1 \in A$. Since S is a maximal element of A, then $S_1 \subset S$. In particular, $\alpha \cup \gamma \in S$ for all $\gamma \in S$. It is now trivial that S is a MSI.

Corollary 5. *If $\alpha \in C$, $\alpha \neq 0$, then there is a maximal sum ideal containing α.*

For the set K whose only member is α is a product system not containing 0.

Theorem 6. *If S is a maximal sum ideal and $\alpha \in C$, then either $\alpha \in S$ or $\alpha' \in S$.*

Proof. Suppose that $\alpha \cap \beta \neq 0$ for all $\beta \in S$. Let K be the class consisting of S and all elements of the form $\alpha \cap \beta$ where $\beta \in S$. Then K is a product system and $0 \notin K$. Let S_1 be a maximal sum ideal containing K. Then $S \subset S_1$, and since S is a maximal ideal, we must have $S = S_1$. But $\alpha = \alpha \cap 1 \in K \subset S_1$.

On the other hand, if there is a $\beta \in S$ such that $\alpha \cap \beta = 0$, then $\alpha' = \beta \cup \alpha' \in S$.

COROLLARY 6a. *If S is a maximal sum ideal and $\alpha \cup \beta \in S$, then $\alpha \in S$ or $\beta \in S$.*

For if $\alpha \notin S$, then $\alpha' \in S$, so that $\beta \cap \alpha' = (\alpha \cup \beta) \cap \alpha' \in S$, and therefore $\beta = (\beta \cap \alpha') \cup \beta \in S$.

Let $T(\alpha)$ be the class of all MSI which contain α, and let C_1 be the class of all classes of the form $T(\alpha)$.

THEOREM 7. *The triple $(C_1, \cap, *)$, where $T(\alpha)^* = T(1) - T(\alpha)$ is a Boolean algebra isomorphic with B. This isomorphism is generated by the relation whereby α corresponds to $T(\alpha)$.*

Proof. First we shall prove that $T(\alpha \cap \beta) = T(\alpha) \cap T(\beta)$. If $P \in T(\alpha) \cap T(\beta)$, then $\alpha \in P$ and $\beta \in P$. Hence $\alpha \cap \beta \in P$, so that $P \in T(\alpha \cap \beta)$. Conversely, if $P \in T(\alpha \cap \beta)$, then $\alpha \cap \beta \in P$. Since $\alpha \cap \beta \subset \alpha$ and $\alpha \cap \beta \subset \beta$, then $\alpha \in P$ and $\beta \in P$, so that $P \in T(\alpha) \cap T(\beta)$.

Next we show that $T(\alpha') = T(1) - T(\alpha) = T(\alpha)^*$. Now by what we have just proved, $T(\alpha) \cap T(\alpha') = T(0)$. But no MSI contains 0; hence $T(0)$ is the null class and $T(\alpha) \cap T(\alpha') = 0$. But $T(1)$ contains all MSI. It follows that $T(\alpha') \subset T(1) - T(\alpha) = T(\alpha)^*$. Now suppose that P is a MSI which does not contain α. Then, by Theorem 6, $\alpha' \in P$, so that $P \in T(\alpha')$. Putting all this together, we see that $T(1) - T(\alpha) \subset T(\alpha')$, from which we infer that $T(\alpha') = T(\alpha)^*$.

All that remains is to show that the correspondence between C and C_1 defined by the relation between α and $T(\alpha)$ is a one-to-one correspondence. But if $\alpha \neq \beta$, then either $\alpha \cap \beta' \neq 0$ or $\beta \cap \alpha' \neq 0$, say $\alpha \cap \beta' \neq 0$. Then there is a MSI P such that $\alpha \cap \beta' \in P$. That is, $P \in T(\alpha \cap \beta') = T(\alpha) \cap (T(1) - T(\beta)) = T(\alpha) - T(\beta)$. Therefore $T(\alpha) \neq T(\beta)$.

If B is a Boolean algebra, and C_1 is a subclass of C which is closed under the operations $\cap$ and $'$ (i.e. whenever α and β are in C_1, then $\alpha \cap \beta$ and α' are in C_1), then the triple $B_1 = (C_1, \cap, ')$ is also a Boolean algebra. In such a case we say that B_1 is a *subalgebra* of B. Then the algebra $(C_1, \cap, *)$ defined in Theorem

7 is a subalgebra of the algebra of all subclasses of $T(1)$, which is the class of all maximal sum ideals of B.

COROLLARY 7a. *Every Boolean algebra is isomorphic to a subalgebra of the algebra of all subclasses of some class.*

Thus every Boolean algebra is isomorphic to some algebra of classes. This to a large extent justifies the prominent place given to Boolean algebras in the study of the logic of classes.

Under what conditions is a Boolean algebra isomorphic to the algebra of all subclasses of some class? In order to answer this question we must introduce a few additional concepts.

If B is a Boolean algebra and A is any class of elements in C, then we say that β is a *least upper bound*, or *union*, of A if

(1) for all $\alpha \in A$, $\alpha \subset \beta$,

and (2) if $\alpha \subset \gamma$ for all $\alpha \in A$, then $\beta \subset \gamma$.

Clearly, if β and δ are unions of A, then $\beta = \delta$. For by the second condition, $\beta \subset \delta$ and $\delta \subset \beta$. Thus A has at most one union, so that we may speak of *the* union of A if one exists. In that case we shall denote it by $\bigcup(A)$ or $\bigcup_{\alpha \in A} \alpha$. If every non-empty subclass A of C has a union, we say that B is a *complete* Boolean algebra. A Boolean algebra is called *distributive* if for every subclass A of C such that $\bigcup(A)$ exists, and for every element β in C, we have

$$\beta \cap \bigcup(A) = \bigcup_{\alpha \in A} (\beta \cap \alpha).$$

We say that B is an *atomic* Boolean algebra if for every non-zero element α there exists an atom β such that $\beta \subset \alpha$.

THEOREM 8. *A necessary and sufficient condition that the Boolean algebra B be isomorphic to the algebra of all subclasses of some class is that B be complete, distributive, and atomic. In that case B is isomorphic to the algebra of all subclasses of the class of atoms in C.*

Proof. Suppose that B is isomorphic to the algebra of all subclasses of some class $\mathfrak{A}$. Let the subclass of $\mathfrak{A}$ which corresponds to a given element α of C be denoted by $A(\alpha)$. Now if $x \in \mathfrak{A}$ and

$\{x\}$ is the class whose only member is x, then for some β in C, $A(\beta) = \{x\}$. We claim that β is an atom. For if $\gamma \subset \beta$, then $A(\gamma) \subset A(\beta)$. Hence $A(\gamma)$ contains at most one member, namely x. Therefore either $A(\gamma) = 0$, whereupon $\gamma = 0$, or $A(\gamma) = \{x\}$, whereupon $\gamma = \beta$.

If $\alpha \in C$ and $\alpha \neq 0$, then $A(\alpha) \neq 0$. Let $x \in A(\alpha)$, and let $\beta \in C$ be such that $A(\beta) = \{x\}$. Then β is an atom and $\beta \subset \alpha$ since $A(\beta) \subset A\ (\alpha)$. Hence B is atomic.

If $\mathfrak{A}_1$ is any subclass of C, let $\mathfrak{D}$ be the class of all elements x such that $x \in A(\alpha)$ for some $\alpha \in \mathfrak{A}_1$. Let β be the element of C such that $A(\beta) = \mathfrak{D}$. Then if $\alpha \in \mathfrak{A}_1$, then $A(\alpha) \subset \mathfrak{D} = A(\beta)$, so that $\alpha \subset \beta$. Also, if $\alpha \subset \gamma$ for all $\alpha \in \mathfrak{A}_1$, then $A(\alpha) \subset A(\gamma)$ for all α in $\mathfrak{A}_1$. But if $x \in \mathfrak{D}$, there is some α in $\mathfrak{A}_1$ such that $x \in A(\alpha)$, and therefore $x \in A(\gamma)$. This shows that $\mathfrak{D} \subset A(\gamma)$ so that $\beta \subset \gamma$. Thus we have proved that β is the union of $\mathfrak{A}_1$, and therefore that B is complete.

Lastly, if $\mathfrak{A}_1$ is any subclass of C and β is any member of C, we must show that $\beta \cap \bigcup(\mathfrak{A}_1) = \bigcup_{\alpha \in \mathfrak{A}_1}(\beta \cap \alpha)$. Let $\mathfrak{D} = A(\bigcup(\mathfrak{A}_1))$ and $\mathfrak{D}_1 = A(\bigcup_{\alpha \in \mathfrak{A}_1}(\beta \cap \alpha))$. If $x \in A(\beta \cap \bigcup(\mathfrak{A}_1)) = A(\beta) \cap \mathfrak{D}$, then there is an α in $\mathfrak{A}_1$ such that $x \in A(\alpha)$, by the preceding paragraph. Hence $x \in A(\beta) \cap A(\alpha) = A(\beta \cap \alpha) \subset \mathfrak{D}_1$. Consequently $\beta \cap \bigcup(\mathfrak{A}_1) \subset \bigcup_{\alpha \in \mathfrak{A}_1}(\beta \cap \alpha)$. Conversely, if $x \in \mathfrak{D}_1$, then there is an α in $\mathfrak{A}_1$ such that $x \in A(\beta \cap \alpha) = A(\beta) \cap A(\alpha) \subset A(\beta) \cap \mathfrak{D}$. Hence $\bigcup_{\alpha \in \mathfrak{A}_1}(\beta \cap \alpha) \subset \beta \cap \bigcup(\mathfrak{A}_1)$, which completes the proof.

Now suppose that B is complete, distributive, and atomic. Let $\mathfrak{A}$ be the class of all atoms in C, and let $A(\alpha)$ be the class of all atoms β such that $\beta \subset \alpha$. We shall show that the relation between α and $A(\alpha)$ is a one-to-one correspondence between C and the class of all subclasses of $\mathfrak{A}$ whereby B and the algebra of all these subclasses are isomorphic.

Firstly, we show that $A(\alpha \cap \beta) = A(\alpha) \cap A(\beta)$. If $\gamma \in A(\alpha \cap \beta)$, then γ is an atom and $\gamma \subset \alpha \cap \beta$, so that $\gamma \subset \alpha$ and $\gamma \subset \beta$. It follows that $\gamma \in A(\alpha) \cap A(\beta)$, and further, that $A(\alpha \cap \beta) \subset A(\alpha) \cap A(\beta)$. Conversely, if $\gamma \in A(\alpha) \cap A(\beta)$, then γ is an atom and $\gamma \subset \alpha$ and $\gamma \subset \beta$. Hence $\gamma \subset \alpha \cap \beta$, so that $\gamma \in A(\alpha \cap \beta)$.

Next we prove that $A(\alpha') = \mathfrak{A} - A(\alpha) = A(\alpha)^*$. If $\gamma \in A(\alpha')$, then γ is an atom and $\gamma \subset \alpha'$. If $\gamma \in A(\alpha)$ as well, then $\gamma \subset \alpha$, so that $\gamma \subset \alpha \cap \alpha' = 0$, and therefore $\gamma = 0$, which is impossible. This shows that $A(\alpha') \subset \mathfrak{A} - A(\alpha)$. Conversely, if $\gamma \in \mathfrak{A} - A(\alpha)$, then, by T2, $\gamma \cap \alpha = 0$, so that $\gamma \subset \alpha'$. As a consequence, $\gamma \in A(\alpha')$.

Thirdly, we show that if $A(\alpha) = A(\beta)$, then $\alpha = \beta$, which implies that the correspondence is one-to-one. If $\alpha \neq \beta$, then either $\alpha \cap \beta' \neq 0$ or $\beta \cap \alpha' \neq 0$, say $\alpha \cap \beta' \neq 0$. Then there is an atom γ such that $\gamma \subset \alpha \cap \beta'$. Hence $\gamma \in A(\alpha \cap \beta') = A(\alpha) \cap (\mathfrak{A} - A(\beta)) = A(\alpha) - A(\beta)$; therefore $A(\alpha) \neq A(\beta)$.

Finally, we prove that if $\mathfrak{A}_1$ is any subclass of $\mathfrak{A}$, then there is an element α in C such that $A(\alpha) = \mathfrak{A}_1$. Now $\mathfrak{A}_1$ is also a subclass of C, and therefore, by the completeness of B, has a union. Let $\alpha = \bigcup(\mathfrak{A}_1)$. We claim that $A(\alpha) = \mathfrak{A}_1$. For if $\gamma \in \mathfrak{A}_1$, then $\gamma \subset \alpha$, so that $\gamma \in A(\alpha)$. Conversely, if $\gamma \in A(\alpha)$, then $\gamma \subset \alpha$. Therefore $\gamma = \gamma \cap \alpha = \gamma \cap \bigcup(\mathfrak{A}_1) = \bigcup_{\beta \in \mathfrak{A}_1}(\gamma \cap \beta)$. Now if β is an atom and $\beta \neq \gamma$, then by theorem 4, $\beta \cap \gamma = 0$. It follows that if γ were not in $\mathfrak{A}_1$, then $\gamma \cap \beta = 0$ for all β in $\mathfrak{A}_1$, and therefore $\gamma = 0$, which is impossible. Hence if $\gamma \in A(\alpha)$, then $\gamma \in \mathfrak{A}_1$. This completes the proof.

EXERCISES

Ex. 1. We say that the descending chain condition holds if there is no infinite sequence of distinct elements α_n such that $\alpha_{n+1} \subset \alpha_n$ for all n. Similarly for the ascending chain condition. Show that (a) in a Boolean algebra either implies the other, (b) the descending chain condition implies T1, (c) the descending chain condition implies that the number of elements in C is finite.

Ex. 2. Show that if the number of elements of C is finite, and f is a Boolean function of one variable, then the number of solutions of the equation $f(\xi) = \eta$, for any η such that $f(0) \cap f(1) \subset \eta \subset f(0) \cup f(1)$, is equal to 2^k, where k is the number of atoms contained in $f(0)' + f(1)$.

Ex. 3. Let B be the Boolean algebra of all subclasses of some class $\mathfrak{A}$. What are the atoms of B?

Ex. 4. Let C be the class of all classes of integers. Define "$\alpha \equiv \beta$" to mean that $\alpha + \beta$ has a finite number of elements. Show that $\equiv$ is an equivalence relation, and that $(C, \cap, ')$ is a Boolean algebra with respect to $\equiv$. Prove that there are no atoms in this algebra.

Ex. 5. In problem 4 let "$\alpha \equiv_1 \beta$" denote that $\alpha \equiv \beta$ and that the integer 2 is not contained in $\alpha + \beta$. Show that $(C, \cap, ')$ is also a Boolean algebra with respect to $\equiv_1$. What are the atoms of this algebra, if any?

Ex. 6. In problem 3 show that if $\mathfrak{A}$ is infinite, then there are MSI different from the simple type mentioned on p. 21. Hint: Choose a suitable product system and apply theorem 5. Tarski and Ulam, Fundamenta Mathematica, 1930, have proved that the non-trivial MSI outnumber the trivial ones by far. No way is known for constructing one, however, or even of proving their existence without some such assumption as Zorn's lemma or the axiom of choice (III7).

Ex. 7. Prove that if α is an atom, then the class of all β such that $\alpha \subset \beta$ is a MSI.

Ex. 8. Let C be the class of all classes α of integers such that either α or α' contains only a finite number of elements. Show that $(C, \cap, ')$ is a Boolean algebra. Is it complete?

Ex. 9. Show that in a complete Boolean algebra if A is any class of elements in C, then there exists a *greatest lower bound*, or *join*, β of A satisfying
(1) for all α in A, $\beta \subset \alpha$, and
(2) if $\gamma \subset \alpha$ for all $\alpha \in A$, then $\gamma \subset \beta$.

Chapter II

THE LOGIC OF PROPOSITIONS

SECTION 1 FUNDAMENTALS

In the last chapter we studied the general laws underlying the logic of classes. The propositions with which we worked were mostly of the form "$\alpha = \beta$," where α and β are classes. We found out under what conditions such propositions are true and under what conditions one proposition of this type implies another. Now we shall consider what laws governing the logic of propositions are independent of their inner structure.

If p and q are propositions, then "$p \wedge q$" shall denote the proposition that both p and q, and "$p \vee q$" shall denote the proposition that either p or q or both, and "$\sim p$" shall denote the proposition that it is false that p. For example, let "p" denote that Willie is silly, "q" denote that Jane is vain, and "r" denote that man is vile. Then "$\sim p \vee (q \wedge r)$" denotes the proposition that either Willie is not silly, or both Jane is vain and man is vile, or Jane is vain, man is vile, but Willie is not silly.

We shall tentatively think of propositions as having one of two truth values, "truth" or "falsity," which we shall denote by "t" and "f." Then the truth values of $p \wedge q$, $p \vee q$, and $\sim p$ are determined by those of p and q. This is indicated in the following tables:

p	q	$p \wedge q$	$p \vee q$
t	t	t	t
t	f	f	t
f	t	f	t
f	f	f	f

p	$\sim p$
t	f
f	t

We shall say that two propositions are *equivalent* if they have the same truth value, and shall denote this relation by "$p\ E\ q$." The statement "$p\ E\ q$" is a sentence in the syntax language, not in the object language.

The following may be easily verified, either directly or by means of the above truth tables:

(1) $p \wedge q\ E\ q \wedge p$,
(2) $p \wedge (q \wedge r)\ E\ (p \wedge q) \wedge r$,
(3) if $p \wedge q\ E\ p$, then $p \wedge (\sim q)\ E\ r \wedge (\sim r)$, and
(4) if $p \wedge (\sim q)\ E\ r \wedge (\sim r)$, then $p \wedge q\ E\ p$.

Also we have

(5) if $p\ E\ q$, then $\sim p\ E \sim q$, and
(6) if $p\ E\ q$, then $p \wedge r\ E\ q \wedge r$ and $r \wedge p\ E\ r \wedge q$.

Thus we see that the laws of Boolean algebra also hold for the logic of propositions with "$\wedge$", "$\sim$", and "E," in the places of "$\cap$", "$'$", and "$=$". In fact, the symbols "t" and "f" form a two-element Boolean algebra with respect to the operations $\wedge$ and $\sim$ defined by the above tables. The algebra of propositions is, then, essentially the same as the algebra of classes. We are thus led to the following formulation of the logic of propositions as a deductive science.

The undefined terms in our system are a non-empty class C, two operations $\wedge$ and $\sim$ defined on C, and a relation E defined between the members of C. The unproved propositions are:

A1′. *If p and q are in C, then $\sim p$ and $p \wedge q$ are uniquely determined members of C.*
A2′. *If p and q are in C, then $p \wedge q\ E\ q \wedge p$.*
A3′. *If p, q, and r are in C, then $(p \wedge q) \wedge r\ E\ p \wedge (q \wedge r)$.*
A4′. *If p, q, and r are in C, and $p \wedge q\ E\ p$, then $p \wedge \sim q\ E\ r \wedge \sim r$.*
A5′. *If p, q, and r are in C, and $p \wedge \sim q\ E\ r \wedge \sim r$, then $p \wedge q\ E\ p$.*
A6′. *If p and q are in C and $p\ E\ q$, then $\sim p\ E \sim q$.*

A7′. *If* p, q, *and* r *are in* C, *and* $p\ E\ q$, *then* $p \wedge r\ E\ q \wedge r$ *and* $r \wedge p\ E\ r \wedge q$.
A8′. *If* p *is in* C, *then* $p\ E\ p$.
A9′. *If* p *and* q *are in* C, *and* $p\ E\ q$, *then* $q\ E\ p$.
A10′. *If* p, q, *and* r *are in* C, *and* $p\ E\ q$, *and* $q\ E\ r$, *then* $p\ E\ r$.

It is now clear that $(C, \wedge, \sim, E)$ is a Boolean algebra with respect to the equivalence relation E. In other words, the logic of classes and the logic of propositions are models of the same deductive science, namely that of Boolean algebra. All theorems in Boolean algebra hold for both logics. Theorem 1.2.23 gives us a criterion for determining whether a sentence of the form "$p\ E\ q$" is or is not universally valid in the logic of propositions, where p and q are expressed as Boolean functions of arbitrary propositions.

There is one combination, namely "$(\sim p) \vee q$" or "$\sim(p \wedge (\sim q))$," which has many of the intuitive properties of an implication relation. It is therefore called *material implication* and is symbolized by "$p \supset q$." There has been some controversy over the question of whether this is a suitable interpretation of the proposition that if p then q, and we shall not commit ourselves on this question. We merely remark that for most mathematical purposes this interpretation is entirely adequate. The determination of its truth value from those of p and q is shown by the table:

p	q	$p \supset q$
t	t	t
t	f	f
f	t	t
f	f	t

Thus with this interpretation a false proposition implies any proposition and a true proposition is implied by any proposition. The proposition $p \supset q$ is false if and only if p is true and q is false. Some philosophers have argued that these properties of material implication disagree with the intuitive meaning of implication. Nevertheless, these properties do agree with the interpretation of implication used in practice by mathematicians.

Note carefully that while "$\alpha \subset \beta$" expresses a relation between elements in a Boolean algebra and is thus a sentence in the syntax language, $p \supset q$ is an element of C, and "$p \supset q$" is a sentence in the object language.

SECTION 2 ALTERNATIVE FORMULATIONS

The formulation of the propositional logic based on A1′–A10′ is entirely adequate and shows very clearly the relation between the logic of propositions and Boolean algebra. There are, however, other approaches to the logic of propositions which are, in some ways, more acceptable intuitively.

The first one which we shall consider has the following primitive frame:

Undefined terms: a class C, a class $\mathfrak{T}$, a binary operation $\supset$, and a unary operation $\sim$;

Unproved propositions:

A1″. *If p is in $\mathfrak{T}$, then p is in C;*

A2″. *If p and q are in C, then $p \supset q$ is a uniquely determined element of C;*

A3″. *If p is in C, then $\sim p$ is a uniquely determined element of C;*

A4″. *If p, q, and r are in C, then $[p \supset (q \supset r)] \supset [(p \supset q) \supset (p \supset r)]$ is in $\mathfrak{T}$;*

A5″. *If p and q are in C, then $p \supset (q \supset p)$ is in $\mathfrak{T}$;*

A6″. *If p and q are in C, then $[(\sim p) \supset (\sim q)] \supset [q \supset p]$ is in $\mathfrak{T}$;*

A7″. *If p and $p \supset q$ are in $\mathfrak{T}$, then q is in $\mathfrak{T}$.*

An ordered quadruple $(C, \mathfrak{T}, \supset, \sim)$ satisfying these postulates will be called a *Boolean propositional logic.*

In the concrete interpretation which we have in mind, C is the class of propositions, $\mathfrak{T}$ is the class of true propositions, $p \supset q$ is the proposition that if p, then q, and $\sim p$ is the proposition that it is false that p. We shall abbreviate the statement "p is in $\mathfrak{T}$" by "$\vdash p$," which may be read "We assert that p" or "It is true that p." Of course, "$\vdash p$" is a sentence in the syntax language.

For brevity we shall adopt certain conventions for omitting parentheses or replacing them by dots. The symbols $\supset$, $\vee$, $\wedge$, and $\sim$ shall be called *connectives* and this shall be their *order of seniority*, so that "$\supset$" is senior to the symbols that follow it in this list, etc. We shall write sentences in the object language using dots as punctuation instead of parentheses. A *point* is a symbol consisting of zero or more dots. We use points on the right of unary connectives such as "$\sim$" or on either side of binary connectives. A point to the right of a connective will be called a *right point*, and one to the left will be called a *left point*; the point will be said to be *attached* to the connective in question. Each point in a sentence indicates a certain part, which is itself a sentence and would be enclosed in parentheses in the old notation. This part is called the *scope* of the point. The scope is determined by the following rules.

I. If α and β are points in a sentence, then α is *senior* to β if and only if either
   (a) α consists of more dots than β; or
   (b) α and β have the same number of dots, but α is attached to a connective senior to that to which β is attached; or
   (c) α and β are the same with respect to (a) and (b) but α lies to the right of β.

II. The scope of any right point extends to the right until the first (if any) left point which is senior to the given point and all intermediate right points.

III. The same as II with "right" and "left" interchanged.

Thus in the sentence "$p \supset q \supset r$" the points all consist of zero dots and may be identified thus "$p_1 \supset_2 q_3 \supset_4 r$." Their order of seniority from highest to lowest is 4, 3, 2, 1 (See I(c).). The scope of "3" is "$p \supset q$," and the scope of "4" is "r." If we write this sentence in the parentheses notation, we obtain

"$(p \supset q) \supset r$," where we have left out parentheses enclosing single letters. The conclusion of A4$''$ could now be written

$$\text{“}p \supset .q \supset r. \supset .p \supset q \supset .p \supset r\text{”},$$

but we shall often put in extra dots to make the scopes more obvious. The purpose of language being communication, it is more important to write legibly than to be stingy with dots. We shall therefore prefer to write this sentence thus:

$$\text{“}p \supset .q \supset r: \supset :p \supset q \supset .p \supset r\text{”},$$

or even thus:

$$\text{“}p. \supset .q \supset r: \supset :p \supset q. \supset .p \supset r\text{”},$$

although the first form is more economical.

The conclusions of A5$''$ and A6$''$ may be written as follows:

$$\text{“}p \supset .q \supset p\text{”},$$

and $$\text{“}\sim p \supset \sim q. \supset .q \supset p\text{”}.$$

We introduce the following definitions:

D1. "$p \vee q$" *for* "$\sim p \supset q$."
D2. "$p \wedge q$" *for* "$\sim .p \supset \sim q$."
D3. "$p \equiv q$" *for* "$p \supset q. \wedge .q \supset p$."

We shall take "$\equiv$" as senior to "$\supset$."

On the basis of A1$''$–A7$''$ we can prove the following theorems. We shall usually omit the explicit statement that the elements mentioned in these theorems are members of C.

T1. $\vdash p \supset p$.
Proof. (1) $\vdash p \supset .q \supset p \supset p$. (A5$''$)
(2) $\vdash p \supset .q \supset p$. (A5$''$)
(3) $\vdash (1) \supset .(2) \supset .$T1. (A4$''$)

Here step (3) indicates that the statement

$$\vdash p \supset .q \supset p \supset p: \supset :.p \supset .q \supset p: \supset .p \supset p$$

follows from A4″, and that certain parts are identifiable with sentences which were proved in previous steps. Two applications of A7″ yield the desired result. Explicit mention of such applications of A7″ will sometimes be omitted.

T2. $\vdash q \supset r \supset .p \supset q \supset .p \supset r.$

Proof. (1) $\vdash p \supset .q \supset r : \supset :p \supset q \supset .p \supset r.$ (A4″)

(2) $\vdash (1) \supset .q \supset r \supset (1)$ (A5″)

(3) $\vdash q \supset r \supset (1)$ (A7″)

(4) $\vdash q \supset r . \supset :p \supset .q \supset r$ (A5″)

(5) $\vdash (3) \supset .(4) \supset .\mathrm{T2}.$ (A4″)

T3. $\vdash \sim p \supset .p \supset q.$

Proof. (1) $\vdash \sim q \supset \sim p \supset .p \supset q.$ (A6″)

(2) $\vdash \sim p \supset .\sim q \supset \sim p$ (A5″)

(3) $\vdash (1) \supset .(2) \supset .\mathrm{T3}$ (T2)

T4. $\vdash \sim\sim p \supset p.$

Proof. (1) $\vdash \sim\sim p \supset .\sim p \supset \sim\sim\sim p$ (T3)

(2) $\vdash \sim p \supset \sim\sim\sim p . \supset .\sim\sim p \supset p.$ (A6″)

(3) $\vdash (2) \supset :(1) \supset :\sim\sim p \supset .\sim\sim p \supset p$ (T2)

(4) $\vdash \sim\sim p \supset .\sim\sim p \supset p.$ (A7″)

(5) $\vdash \sim\sim p \supset \sim\sim p$ (T1)

(6) $\vdash (4) \supset .(5) \supset .\mathrm{T4}$ (A4″)

T5. $\vdash p \supset \sim\sim p$

Proof. (1) $\vdash \sim\sim\sim p \supset \sim p$ (T4)

(2) $\vdash (1) \supset \mathrm{T5}$ (A6″)

T6. $\vdash p \supset .p \supset q \supset q$

Proof. (1) $\vdash p \supset q \supset .p \supset q$ (T1)

(2) $\vdash (1) \supset :p \supset q \supset p . \supset .p \supset q \supset q$ (A4″)

(3) $\vdash p \supset q \supset p . \supset .p \supset q \supset q$ (A7″)

(4) $\vdash p \supset .p \supset q \supset p$ (A5″)

(5) $\vdash (3) \supset .(4) \supset \mathrm{T6}$ (T2)

T7. $\vdash p \supset .q \supset r : \supset :q \supset .p \supset r$

Proof. (1) $\vdash p \supset q \supset .p \supset r : \supset :.q \supset .p \supset q : \supset :p \supset .q \supset r$ (T2)

(2) $\vdash p \supset .q \supset r : \supset : p \supset q \supset .p \supset r$ (A4″)
(3) $\vdash q \supset .p \supset q$ (A5″)
(4) $\vdash (1) \supset :(2) \supset : p \supset q \supset r . \supset :(3) \supset :q \supset .p \supset r$ (T2)
(5) $\vdash p \supset .q \supset r . \supset :(3) \supset :q \supset .p \supset r$ (A7″)
(6) $\vdash (3) \supset ::(3) \supset :q \supset .p \supset r : \supset :.q \supset .p \supset r$ (T6)
(7) $\vdash (3) \supset :q \supset .p \supset r .: \supset :.q \supset .p \supset r$ (A7″)
(8) $\vdash (7) \supset .(5) \supset$ T7 (T2)

T8. $\vdash p \supset q : \supset :q \supset r \supset .p \supset r$ (T7, T2)
T9. $\vdash p \supset \sim q \supset .q \supset \sim p$
Proof. (1) $\vdash \sim\sim p \supset p$ (T4)
(2) $\vdash (1) : \supset :p \supset \sim q \supset .\sim\sim p \supset \sim q$ (T8)
(3) $\vdash p \supset \sim q \supset .\sim\sim p \supset \sim q$ (A7″)
(4) $\vdash \sim\sim p \supset \sim q . \supset .q \supset \sim p$ (A6″)
(5) $\vdash (3) \supset .(4) \supset$ T9

T10. $\vdash \sim p \supset q \supset .\sim q \supset p$
T11. $\vdash p \supset q \supset .\sim q \supset \sim p$

The proofs of T10 and T11 are similar to that of T9 and may be left to the reader as exercises.

T12. $\vdash p \wedge q \supset q \wedge p$ (T9, T11, D2)
T13. $\vdash p \supset .q \supset p \wedge q$
Proof. (1) $\vdash p \supset .p \supset \sim q \supset \sim q$ (T6)
(2) $\vdash p \supset \sim q \supset \sim q . \supset .q \supset p \wedge q$ (T9, D2)
(3) $\vdash (1) \supset .(2) \supset$ T13 (T8)

T14. $\vdash p \supset q \supset .q \supset p \supset .p \equiv q$ (T13, D3)
T15. $\vdash p \wedge q \supset p$
Proof. (1) $\vdash \sim p \supset .p \supset \sim q$ (T3)
(2) $\vdash p \supset \sim q \supset .\sim .p \wedge q$ (T5, D2)
(3) $\vdash (1) \supset .(2) \supset .\sim p \supset .\sim .p \wedge q$ (T8)
(4) $\vdash \sim p \supset .\sim .p \wedge q : \supset :$ T15 (A6″)

T16. $\vdash p \wedge q \supset q$ (T12, T15)
T17. $\vdash p \wedge q \equiv q \wedge p$ (T12, T14)
T18. $\vdash r \supset p \supset .r \supset q \supset .r \supset p \wedge q$

Proof. (1) $\vdash p \supset .q \supset p \wedge q$ (T13)
(2) $\vdash (1) \supset .r \supset (1)$ (A5″)
(3) $\vdash r \supset (1). \supset .\text{T18}$ (A4″)

T19. $\vdash p \wedge .q \wedge r. \equiv .p \wedge q. \wedge r$
Proof. (1) $\vdash p \wedge .q \wedge r. \supset p$ (T15)
(2) $\vdash p \wedge .q \wedge r. \supset .q \wedge r$ (T16)
(3) $\vdash q \wedge r \supset q$ (T15)
(4) $\vdash (2) \supset .(3) \supset .p \wedge .q \wedge r. \supset q$ (T8)
(5) $\vdash p \wedge .q \wedge r. \supset q$ (A7″)
(6) $\vdash (1) \supset :(5) \supset :p \wedge .q \wedge r. \supset p \wedge q$ (T18)
(7) $\vdash p \wedge .q \wedge r. \supset p \wedge q$ (T16)
(8) $\vdash q \wedge r \supset r$
(9) $\vdash p \wedge .q \wedge r. \supset .r$ ((2), (8), T8)
(10) $\vdash p \wedge .q \wedge r. \supset .p \wedge q. \wedge r$ ((7), (9), T18)

Similarly we prove that

(11) $\vdash p \wedge q. \wedge r. \supset .p \wedge .q \wedge r$
Hence, (12) $\vdash (10) \supset .(11) \supset \text{T19}$ (T14)

T20. *If* $\vdash p$ *and* $\vdash p \equiv q$, *then* $\vdash q$.
Proof. (1) $\vdash p \equiv q. \supset p \supset q$ (T15)

T20 follows from (1) and A7″.

T21. $\vdash p \equiv q. \supset .\sim p \equiv \sim q$
Proof. (1) $\vdash p \equiv q. \supset .p \supset q$ (T15)
(2) $\vdash p \supset q \supset .\sim q \supset \sim p$ (T11)
(3) $\vdash p \equiv q. \supset .\sim q \supset \sim p$ ((1), (2), T8)
(4) $\vdash p \equiv q. \supset .\sim p \supset \sim q$ (T16, T11, T8)
(5) $\vdash p \equiv q. \supset .\sim p \equiv \sim q$ ((3), (4), T18, D3)

T22. $\vdash p \supset q. \equiv .p \wedge q \equiv p$
Proof. (1) $\vdash p \wedge q \supset p$ (T15)
(2) $\vdash p \supset q. \supset .p \wedge q \supset p$ ((1), A5″)
(3) $\vdash \text{T1} \supset .p \supset q \supset .p \supset p \wedge q$ (T18)
(4) $\vdash p \supset q. \supset .p \wedge q \equiv p$ ((2), (3), T18, D3)
(5) $\vdash p \wedge q \equiv p. \supset .p \supset p \wedge q$ (T16, D3)

(6) $\vdash T16 \supset .p \supset p \wedge q \supset .p \supset q$ (T8)

(7) $\vdash p \wedge q \equiv p. \supset .p \supset q$ ((5), (6), A7″, T8)

(8) $\vdash (4) \supset .(7) \supset T22$ (T14)

T23. $\vdash \sim .p \wedge \sim p$ (T5)

T24. $\vdash p \equiv p$ (T1, T13)

T25. $\vdash p \equiv q. \equiv .q \equiv p$ (T17, D3)

T26. $\vdash p \equiv q \supset .p \supset r \equiv q \supset r$

Proof. (1) $\vdash p \equiv q \supset .q \supset p$ (T16)

(2) $\vdash q \supset p \supset .p \supset r \supset .q \supset r$ (T8)

(3) $\vdash (1) \supset .(2) \supset .p \equiv q \supset .p \supset r \supset .q \supset r$ (T8)

Similarly,

(4) $\vdash p \equiv q \supset .q \supset r \supset .p \supset r$

(5) $\vdash (1) \supset .(4) \supset .T26$ (T18)

T27. $\vdash p \equiv q \supset .r \supset p \equiv r \supset q$ (Similar to T26)

T28. $\vdash p \equiv q \supset :q \equiv r. \equiv .p \equiv r$ (T26, T27, T25, T21)

T29. $\vdash \sim\sim p \equiv p$ (T4, T5)

T30. $\vdash p \supset q. \equiv .\sim .p \wedge \sim q$ (T29, T28, T26)

T31. $\vdash \sim p. \equiv .p \equiv r \wedge \sim r$

Proof. (1) $\vdash \sim p \supset .p \supset r \wedge \sim r$ (T3)

(2) $\vdash T23 \supset .r \wedge \sim r \supset p$ (T3)

(3) $\vdash \sim p \supset .r \wedge \sim r \supset p$ (A5″, (2))

(4) $\vdash \sim p \supset .p \equiv r \wedge \sim r$ ((1), (2), T18)

(5) $\vdash p \equiv r \wedge \sim r. \supset .p \supset r \wedge \sim r$ (T15)

(6) $\vdash p \supset r \wedge \sim r \supset : \sim .r \wedge \sim r. \supset \sim p$ (T11)

(7) $\vdash T23 \supset .p \supset r \wedge \sim r \supset \sim p$ ((6), T7)

(8) $\vdash p \equiv r \wedge \sim r. \supset p$ ((5), (7), T8)

(9) $\vdash p. \equiv .p \equiv r \wedge \sim r$ (T14)

T32. $\vdash p \supset q. \equiv .p \wedge \sim q \equiv r \wedge \sim r$ (T31, T30)

T33. $\vdash p \wedge q \equiv p. \equiv .p \wedge \sim q \equiv r \wedge \sim r$ (T32, T22)

T34. *If* $\vdash p \wedge q \equiv p$, *then* $\vdash p \wedge \sim q \equiv r \wedge \sim r$ (T20, T33)

T35. *If* $\vdash p \wedge \sim q \equiv r \wedge \sim r$, *then* $\vdash p \wedge q \equiv p$ (T25, T33, T22)

T36. $\vdash p \equiv q. \supset .p \wedge r \equiv q \wedge r$ (T26, T21)

T37. $\vdash p \equiv q. \supset .r \wedge p \equiv r \wedge q$ (T27, T21)

D4. "$p\ E\ q$" *for* "$\vdash p \equiv q$."

It is now easy to verify that $(C, \wedge, \sim, E)$ is a Boolean algebra with respect to the equivalence relation E. Conversely if $(C, \wedge, \sim, E)$ is a Boolean algebra with respect to the equivalence relation E, and we define the class $\mathfrak{T}$ as the class of all members p of C such that $p\ E \sim(p \wedge \sim p)$, and define "$p \supset q$" as "$\sim(p \wedge \sim q)$", then $(C, \mathfrak{T}, \supset, \sim)$ is a Boolean propositional logic. This shows that the two concepts are equivalent.

An alternative approach is possible in which we fix our attention not on the classes C and $\mathfrak{T}$, and the properties of the operations $\supset$ and $\sim$, but on the object language in which we talk about these entities. That is, we can set up a system of rules for the manipulation of the signs without making any assumptions at all about the things they denote, or indeed, without assuming that the signs denote anything at all.

We take as our alphabet the signs (,), $\supset$, $\sim$, and the infinite list of "letters" $p_1, p_2, p_3, \cdots$. The latter we call *propositional variables.* A finite sequence of signs, written from left to right, will be called a *string.* We shall use capital Latin letters to denote strings, i.e., as names of strings. The notion of a string is expressed in the syntax language, while the strings themselves are in the object language.

A *sentence* is a string formed according to the following rules:

(1) a string consisting of a single propositional variable is a sentence.
(2) if A and B are sentences, then $(A \supset B)$ and $(\sim A)$ are sentences.

Here "$(A \supset B)$" denotes the string consisting of "(", then the signs of A in order, then "$\supset$", then the signs of B, and finally ")". A string of signs in our alphabet and capital Latin letters will always be interpreted in this way. If A and B are strings, then $S(B \mid p_i \mid A)$ is the string obtained by substituting B for "p_i" throughout A.

We take the following strings as axioms:

A1a. $((p_1 \supset (p_2 \supset p_3)) \supset ((p_1 \supset p_2) \supset (p_1 \supset p_3)))$.
A2a. $(p_1 \supset (p_2 \supset p_1))$.
A3a. $(((\sim p_1) \supset (\sim p_2)) \supset (p_2 \supset p_1))$,

and the following "rules of inference":

R1a. If A and $(A \supset B)$, then B.

R2a. If B is a sentence and A is a theorem, then $S(B \mid p_i \mid A)$.

These axioms are to be used as an initial supply of strings, and the theorems are the axioms themselves, and all strings obtainable by a finite number of applications of the rules to the axioms or the strings already obtained. For example, the first step in the proof of T1 now consists in observing that "$(p_2 \supset p_1)$" is a sentence and taking the string $(p_1 \supset (p_2 \supset p_1))$ for A, and applying R2a to obtain $S((p_2 \supset p_1) \mid p_2 \mid A)$, which is "$(p_1 \supset ((p_2 \supset p_1) \supset p_1))$."

In our previous treatment a rule of substitution, such as R2a, was unnecessary, since if A is a sentence and a letter, say "p", occurs in A, and if $\vdash A$ is proved for all members p of C, then we may replace "p" by any other name of any member of C. Thus R2a amounts to the observation that no members of C are singled out by A1″–A7″ as having special properties expressible in the object language, so that anything provable from these assumptions alone holds for all members of C. In other words, R2a is a statement of a property of the object language, i.e. that the only true propositions expressible in this language are generally true propositions, and has nothing to do with the properties of C.

Nevertheless, the two points of view are formally equivalent, since the provable sentences are exactly the same in the two theories. The difference is that previously it was assumed that the strings had meanings, and whenever meanings are assigned so that A1″–A7″ are true, then all the theorems automatically become true propositions. In the second point of view we first develop a language by applying certain rules without any reference to any meaning of the signs. If we wish to use this language for any purpose, then we must give rules for interpreting it. In this particular case it is easy to give an acceptable interpretation and to see intuitively that the interpretation is satisfactory. It is, however, a very difficult problem to define rigorously what is meant by an interpretation of a language, and to give criteria by means of which one can decide whether a proposed interpretation is acceptable. This difficulty is avoided when from the beginning we take the signs as names for various entities.

The second formulation is still not entirely satisfactory, since the notion of substitution is a rather complicated one. We could, of course, define that notion and thus make it available for a rigorous theory. But this makes it necessary to use rather heavy machinery in the unanalyzed syntax language even for the proofs of very simple theorems.

Of course, when we wish to prove deeper theorems about the system, such as T1.1.41, we must use a great deal of the syntax language in any case, but in the simpler parts of the theory we should try to reduce its use to a minimum, just because its properties are not stated explicitly. If we tried to analyze the syntax language as well, we should have to communicate this analysis in a language whose meaning and structure was already assumed to be known, and so on; this would force us into a paradox akin to the "Achilles and the Tortoise" paradox of Lewis Carroll ([67] 2, 3. See also "The Collected Works of Lewis Carroll," The Modern Library, New York).

We may solve this difficulty by incorporating these troublesome parts of the syntax language in the object language. While we are at it, we may as well get rid of the infinite alphabet, involving numerical subscripts, which occurs in the last formulation. To do this, we identify the subscripts with strings in a new sign "1," and in order to retain the uniform convention of writing strings in linear order, we place the 1's on the same line as the rest of the signs. In this way we avoid even this trivial unanalyzed use of arithmetic in the logic of propositions.

In this way we arrive at the following formulation:

Alphabet: S, $\vdash$, V, $\supset$, $\sim$, (,), p, 1, $\mathfrak{S}$, $=$, $\neq$, |.

Axioms: A1b. Vp

A2b. $p = p$

A3b. $1 = 1$

A4b. $\supset = \supset$

A5b. $\sim = \sim$

A6b. $(= ($

A7b. $) =)$
A8b. $\vdash((p \supset (p1 \supset p11)) \supset ((p \supset p1) \supset (p \supset p11)))$
A9b. $(p \supset (p1 \supset p))$
A10b. $(((\sim p) \supset (\sim p1)) \supset (p1 \supset p))$

Rules: R1b. $VA \rightarrow VA1$
R2b. $A = B, C = D \rightarrow AC = BD$
R3b. $A = B \rightarrow B = A$
R4b. $A = B, B = C \rightarrow A = C$
R5b. $\vdash A, A = B \rightarrow \vdash B$
R6b. $VA \rightarrow p \neq A1$
R7b. $A \neq B \rightarrow A1 \neq B1$
R8b. $A \neq B \rightarrow B \neq A$
R9b. $VA \rightarrow \mathfrak{S}A$
R10b. $\mathfrak{S}A \rightarrow \mathfrak{S}(\sim A)$
R11b. $\mathfrak{S}A, \mathfrak{S}B \rightarrow \mathfrak{S}(A \supset B)$
R12b. $VA, \mathfrak{S}B \rightarrow S(B \mid A \mid A) = B$
R13b. $VA, \mathfrak{S}B, VC, A \neq C \rightarrow S(B \mid A \mid C) = C$
R14b. $VA, \mathfrak{S}B, \mathfrak{S}C, \mathfrak{S}D \rightarrow S(B \mid A \mid (C \supset D)) = (S(B \mid A \mid C) \supset S(B \mid A \mid D))$
R15b. $VA, \mathfrak{S}B, \mathfrak{S}C \rightarrow S(B \mid A \mid (\sim C)) = (\sim S(B \mid A \mid C))$
R16b. $\vdash A, \vdash(A \supset B) \rightarrow \vdash B$
R17b. $VA, \mathfrak{S}B, \mathfrak{S}C, \vdash C \rightarrow \vdash S(B \mid A \mid C)$

Here again the axioms are to be taken as an initial supply of strings. The rules are to be understood as meaning that whenever we already have the strings indicated to the left of the arrow, then the string to the right is to be taken as well. The letters A, B, C, and D denote arbitrary strings.

For example, if we start with A1b and apply R1b repeatedly, we obtain the strings

(1) $Vp, Vp1, Vp11, Vp111, \cdots$.

We may then apply R6b to these strings and get

(2) $p \neq p1, p \neq p11, p \neq p111, \cdots$.

Application of R7b yields

(3) $p1 \neq p11,\ p11 \neq p111,\ \cdots,$
$p1 \neq p111,\ p11 \neq p1111,\ \cdots.$

By R9b applied to the strings in (1), we find that the initial "V" may be replaced by "$\mathfrak{S}$". Then R11b gives us

(4) $\mathfrak{S}(p1 \supset p),\ \mathfrak{S}(p \supset (p1 \supset p)),\ \mathfrak{S}(p11 \supset (p1 \supset (p11 \supset p))),$ etc.

Now we may use R17b and A9b to obtain

(5) $\vdash S((p1 \supset p) \mid p1 \mid (p \supset (p1 \supset p))).$

To save time we shall merely summarize the next inferences:

(6) $S((p1 \supset p) \mid p1 \mid (p \supset (p1 \supset p))) = (S((p1 \supset p) \mid p1 \mid p) \supset S((p1 \supset p) \mid p1 \mid (p1 \supset p)))$
(7) $S((p1 \supset p) \mid p1 \mid p) = p$
(8) $S((p1 \supset p) \mid p1 \mid (p1 \supset p)) = (S((p1 \supset p) \mid p1 \mid p1) \supset S((p1 \supset p) \mid p1 \mid p))$
(9) $S((p1 \supset p) \mid p1 \mid p1) = (p1 \supset p)$
(10) $(S((p1 \supset p) \mid p1 \mid p1) = ((p1 \supset p)$ (A6b, (9), R2b)
(11) $(S((p1 \supset p) \mid p1 \mid p1) \supset S((p1 \supset p) \mid p1 \mid p)) = ((p1 \supset p) \supset p)$ ((7), (8), R2b, R4b)
(12) $S((p1 \supset p) \mid p1 \mid (p \supset (p1 \supset p))) = (p \supset ((p1 \supset p) \supset p))$ ((6), (11), R2b, R4b)
(13) $\vdash(p \supset ((p1 \supset p) \supset p))$ ((5), (12), R5b)

Thus we see what is involved in this formulation in order to perform the first step in the proof of T1. We have, in fact, omitted a few steps (applications of R2b) in (10), (11), and (12). This situation arises because we have analyzed the rules R1a and R2a and the definition of a sentence into "atomic" steps. Steps (4)–(13) are what we really do in one fell swoop when we substitute "$(p1 \supset p)$" for "$p1$" in A9b. This illustrates the complexity of the process of substitution. In this formulation we have reduced the use of the syntax language to a bare minimum at the cost of greatly increasing the lengths of proofs. On the other hand, the present object language is much richer, so that many syntactical theorems about the logic of propositions now become theorems in this precisely formulated object language. The advantages and disadvantages of these points of view will be discussed later in more detail. In the last chapter (p. 157–159) we give still another analysis of the object language of Boolean algebra.

EXERCISES

Ex. 1. Prove (a) $\vdash p_1 \supset .p_2 \supset \cdots \supset .p_k \supset q :\equiv: p_1 \wedge p_2 \wedge \cdots \wedge p_k \supset q.$

(b) $\vdash \sim .p \equiv \sim p.$

(c) $\vdash p \vee \sim p.$

(d) $\vdash p \equiv q . \vee . p \equiv \sim q.$

(e) $\vdash p \supset q . \vee . q \supset p.$

(f) $\vdash p \equiv q . \equiv . p \wedge q \vee \sim p \wedge \sim q.$

(g) $\vdash p . \supset . p \wedge q \equiv q.$

(h) $\vdash p \supset p \vee q.$

(i) $\vdash p \vee q \equiv q \vee p.$

(j) $\vdash p \wedge . p \equiv q . \supset q.$

Ex. 2. Prove the independence of A4″–A6″.

Ex. 3. Prove that if f is any Boolean function of one variable, then $\vdash p \equiv q . \supset . f(p) \equiv f(q).$

Ex. 4. (a). Prove that if f is any Boolean function of one variable, then

$$\vdash f(p \supset p) \wedge f(\sim(p \supset p)) \supset f(q).$$

(b). State and prove the analogous theorems for Boolean functions of several variables.

Ex. 5. Show how problem 4 can be used to decide whether for a given Boolean function f, the statement $\vdash f(p_1, \cdots, p_k)$ is a theorem.

Ex. 6. Show that a necessary and sufficient condition that $\vdash f(p_1, \cdots, p_k) \supset g(p_1, \cdots, p_k)$ be a theorem is that whenever $\vdash f(p_1, \cdots, p_k)$ then $\vdash g(p_1, \cdots, p_k)$.

SECTION 3 DEDUCTIVE SYSTEMS

By making use of the concepts introduced in the study of Boolean algebras we can clarify the foundations of the logic of propositions and study the nature of deductive systems from a rather general point of view. As we have remarked before, the propositional calculus forms a Boolean algebra with the relation E playing the role of the equality relation $=$. On the other hand, if $B = (C, \cap, ')$ is a Boolean algebra, and we define "$p \supset q$" as "$p' \cup q$" or "$(p \cap q')'$" and "$\sim p$" as "p'", then

$$p \supset (q \supset p) = p' \cup (q' \cup p) = p' \cup p \cup q = 1,$$

and similarly for the formulae appearing in A4″ and A6″. If $\mathfrak{T}$ is a sub-class of C such that A4″–A7″ are satisfied, then $1 \in \mathfrak{T}$. By T9″, $p, q \in \mathfrak{T}$ implies that $p \cap q \in \mathfrak{T}$; furthermore

$$p \supset (p \cup q) = p' \cup (p \cup q) = 1 \in \mathfrak{T},$$

so that $p \in \mathfrak{T}$, $q \in C$ implies that $p \cup q \in \mathfrak{T}$. Thus if $\mathfrak{T}$ is a subclass of C satisfying A4″–A7″, then $\mathfrak{T}$ is a sum ideal. Conversely, if $\mathfrak{T}$ is a sum ideal, then $1 \in \mathfrak{T}$ so that A4″–A6″ are automatically satisfied. Besides, if p and $p \supset q = p' \cup q \in \mathfrak{T}$, then $q = q \cup (p \cap (p' \cup q)) \in \mathfrak{T}$, which yields A7″. We thus have proved

THEOREM 1. *If $B = (C, \cap, ')$ is a Boolean algebra, and we define "$p \supset q$" as "$(p \cap q')'$" and "$\sim p$" as "p'", then for the subclass $\mathfrak{T}$ of C to satisfy* A4″–A7″ *it is necessary and sufficient that $\mathfrak{T}$ be a sum ideal.*

We shall, in this section, revert to the notations of chapter I, supplemented by the symbols "$\vdash$" and "$\supset$". In many deductive theories we wish the axioms to be categorical, that is, that the system should be adequate to decide the truth or falsity of any proposition which can be formulated in the system. In the frame of A1″–A7″ we can give this demand the strong form that for every $p \in C$ either $\vdash p$ or $\vdash p'$, i.e. $p \in \mathfrak{T}$ or $p' \in \mathfrak{T}$. As a consequence of lemma 6 we obtain

THEOREM 2. *A necessary and sufficient condition that a propositional logic be categorical is that $\mathfrak{T}$ be a maximal sum ideal.*

Proof. By lemma 6, if $\mathfrak{T}$ is a MSI, then the logic is categorical. Conversely, if the logic is categorical and $\mathfrak{S}$ is a sum ideal containing $\mathfrak{T}$, and $\mathfrak{S} \neq \mathfrak{T}$, then there is a $p \in \mathfrak{S}$ such that $p \notin \mathfrak{T}$. Hence $p' \in \mathfrak{T} \subset \mathfrak{S}$, so that $0 = p \cap p' \in \mathfrak{S}$. Therefore $\mathfrak{S} = C$. This shows that $\mathfrak{T}$ is a MSI.

If $\mathfrak{X}$ is any subclass of C, then the sequence $p_1, \cdots, p_n$ is said to be a *proof of q from the hypotheses* $\mathfrak{X}$ if $q = p_n$ and if for each i, $1 \leq i \leq n$, either p_i is in $\mathfrak{T}$ or p_i is in $\mathfrak{X}$, or there are j, k such that $1 \leq j, k < i$ and $p_k = (p_j \supset p_i)$. We shall say that q is a *consequence* of $\mathfrak{X}$ if there is a proof of q from the hypotheses $\mathfrak{X}$*. We shall denote the class of consequences of $\mathfrak{X}$ by "$\bar{\mathfrak{X}}$". Of course, the notion of a consequence of $\mathfrak{X}$ is relative to the sum ideal $\mathfrak{T}$ initially chosen as the class of true propositions. If $\mathfrak{T}$ is taken to be the class whose only member is 1 (i.e. $p \supset p$ for some $p \in C$), then $\bar{\mathfrak{X}}$ becomes in a sense the class of *logical* consequences of $\mathfrak{X}$, i.e. the class of all propositions which follow from $\mathfrak{X}$ under no assumptions as to "extralogical" truths.

THEOREM 3. *If $\mathfrak{X}$ is a finite subclass of C, $\mathfrak{X} = \{r_1, \cdots, r_k\}$, then q is a consequence of $\mathfrak{X}$ if and only if $\vdash r_1 \cap r_2 \cap \cdots \cap r_k \supset q$.*

(We omit parentheses here with T2.2.19 as justification.)

Proof. Let $p_1, \cdots, p_n$ be a proof of q from the hypotheses $\mathfrak{X}$. Let $s = r_1 \cap \cdots \cap r_k$. We shall prove by induction that $\vdash s \supset p_i$, $i = 1, \cdots, n$, the last case of which is the desired assertion.

Now either $\vdash p_1$ or $p_1 \in \mathfrak{X}$. In the first case, the assertion "$\vdash s \supset p_1$" follows from A5″, and in the second case, from repeated applications of T2.2.15 and T2.2.16.

Suppose that $\vdash s \supset p_j$ for $1 \leq j < i$. If either $\vdash p_i$ or $p_i \in \mathfrak{X}$, then the argument just used for $i = 1$ applies. If there are j, k such that $1 \leq j, k < i$ and $p_k = p_j \supset p_i$, then $\vdash s \supset p_k \supset .s \supset$

*We shall say that q is a consequence of the proposition p if q is a consequence of the class $\{p\}$.

$p_i \supset .s \supset p_i$ (A4″), so that the assertion that $\vdash s \supset p_i$ follows by two applications of A7″.

Conversely, if $\vdash r_1 \cap r_2 \cap \cdots \cap r_k \supset q$, then q is a consequence of $\mathfrak{X}$. For r_1, $r_1 \supset .r_2 \supset r_1 \cap r_2$, $r_2 \supset r_1 \cap r_2$, r_2, $r_1 \cap r_2$, $r_1 \cap r_2 \supset .r_3 \supset r_1 \cap r_2 \cap r_3$, $r_3 \supset r_1 \cap r_2 \cap r_3$, r_3, $r_1 \cap r_2 \cap r_3$, $\cdots$, $r_1 \cap r_2 \cap \cdots \cap r_k$, $r_1 \cap r_2 \cap \cdots \cap r_k \supset q$, q is a proof of q from the hypotheses $\mathfrak{X}$.

Corollary 3a. *If $\mathfrak{X}$ is a non-empty subclass of C, then q is a consequence of $\mathfrak{X}$ if and only if there are elements $r_1, \cdots, r_k$ of $\mathfrak{X}$ such that $\vdash r_1 \cap \cdots \cap r_k \supset q$.*

For the latter condition certainly implies that q is a consequence of $\mathfrak{X}$. On the other hand, if $p_1, \cdots, p_n$ is a proof of q from the hypotheses $\mathfrak{X}$, and if $r_1, \cdots, r_k$ are the elements of $\mathfrak{X}$ occurring in this proof, then q is a consequence of $\{r_1, \cdots, r_k\}$, so that theorem 3 applies.

Corollary 3b. *The element q is a consequence of the null class if and only if $\vdash q$.*

For then q is also a consequence of $q \supset q$, so that $\vdash q$ follows from T2.2.1.

Corollary 3c. *The element q is a consequence of p if and only if $\vdash p \supset q$.*

This is the case $k = 1$ of theorem 3.

Corollaries 3a and 3c constitute the so-called *deduction theorem* of the Boolean propositional logic. We shall denote that q is a consequence of $\mathfrak{X}$ by "$\mathfrak{X} \vdash q$"; if $\mathfrak{X} = \{r_1, \cdots, r_k\}$, then we may also write "$r_1, \cdots, r_k \vdash q$". The use of the deduction theorem would have simplified many of the proofs in the preceding section.

Theorem 4. *$\bar{\mathfrak{X}}$ is the smallest sum ideal containing both $\mathfrak{X}$ and $\mathfrak{T}$.*

Proof. If $\mathfrak{X}$ is the null class, then $\bar{\mathfrak{X}} = \mathfrak{T}$ and is certainly the smallest sum ideal containing $\mathfrak{X}$ and $\mathfrak{T}$. Suppose that $\mathfrak{X}$ is not empty. Let $\mathfrak{S}$ be any sum ideal containing $\mathfrak{X}$ and $\mathfrak{T}$. If $q \in \bar{\mathfrak{X}}$, then there are elements $r_1, \cdots, r_k \in \mathfrak{X}$ such that $\vdash r_1 \cap \cdots$

$\cap r_k \supset q$. Hence $r_1 \cap \cdots \cap r_k \in \mathfrak{S}$ and $r_1 \cap \cdots \cap r_k \supset q \in \mathfrak{S}$, so that $q \in \mathfrak{S}$, by theorem 1. This shows that every sum ideal containing $\mathfrak{X}$ and $\mathfrak{T}$ also contains $\overline{\mathfrak{X}}$. It remains to show that $\overline{\mathfrak{X}}$ is itself a sum ideal containing both $\mathfrak{X}$ and $\mathfrak{T}$.

If $q \in \mathfrak{X}$ or $\mathfrak{T}$, then q itself is a proof of q from the hypotheses $\mathfrak{X}$. Therefore $\overline{\mathfrak{X}}$ does contain $\mathfrak{X}$ and $\mathfrak{T}$.

If q_1 and $q_2 \in \overline{\mathfrak{X}}$, then there are elements $r_1, \cdots, r_m, r_{m+1}, \cdots, r_n$ in $\mathfrak{X}$ such that

$$\vdash r_1 \cap \cdots \cap r_m \supset q_1 \text{ and } \vdash r_{m+1} \cap \cdots \cap r_n \supset q_2 .$$

But

$$\vdash r_1 \cap \cdots \cap r_n \supset r_1 \cap \cdots \cap r_m \text{ and}$$
$$\vdash r_1 \cap \cdots \cap r_n \supset r_{m+1} \cap \cdots \cap r_n, \text{ by T2.2.15, T2.2.16.}$$

Then $q_1 \cap q_2 \in \overline{\mathfrak{X}}$, by T2.2.8 and T2.2.18. If $q \in \overline{\mathfrak{X}}$ and $r \in C$, then $\vdash q \supset q \cup r$ (see p. 43). Consequently, if we adjoin $q \supset q \cup r$, $q \cup r$ to any proof of q from the hypotheses $\mathfrak{X}$, we obtain a proof of $q \cup r$. Hence $q \cup r \in \overline{\mathfrak{X}}$, which completes the proof that $\overline{\mathfrak{X}}$ is a sum ideal.

The following properties are easy to prove:

$$\overline{\overline{\mathfrak{X}}} = \overline{\mathfrak{X}},$$

$$\overline{\{p \cap p'\}} = \overline{\{p, p'\}} = C,$$

if $q, r \in C$, then $q \supset r \in \overline{\mathfrak{X}}$, if and only if $r \in \overline{\mathfrak{X} \cup \{q\}}$,

$$\overline{0} = \overline{\{1\}} = \overline{\{p\}} \cap \overline{\{p'\}} = \mathfrak{T}.$$

Here $\{p, q, \cdots\}$ is the class whose only members are $p, q, \cdots$, and the connectives "$\cap$" and "$\cup$" are the usual ones in the algebra of classes.

We may say that a subclass $\mathfrak{X}$ of C is a *deductive system* if it contains all of its consequences, i.e. if $\overline{\mathfrak{X}} \subset \mathfrak{X}$. But, by theorem 4, $\mathfrak{X} \subset \overline{\mathfrak{X}}$, so that this condition is equivalent to $\mathfrak{X} = \overline{\mathfrak{X}}$, and this implies that $\mathfrak{X}$ is a sum ideal containing $\mathfrak{T}$. Conversely, if $\mathfrak{X}$ is a sum ideal containing $\mathfrak{T}$, then $\mathfrak{X} = \overline{\mathfrak{X}}$, by theorem 4. Thus the concept of a deductive system coincides with that of a sum ideal containing $\mathfrak{T}$. An equivalent condition is that there is a $\mathfrak{Y} \subset C$

such that $\mathfrak{X} = \overline{\mathfrak{Y}}$. In other words, a deductive system is the set of all consequences of some given class of propositions. To say that a class $\mathfrak{X}$ of propositions is consistent means that there is no proposition q such that both q and q' are consequences of $\mathfrak{X}$. But $q, q' \in \overline{\mathfrak{X}}$ implies that $0 = q \cap q' \in \overline{\mathfrak{X}}$, and $0 \in \overline{\mathfrak{X}}$ implies that $r = r \cup 0 \in \overline{\mathfrak{X}}$ for all $r \in C$.

Hence $0 \in \overline{\mathfrak{X}}$ if and only if $\overline{\mathfrak{X}} = C$. Thus $\mathfrak{X}$ is consistent when and only when $\overline{\mathfrak{X}}$ is a proper sum ideal or equivalently, when not all propositions are consequences of $\mathfrak{X}$.

We see then that many of the "metalogical" concepts arising in the study of deductive theories are subsumed by the notions of modern algebra. This is discussed in detail by Stone and Tarski, who arrived at this result independently from quite different points of view. As these authors have shown, there is a close connection between the properties of deductive systems and Brouwer's "intuitionistic" logic as formalized by Heyting (see the next section).

We are now able to throw new light on the concept of truth value. As we have noted before, the truth values form a two-element Boolean algebra with respect to the operations $\cap$ and $'$, and may therefore be identified with the elements 0 and 1. Now suppose we have a method of assigning truth values to all propositions in agreement with the tables of II1. That is, we have a function v defined on the Boolean algebra of all propositions and taking on only the values 0 and 1, and such that

$$v(p') = v(p)', \qquad v(p \cap q) = v(p) \cap v(q),$$

which merely states algebraically that the assignment of truth values really does what we want it to do. Such a function is called by algebraists a *homomorphism* of the given Boolean algebra B onto the two-element Boolean algebra. Let $\mathfrak{T}$ be the class of propositions with the truth value "truth", i.e. such that $v(p) = 1$.

It turns out that $\mathfrak{T}$ is a MSI. For if $p, q \in \mathfrak{T}$, then $v(p) = v(q) = 1$, so that $v(p \cap q) = v(p) \cap v(q) = 1 \cap 1 = 1$, and $p \cap q \in \mathfrak{T}$. If $p \in \mathfrak{T}, q \in C$, then $v(p \cup q) = v((p' \cap q')') = v(p' \cap q')' = (v(p') \cap v(q'))' = (v(p)' \cap v(q)')' = v(p) \cup v(q) =$

$1 \cup v(q) = 1$ so that $p \cup q$ is also in $\mathfrak{T}$. This shows that $\mathfrak{T}$ is a sum ideal. But $v(p) = 1$ or $v(p) = 0$, and if $v(p) = 0$, then $v(p') = v(p)' = 0' = 1$. Hence for every proposition p, either $p \in \mathfrak{T}$ or $p' \in \mathfrak{T}$. Consequently $\mathfrak{T}$ is a MSI.

Conversely, if $\mathfrak{T}$ is a MSI, and we define v by the table:

$$v(p) = \begin{cases} 1 & \text{if } p \in \mathfrak{T} \\ 0 & \text{if } p \notin \mathfrak{T} \end{cases}$$

then v is a homomorphism of the algebra of propositions onto the two-element Boolean algebra. For either $p \in \mathfrak{T}$ or $p' \in \mathfrak{T}$, and not both. In the first case $v(p') = 0 = v(p)'$, and in the second, $v(p') = 1 = v(p)'$. Similarly we show that $v(p \cap q) = v(p) \cap v(q)$. This proves

THEOREM 5. *An assignment of truth values is possible in a Boolean propositional logic if and only if the logic is categorical.*

Since logics adequate for mathematics and belonging to a certain very general class cannot be categorical, by Gödel's theorem, it follows that in general it is impossible to assign truth values to all propositions in an adequate logic.

The concepts introduced here aid us in clearing up a number of common misconceptions as to the nature of the Boolean propositional logic.

In some quarters it is held that in the Boolean logic there are only two distinct propositions, 0 and 1. This is manifestly wrong since no special assumption as to the number of elements of C is forced on us. Even if we consider propositions p and q as the same if $p\ E\ q$, (algebraically, we consider the Boolean algebra of equivalence classes), then this conclusion is not forced on us. In fact, it is the same as saying that $\mathfrak{T}$ is a MSI, i.e. that the logic is categorical. As we have mentioned above, the most interesting logics so far constructed are not categorical, and no way is known to make them so. Even if the logic is categorical, then we may still make distinctions between propositions other than those expressible in terms of truth values.

The mistake arises from confusing the object language with the syntax language. The following are theorems in the Boolean logic:

$\vdash p \vee \sim p,$

$\vdash p \equiv .p \equiv 1.$ (1 is $r \supset r$ for a fixed r)

$\vdash \sim p \equiv .p \equiv 0.$ (0 is $1'$).

(1) $\vdash p \equiv 0 . \vee . p \equiv 1$, for all p in C.

The statement that

(2) $\vdash p \equiv 0$ or $\vdash p \equiv 1$, for all p in C,

is true if and only if the logic is categorical. In a loose translation into English (1) and (2) seem to mean the same, but the "or" or "$\vee$" of the object language is not the same as the "or" of the syntax language. The difference is clearer if we read "$\vdash p$" as "it is provable that p". Then (2) holds only if all sentences in the logic are decidable in that logic, which means that the logic is either so simple that only fairly trivial propositions are expressible in it, or so powerful that it transcends all logics so far constructed.

As we shall see in the next section, the Boolean logic has been criticized on the ground that it deals only with the truth and falsity of propositions, and omits such properties as possibility and necessity, the so-called modal distinctions. Of course, the only functions of propositions expressible in the present object language are Boolean functions, whose trivial nature is revealed by T1.1.21. There is, however, nothing to stop us from considering non-Boolean functions of elements in a Boolean algebra, and this gives us the possibility of studying modal logic by merely extending the framework of Boolean logic. The introduction of non-Boolean functions is analogous to the extension of ordinary algebra by the consideration of polynomials and even more general functions instead of merely linear functions. A small but significant beginning in this direction has been made by McKinsey and Tarski (e.g. [IX]96), but much still remains to be done.

EXERCISES

Ex. 1. Prove the statements on p. 47.

Ex. 2. Let $\mathfrak{T}$ be a sum ideal, and define "$p = q$" as "$\vdash p \equiv q$". State in words the meaning of the statement that the proposition p is an atom in the corresponding logic. Is it likely that in an intuitively acceptable propositional logic there exist atoms?

Ex. 3. Let us say that one logic L_1 is an *extension* of another one, L_2, if the corresponding classes of true propositions are related by $\mathfrak{T}_2 \subset \mathfrak{T}_1$. Prove, by T1.3.5, that every logic has a categorical extension. Is it likely that such an extension can be defined constructively when the original logic is non-trivial?

SECTION 4 MANY VALUED LOGICS MODAL LOGICS INTUITIONISM

The logic of propositions developed in the last two sections is based on the properties of the two truth values "truth", and "falsity", which were taken as intuitively evident. Some scholars have, however, proposed systems of logic with more than two truth values. Various interpretations have been given for these logics. Thus the truth values in a four valued logic might be interpreted as "truth", "plausibility", "implausibility", and "falsity".

In the system proposed by Post, there are n truth values which may be denoted by $1, 2, 3, \cdots, [n-1]$, and n. Here we write $[n-1]$ in brackets to indicate the $n-1$st truth value rather than the result of the arithmetical operation of subtraction.

The operations $\cup$, $\cap$, and $'$ (interpreted as "either . . . or . . .", "both . . . and . . .", and "not . . .") are defined by the tables

$\cup$	1	2	3	$\cdots$	n
1	1	1	1	$\cdots$	1
2	1	2	2	$\cdots$	2
3	1	2	3	$\cdots$	3
$\cdot$	$\cdot$	$\cdot$	$\cdot$	$\cdots$	$\cdot$
$\cdot$	$\cdot$	$\cdot$	$\cdot$	$\cdots$	$\cdot$
$\cdot$	$\cdot$	$\cdot$	$\cdot$	$\cdots$	$\cdot$
n	1	2	3	$\cdots$	n

$\cap$	1	2	3	$\cdots$	n
1	1	2	3	$\cdots$	n
2	2	2	3	$\cdots$	n
3	3	3	3	$\cdots$	n
$\cdot$	$\cdot$	$\cdot$	$\cdot$	$\cdots$	$\cdot$
$\cdot$	$\cdot$	$\cdot$	$\cdot$	$\cdots$	$\cdot$
$\cdot$	$\cdot$	$\cdot$	$\cdot$	$\cdots$	$\cdot$
n	n	n	n	$\cdots$	n

p	p'
1	2
2	3
3	4
$\cdot$	$\cdot$
$\cdot$	$\cdot$
$\cdot$	$\cdot$
$[n-1]$	n
n	1

Observe that n plays the same role as 0 or f in the two valued scheme.

The properties of these operations can now be developed on the basis of these tables. We can also set up a system of postulates for the system and present it as a deductive science. Also we can develop an algebra of classes and an abstract algebra corresponding to this logic of propositions in the same way that Boolean algebra corresponds to the two valued logic. These algebras have been called *Post algebras.* We shall give, for example, a set of postulates for the four valued Post algebras.

Our undefined terms are a class C, and two operations $\cup$ and $'$, and an undefined relation $=$. The postulates and first few definitions are:

P1. *If p and q are in C, then $p \cup q$ and p' are uniquely determined elements of C.*

P2. *If p and q are in C, then $p \cup q = q \cup p$.*

P3. *If p, q, and r are in C, then $(p \cup q) \cup r = p \cup (q \cup r)$.*

P4. *If p is in C, then $p \cup p = p$.*

D1. $p \cup q \cup r = (p \cup q) \cup r,$

$p \cup q \cup r \cup s = (p \cup q \cup r) \cup s$, *etc.*

D2. $p^0 = p. \quad p^{k+1} = (p^k)'.$

D3. $1(p) = \sum_{m=0}^{3} p^m = p \cup p' \cup p'' \cup p'''.$

D4. $2(p) = (1(p))', 3(p) = (2(p))', 4(p) = (3(p))'$.
P5. *If p is in C, then* $1(p) = (1(p))'''' = (4(p))'$.
D5. $\varphi_1(p) = (p' \cup p'' \cup p''')'''$.
D6. $\varphi_k(p) = ((p \cup 2(p))''' \cup p^k)''', k = 2, 3$.
D7. $-p = \varphi_1(p') \cup \varphi_2(p'') \cup \varphi_3(p''')$.
D8. $p \cap q = -(-p \cup -q)$.
D9. $p \cap q \cap r = (p \cap q) \cap r,$
$p \cap q \cap r \cap s = (p \cap q \cap r) \cap s,$ *etc.*
P6. *If p, q, and r are in C, then*
$p \cup (q \cap r) = (p \cup q) \cap (p \cup r)$.
P7. *If p and q are in C, then*
$(p \cap q) \cup (p \cap q') \cup (p \cap q'') \cup (p \cap q''') = p$.
P8. *If p is in C, then* $p = \varphi_1(p) \cup (2(p) \cap \varphi_1(p''')) \cup (3(p) \cap \varphi_1(p'')) \cup (4(p) \cap \varphi_1(p'))$.
P9. *If* p, q_0, q_1, q_2, *and* q_3 *are in C, then*
$$((q_0 \cap \varphi_1(p)) \cup (q_1 \cap \varphi_1(p')) \cup (q_2 \cap \varphi_1(p'')) \cup (q_3 \cap \varphi_1(p''')))' = (q_0' \cap \varphi_1(p)) \cup (q_1' \cap \varphi_1(p')) \cup (q_2' \cap \varphi_1(p'')) \cup (q_3' \cap \varphi_1(p''')).$$

An analogue to T1.1.41 is that every "Post" function f of one variable can be represented in the form:

$$f(p) = (q_0 \cap \varphi_1(p)) \cup (q_1 \cap \varphi_1(p')) \cup (q_2 \cap \varphi_1(p'')) \cup (q_3 \cap \varphi_1(p''')),$$

where q_0, q_1, q_2, and q_3 are constant elements. From this it follows that every function definable by 4-valued truth tables is a Post function, i.e. the algebra is "functionally complete." There is also a decision procedure analogous to that of T1.2.24. The many valued logics proposed by Łukasiewicz and Tarski are not functionally complete.

A typical concrete example of a Post algebra is this. We suppose that some class A is given. Then C is the class of all functions defined on A and with values among the integers from 1 to n. If f and g are such functions, then

$f \cup g$ is the function such that for all a in A

$$(f \cup g)(a) = \min (f(a), g(a)),$$

and $f \cap g$ is the function such that for all a in A

$$(f \cap g)(a) = \max\,(f(a), g(a)).$$

Also, if f is in C, then

f' is the function such that

$$f'(a) = \begin{cases} f(a) + 1 & \text{if } f(a) < n \\ 1 & \text{if } f(a) = n. \end{cases}$$

It is easy to check that with this interpretation all the postulates are verified. A Post algebra P_1 is a subalgebra of P if C_1 is a subclass of C, and $\cap$ and $'$ are defined as in P. It has been proved by Wade that every Post algebra is isomorphic to a subalgebra of an algebra of the type described above. We may think of the elements in C as properties of the elements of A, so that the equation $f(a) = k$ expresses that the proposition that the element a has the property denoted by "f" has the truth value k.

As we have mentioned before, many philosophers object to the interpretation of "$p \supset q$" as "p implies q", mainly because of the so-called "paradoxes" of material implication. These are embodied, for example, in A5″ and T2.2.3 above. According to A5″, any proposition implies that Gieseking played before Hitler, and by T2.2.3, the proposition that Schacht was not a Nazi implies every proposition. Many philosophers (and also some mathematicians) have insisted that "p implies q" must have the intuitive properties of "q is deducible from p", and that there is no reasonable way of deducing that Columbus discovered America from the assumption that Schacht was not a Nazi. They say that this is because there is no inner connection between these two propositions. This argument is usually vaguely expressed. Many authors seem to mean that while in the existing real world Schacht was a Nazi and Columbus discovered America, a world is imaginable or possible in which Schacht was not a Nazi, and Columbus did not discover America. For determinists like Spinoza and Mark Twain (see "The Mysterious Stranger") this argument would not hold water. In many presentations of this argument there seems to be a confusion between this proposition and some such proposition as that for all x and y, if x is a Nazi then y discovered America. In others, the intended meaning seems to be that if the proposition "Schacht was not a Nazi" is added to the postulates, then "Columbus discovered America" is not a theorem. That is, the proposition "p implies q" is interpreted to mean that if p is adjoined to the postulates, then q is provable. This relation between p and q is, however, clearly expressed as a sentence in the syntax language, not in the object language. Similarly, the demand that "p implies q" mean that "$p \supset q$" is "analytic" or a "tautology" is again an interpretation of implication as a relation in the syntax language. One may attempt to reconcile this view with our previous one as follows. A binary operation I in C is to be a satisfactory "implication" operation if $\vdash p\ I\ q$ when and only when if $\vdash p$ is added to the postulates, then $\vdash q$ is deducible as a theorem. In this sense $\supset$ is a satisfactory implication operation according to the corollary 2.3.3a. We shall discuss below some of the attempts to construct logics with satisfactory implication operations.

Another objection which has been raised to the propositional logic developed above is that there are other relations between propositions other than those which depend upon their truth values. This is usually accompanied by a contention that two classes α and β may consist of exactly the same members, yet may be different because of a conceptual difference in their connotations. For example, the class of unicorns has the same members as the class of centaurs since both are empty, but these classes are different because the concept of a centaur differs from that of a unicorn. It is true that such distinctions play no role in mathematical reasoning as it is actually used, but it is contended that the principles of logic used in this reasoning are inadequate and incomplete just because they neglect these relations between classes in intension. Analogous to these intensional relations between classes are certain "modal" relations between propositions, i.e. relations involving the concept of possibility.

A third objection to the Boolean propositional logic goes back to Kronecker, and has been advanced in modern times especially by Brouwer and Weyl, and in more or less extreme form by others, notably Lusin. This objection originates in the question of the meaning of existence. The proponents of the point of view under discussion hold that an object exists only if a method is given for constructing it. Of course this depends upon the permissible methods of construction, but once they are defined explicitly, we have a criterion for existence. Now we may be able to deduce a contradiction from a proposition p of the form "for all x, $x \in \alpha$" without being able to give a construction for an x such that $x \notin \alpha$. The "intuitionists" would then deny that the proposition that there exists an x such that $x \notin \alpha$ is true, i.e. neither p nor $\sim p$ would be true. Thus they say that the law that $\vdash p \vee \sim p$ is invalid. Clearly a step is overlooked here. For $\vdash p \vee \sim p$ does not have as a consequence $\vdash p$ or $\vdash \sim p$. This conclusion follows only if $\mathfrak{T}$ is a MSI, i.e. if the logic is categorical. The intuitionists demand that in a satisfactory logic $p \vee q$ be provable if and only if either p or q is provable. Hence the intuitionists would object to any Boolean propositional logic which was not categorical. Gödel has proved, however, that for a large class of Boolean propositional logics, which includes all that have been proposed so far which are adequate for arithmetic, that they cannot be categorical. Thus all Boolean propositional logics of this large class fall under the ban of the intuitionists.

The motivation of the intuitionists' criterion for existence is that the naive application of the law $\vdash p \vee \sim p$ to existential propositions involving infinite classes is known to lead to contradiction, as we shall see in the next chapter. Gödel has shown that various Boolean propositional logics which have been proposed up to now and which are adequate for arithmetic, if consistent, are inadequate to prove their own consistency, so that in this sense no Boolean logic of this very general type can be "safe" in the sense that one can prove, using the methods of reasoning which can be formulated within the logic, that no contradiction can arise. The intuitionists say that a logic based on their principles is "safe", that the restrictions thus placed on the naive logic which is known to lead to contradictions, are natural, that their criteria correspond to intuitively acceptable "natural" laws of thought, and that the restrictions which have been proposed in the so far proposed Boolean logics in order to avoid the known paradoxes are ad hoc, i.e. manufactured for that specific purpose. One outstanding difficulty is the proof that the intuitionistic logic is actually "safe". According to another result of Gödel, if the intuitionistic arithmetic is consistent, then so is the arithmetic based on the Boolean logic, so that the latter is as "safe" as the former. On the other hand, Gödel's work shows that every sentence in the latter can be translated into a sentence in the intuitionist arithmetic such that either both are provable in their respective logics or both are unprovable. Thus the intuitionist arithmetic is as adequate as the Boolean arithmetic.

A formulation of the intuitionistic propositional calculus as a deductive science has been given by Heyting. The undefined terms are: a class C, a subclass $\mathfrak{T}$, three binary operations $\cap$, $\cup$, and $\supset$, and a unary operation $\sim$. As before, we shall use "$\vdash p$" for "p is in $\mathfrak{T}$". The unproved propositions are:

I1. *If p and q are in C, then $p \cap q$, $p \cup q$, $p \supset q$, and $\sim p$ are uniquely determined elements of C.*

I2. *If $\vdash p$ and $\vdash p \supset q$, then $\vdash q$.*

I3. *If p and q are in C, then $\vdash p \supset .q \supset p$.*

I4. *If p, q, and r are in C, then $\vdash p \supset .q \supset r. \supset .p \supset q \supset .p \supset r$.*

I5. *If p and q are in C, then $\vdash p \supset .q \supset p \cap q$.*

I6. *If p and q are in C, then $\vdash p \cap q \supset p$.*

I7. *If p and q are in C, then $\vdash p \cap q \supset q$.*

I8. *If p and q are in C, then $\vdash p \supset p \cup q$.*

I9. *If p and q are in C, then $\vdash q \supset p \cup q$.*

I10. *If p, q, and r are in C, then $\vdash p \supset r \supset .q \supset r \supset .p \cup q \supset r$.*

I11. *If p and q are in C, then $\vdash p \supset q \supset .p \supset \sim q \supset \sim p$.*

I12. *If p and q are in C, then $\vdash \sim p \supset .p \supset q$.*

It will be observed that all of these are valid in the Boolean propositional logic. Among the consequences are such theorems as

$$\vdash p \supset \sim\sim p, \vdash \sim\sim\sim p \supset \sim p, \text{ and } \vdash \sim\sim . p \cup \sim p.$$

On the other hand, neither $\vdash p \cup \sim p$ nor $\vdash \sim\sim p \supset p$ are theorems. Glivenko has shown that if $\vdash \sim A$ is provable in the Boolean propositional logic, where A is a formula expressed in that system, then $\vdash \sim A$ is provable in the intuitionistic logic. Gödel has demonstrated other important relations between the Boolean and the intuitionistic logics. Gentzen has found a procedure for determining whether a formula in the intuitionistic logic is provable from I1–I12 above. The operations $\cap$, $\cup$, $\supset$, and $\sim$ are independent; none of them can be defined in terms of the others. In other respects the sentence "$\sim p$" has many properties in common with the formulae representing "p is impossible" in the modal logics discussed below. From this point of view, the intuitionist logic may be considered as a modal logic.

Brouwer, Weyl, and others have been engaged for many years now in a vast program of redoing as much of classical mathematics as possible from the intuitionist point of view. It results from their labors that a surprising amount still holds, other parts can be retained in a modified but more complicated form, and still other parts cannot be saved at all. It must be emphasized that much of this work is of value and importance even for those who admit types of reasoning which the intuitionists reject. For an intuitionist proof that an object exists is tantamount to a construction of that object by certain well defined methods and this property may be in itself interesting and important, just as Gauss' proof that the angle $2\pi/17$ can be constructed by means of straight edge and compass gives important additional information about this number.

The most widely known and most extensively studied modal logics are those proposed by Lewis. The undefined terms are a class C, a subclass $\mathfrak{T}$, a binary operation $\cap$, and two unary operations $\sim$ and P ("Pp" is to be interpreted as "it is possible that p".). We use our earlier notational conventions, and take "$\sim$" as senior to "P". We first introduce a definition

D1. "$p < q$" for "$\sim P \,.\, p \cap \sim q$". (We take "$<$" as senior to "$\cap$".)

In the basic logic of Lewis we may take the following as unproved propositions:

L0. *If p and q are in C, then $p \cap q$, $\sim p$, and Pp are uniquely determined members of C.*

If p, q, and r are in C, then

L1. $\vdash p \cap q < q \cap p$.
L2. $\vdash p \cap q < p$.
L3. $\vdash p < p \cap p$.
L4. $\vdash p \cap q \,.\!\cap.\, r \,.<.\, p \cap \,.q \cap r$.
L5. $\vdash p < q \,.\!\cap.\, q < r \,.<.\, p < r$.
L6. $\vdash p \cap \,.p < q. < q$.
L7. *If* $\vdash p$ *and* $\vdash q$, *then* $\vdash p \cap q$.
L8. *If* $\vdash p$ *and* $\vdash p < q$, *then* $\vdash q$.
L9. *If* $\vdash p < q$, *then* $\vdash Pp < Pq$.
L10. *If* $\vdash p < q$, *then* $\vdash \sim q < \sim p$.
L11. *If* $\vdash p < q$, *then* $\vdash p \cap r < q \cap r$.

In Lewis' formulation L9, L10, and L11 are replaced by the more complicated assumption Ex. 3(i) below, and Ex. 3 (c) and Ex. 3 (g) are also taken as postulates. His postulate

B9. *There are p and q in C such that* $\vdash P \,.p \cap q \,.\!\cap.\, P \,.p \cap \sim q$

serves to distinguish his system from the Boolean propositional logic.

His purpose is "to develop a calculus based on a meaning of 'implies' such that 'p implies q' will be synonymous with 'q is deductible from p'." A further object is to avoid the "paradoxes" of material implication. Among the consequences of L0–L11 are, however,

$$\vdash \sim P\, p. < .p < q,$$

and $$\vdash \sim P \sim p. < .q < p,$$

so that analogues to these "paradoxes" reappear in Lewis' system. It seems, then, that the claim of having avoided these paradoxes is not justified by the formal system itself, but rather by the interpretation assigned to it. As far as the first more serious purpose is concerned, no one has, until recently, published any theorem of the type of the deduction theorem for Lewis' system, and this is essential for the achievement of that purpose. In a recent paper Miss Barcan discusses theorems of this type for logics of propositions (and also of propositional functions) based on Lewis' "strict" implication. She shows that if p and q are in C, then "$\vdash Pp > Pq$" is deducible from "$\vdash p < q$", but that "$\vdash p < q \,.\!<\!.\, Pp < Pq$" is not deducible from L0–L11. If, however, the postulate

B12. *If p is in C, then* $\vdash PPp < Pp$

is added, then the deduction theorem holds in the weakened form:

If $\sim P \sim p_1 , \cdots , \sim P \sim p_k \vdash q$, then

$$\vdash \sim P \sim p_1 < .\sim P \sim p_2 < . \cdots < .\sim P \sim p_k < q.$$

The contention that, from the standpoint of the interpretation as deducibility, "strict" implication is a more satisfactory implication operation than material implication is consequently untenable until a system based on the former is constructed in which the deduction theorem is proved, while in the analogous system in terms of material implication the deduction theorem fails.*

The system L0–L11 is far from categorical, for even such a simple statement as "$\vdash PPp < Pp$" is not decidable on the basis of the postulates. Lewis and others have proposed various additional postulates to complete the system, but no compelling reasons have yet been advanced to decide upon one of these in preference to others.

Two Boolean interpretations of Lewis' system have been

*Since the above was written, Curry's monograph, *A Theory of Formal Deducibility*, Notre Dame Mathematical Lectures No. 6, 1950, has appeared. This book throws new light on the connection between Lewis' system and the theory of deductive systems.

proposed, i.e. constructions within the Boolean logic yielding systems satisfying L0–L11. Henle has shown, for example, that if $B = (C, \mathfrak{T}, \cap, \sim)$ is a Boolean logic and C has more than two elements, and if Pp is defined as 1 for $p \neq 0$ and as 0 for $p = 0$, then L0–L11 are satisfied. Another construction has been given by Fitch, and is presented here in a modified form. Let A be a finite set and B be a Boolean logic. Consider the class $\mathfrak{F}$ of all functions f on A to C (i.e. the functions defined on A with values in C). The family $\mathfrak{F}$ of all such functions forms a Boolean logic with the definitions

$\mathfrak{T}_1$ is the class of all $f \in \mathfrak{F}$ such that $f(a) \in \mathfrak{T}$ for all $a \in A$,
$f \cap g$ is the function such that $(f \cap g)(a) = f(a) \cap g(a)$ for all $a \in A$,
$\sim f$ is the function such that $(\sim f)(a) = \sim f(a)$ for all $a \in A$,
Pf is the function such that $(Pf)(a) = f(b_1) \cup \cdots \cup f(b_k)$ where $b_1, \cdots, b_k$ are the distinct elements of A, and a is an arbitrary element of A.

We can easily check that $(\mathfrak{F}, \mathfrak{T}_1, \cap, \sim, P)$ satisfies L0–L11 if A contains at least two elements. In both of these constructions certain relations hold which are not consequences of the postulates, e.g. $\vdash PPp < Pp$ for all p in C.

Another interesting approach to modal logic is due to H. B. Smith. Unfortunately, due to Smith's defects as an expositor, the main features of his system have remained obscure and misunderstood. In order to explain his point of view we shall need some definitions. By a *modal function* of p we shall mean a function constructed from the variable "p" and the operations $\cap$, $\sim$, and P. By a *simple* modal function of p we shall mean such a function constructed using only the operations $\sim$ and P. An *affirmative* modal function of p is a simple modal function in whose construction the operation $\sim$ enters an even number of times. Thus $P\ (p \cap PP \sim p)$, $\sim PPp$, and $\sim P \sim Pp$ are respectively modal, simple modal, and affirmative modal functions of p. Two modal functions are identical if and only if their equivalence follows using only the laws

(1) $\vdash \sim\sim p \equiv p$ ("$x \equiv y$" means "$x < y . \cap . y < x$")
(2) If $\vdash p \equiv q$, then $\vdash \sim p \equiv \sim q$ and $\vdash Pp \equiv Pq$.

Now Smith places two demands on a system of modal logic, to wit, (A) if M_1 and M_2 are affirmative modal functions of p, then either $\vdash M_1(p) < M_2(p)$ for all p in C or $\vdash M_2(p) < M_1(p)$ for all p in C; (B) if M_1 and M_2 are simple modal functions of p, then $\vdash M_1(p) \equiv M_2(p)$ for all p in C if and only if M_1 and M_2 are identical. We shall not be able to enter into a discussion here of the philosophical background behind these requirements. We shall merely note that (A) is a requirement that the affirmative modalities be linearly ordered (see p. 20), while (B) is a requirement that modal distinctions be preserved. This view may be justified by the fact that the logic of ordinary discourse is too vague for us to identify, say, the proposition that it is necessarily possible that p with the proposition that p. It is very natural to ask whether a linear ordering of the affirmative modal functions is compatible with a maintenance of all modal distinctions, or whether (B) forces a complicated "ramified" theory of modality upon us. Smith shows that (A) and (B) are incompatible with Lewis' L5, the law of the "transitivity" of implication, and proposes that this be replaced by L5′: if $\vdash p < q$ and $\vdash q < r$, then $\vdash p < r$. The use of reasoning in actual practice is too vague to distinguish between these two forms of the intuitive law of transitivity. In any actual case L5′ would be as effective as L5. Smith finds that L9 is also incompatible with (A) and (B). Lewis, himself, has indicated some hesitation about adopting L9. Smith assumes

$$\vdash p < Pp,$$
$$\vdash p < \sim P \sim Pp,$$
$$\vdash p < \sim PP \sim Pp, \text{ etc.}$$

and shows that (A) follows from this infinite list of postulates. He gives, similarly, a series of postulates which yield (B). He then turns to the consideration of modal functions of two variables. The theorem in Lewis' system that

$$\vdash P(p \cup q) \equiv (Pp) \cup (Pq)$$

turns out to be incompatible with (B), and is therefore rejected by Smith. On the other hand,

if $\vdash p \cap \sim q \equiv 0$, then $\vdash p < q$ and therefore $\vdash P\ (p \cup q) \equiv Pq$,
if $\vdash \sim p \cap q \equiv 0$, then $\vdash P\ (p \cup q) \equiv Pp$,
and if $\vdash \sim p \cap \sim q \equiv 0$, then $\vdash P(p \cup q) \equiv 1$.

Thus in order to secure a completeness property analogous to (A) for modal functions of two variables it suffices to assume a law of the form:

if not $\vdash p \cap \sim q \equiv 0$ and not $\vdash \sim p \cap q \equiv 0$ and not $\vdash \sim p \cap \sim q \equiv 0$, then $\vdash P\ (p \cup q) \equiv$ _ _ _ _ ,

where _ _ _ _ indicates a certain combination of simple modal functions of p and q. For such a law to be effectively usable we must adjoin to the postulates what Carnap calls rules of refutation, so that we may be able to prove that various sentences are not asserted. Smith and his pupils have made various suggestions as to the form of such an "expansion formula", and have from them deduced results analogous to (A) for modal functions of two variables. So far, however, no one has given a consistency proof of such a logic which is compatible with (B). It is an interesting problem to determine whether there exist consistent logics satisfying (B) and possessing a completeness property analogous to (A).

Other authors have proposed systems of modal logic. Practically all of these agree on making the logic Boolean with respect to C, $\mathfrak{T}$, $\cap$, and $\sim$, but from there on the various proposals diverge. The laws:

if $\vdash p \equiv q$, then $\vdash Pp \equiv Pq$, and $\vdash \sim p \equiv \sim q$, and
$\vdash p < Pp$ for all p in C,

are also common to most of these systems. It would be of some value to make a systematic study of the structures of all such systems and to determine what additional laws would yield systems satisfying certain simple and natural requirements. The only work in this direction so far published is that of Tarski and McKinsey.

Of those who have criticized the Boolean logic of propositions, only the intuitionists have carried out to any satisfactory extent the constructive part of the critique, that is, to show that a system can be constructed on the basis of the critique which is at least adequate for some considerable portion of mathematics. The work of Miss Barcan can be considered as the first step in the direction of a similar development for strict implication. Rosser and Turquette made some beginnings for the n-valued logics. Such work remains to be done for such systems as Smith's.* It must be emphasized that in very few of these cases have the critics *shown* that the systems they have constructed do not have the features criticized as undesirable in the Boolean logics, nor that they actually possess the properties advocated as desirable at the same time that the corresponding Boolean logics do not possess them. Others who have discussed Boolean logics critically have claimed that certain properties are undesirable without even attempting to give alternative systems *demonstrably* not having these properties. In many other cases the discussions are carried out in the vague intuitive logic, in which the essential distinctions are blurred, and it becomes difficult to pin the authors down and determine just what they want and just what they don't want.

We here suggest the criterion of "put up or shut up" as an aid in evaluating discussions of logic. If one advocates that certain features are desirable in a formal logic, then one should exhibit a system which *demonstrably* possesses those properties. If possible, one should show that the system is adequate at least for arithmetic. If one criticizes certain features in a system of logic, then one should exhibit a reasonably adequate system which *demonstrably* does not possess those properties. Of course, when such a theorem as Gödel's indicates that the desired proof

*If a system of modal logic were so completed as to be adequate for mathematics, the resulting theory would be rich in relations which have no analogues in classical mathematics. Thus to any class α there would correspond a class $P\alpha$ = the class of all x such that $P(x \in \alpha)$. Whether such an enrichment of the classical mathematics would actually be fruitful remains to be seen.

may not exist, then the criterion may be relaxed. A vague informal discussion may be valuable as a guide for future work, but must be regarded as at most a preliminary sketch until the theses have been stated in terms of a precisely formulated object language which is proved to have the desired qualities. Unless such criteria are strictly applied, discussions of logic and the foundations of mathematics are in danger of degenerating into the type of philosophic controversy where one never knows exactly what the problem is, and one never knows surely when the problem is solved.

EXERCISES

Ex. 1. Prove the following from the postulates on p. 52:

(a). $p \cap q = q \cap p$.

(b). $1(p) = 1(q), 2(p) = 2(q), 3(p) = 3(q), 4(p) = 4(q)$. (Hence we may define $1 = 1(p)$, etc.).

(c). $p \cup 1 = 1 \cup p = 1$.

(d). $p \cup (p \cap q) = p$.

(e). $p \cap (p \cup q) = p$,

(f). $p \cap p = -(-p) = p$.

(g). $p \cap 1 = 1 \cap p = p$.

(h). $p \cap (q \cap r) = (p \cap q) \cap r$.

(i). $p \cap (q \cup r) = (p \cap q) \cup (p \cap r)$.

(j). $p'''' = p$.

(k). $p \cap q = p$ if and only if $p \cup q = q$.

(l). $\varphi_2(2) = 4$.

(m). $\varphi_1(2) = \varphi_1(3) = \varphi_1(4) = 4$.

(n). $1 = \varphi_1(1) \cup 4$.

(o). $-4 = 1, 4 = -1$.

(p). $p \cup 4 = 4 \cup p = p$.

(q). $p \cap 4 = 4 \cap p = 4$.

(r). $\varphi_1(1) = 1$.

(s). $2 \cup 3 = 2 \cup 4 = 2$.

(t). $\varphi_2(1) = 2, \varphi_3(1) = 3$.

(u). $\varphi_2(3) = \varphi_2(4) = \varphi_3(2) = \varphi_3(3) = \varphi_3(4) = 4$.

(v). $p \cup q = -(-p \cap -q)$.
(w). $\varphi_1(p) \cup \varphi_1(p') \cup \varphi_1(p'') \cup \varphi_1(p''') = 1$.
(x). If f is a Post function of one variable, then $f(p) = (f(1) \cap \varphi_1(p)) \cup (f(2) \cap \varphi_1(p''')) \cup (f(3) \cap \varphi_1(p'')) \cup (f(4) \cap \varphi_1(p'))$. State and prove the analogous theorem for functions of several variables.
(y). If f is any Post function of one variable, then
$$f(p \cup q) \cup f(p \cap q) = f(p) \cup f(q),$$
and $f(p \cup q) \cap f(p \cap q) = f(p) \cap f(q)$.
(z). $\varphi_1(p \cup q) = \varphi_1(p) \cup \varphi_1(q)$.
In connection with (x), (y), and (z), state an appropriate definition of "Post function."

Ex. 2. Prove the following from the postulates on p. 57:
(a). $\vdash p \supset p$.
(b). $\vdash p \cap p \supset p$.
(c). $\vdash p \supset p \cap p$.
(d). $\vdash p \cup p \supset p$.
(e). $\vdash p \supset p \cup p$.
(f). $\vdash p \cap .p \supset q. \supset q$.
(g). $\vdash q \supset r. \supset .p \supset q \supset .p \supset r$.
(h). $\vdash r \supset p .\supset. r \supset q .\supset. r \supset p \cap q$.
(i). $\vdash p \cap q \supset q \cap p$.
(j). $\vdash p \supset q .\cap. q \supset r :\supset: p \supset r$.
(k) $\vdash p \supset .q \supset r :\supset: p \cap q \supset r$.
(l). $\vdash p \cap q \supset r .\supset. p \supset .q \supset r$.
(m). $\vdash p \supset .p \supset q \supset q$.
(n). $\vdash p \supset q \supset .\sim q \supset \sim p$.
(o). $\vdash p \supset q \supset .p \cap r \supset q \cap r$.
(p). $\vdash p \supset q \supset .p \cup r \supset q \cup r$.
(q). $\vdash p \supset \sim q \supset .q \supset \sim p$.
(r). $\vdash \sim .p \cap \sim p$.
(s). $\vdash \sim .p \cup q .\supset. \sim p \cap \sim q$.
(t). $\vdash \sim p \cap \sim q .\supset. \sim .p \cup q$.
(u). $\vdash \sim .p \cap q .\supset. p \supset \sim q$.
(v). $\vdash p \supset \sim q .\supset. \sim .p \cap q$.
(w). $\vdash \sim p \cup \sim q .\supset. \sim .p \cap q$.
(x). $\vdash p \cap q .\cup. p \cap r .\supset. p \cap .q \cup r$.

(y). $\vdash p \cap .q \cup r .\supset. p \cap q .\cup. p \cap r.$
(z). $\vdash \sim .p \cap q .\cap. p \cup \sim p :\supset: \sim p \cup \sim q.$
(aa). $\vdash \sim \sim .p \cup \sim p.$

Ex. 3. Prove the following from the postulates on p. 59.

(a). $\vdash p \cap p < p.$
(b). $\vdash p < p$
(c). $\vdash P .p \cap q. < Pp.$
(d). $\vdash \sim P .p \cap \sim p.$
(e). $\vdash \sim \sim p < p.$
(f). If $\vdash p < q$, then $\vdash r \cap p < r \cap q.$
(g). $\vdash p < \sim \sim p.$
Define "$p = q$" as "$\vdash p < q .\cap. q < p.$"
(h). State an appropriate definition of the concept of a Lewis function, analogous to that of a Boolean function.
(i). If $p = q$ and f is a Lewis function, then $f(p) = f(q).$
(j). If $p \cap q = p$, then $\vdash p < q.$
(k). If $\vdash p < q$, then $p \cap q = p.$
(l). $p = \sim \sim p.$
(m). $p < q .=. \sim q < \sim p.$
(n). $p \cap q < r .=. p \cap \sim r < \sim q.$
(o). $\vdash p \cap \sim q .<. \sim .p < q.$
(p). $p \cap p = p.$
(q). $\vdash p < Pp.$
(r). $\vdash \sim .p \cap \sim p.$
(s). $\vdash \sim Pp .<. p < q.$
(t). $\vdash \sim P \sim p .<. q < p.$
(u). If $\vdash p < q$ and $\vdash r < s$, then $\vdash p \cap r < q \cap s.$
Define "$p \equiv q$" as "$p < q .\cap. q < p$".
(v). $\vdash \sim Pp .\cap. \sim Pq .<. p \equiv q.$
(w). $\vdash p < q$ if and only if $p \cap \sim q = r \cap \sim r.$
(x). $(C, \cap, \sim, =)$ is a Boolean algebra.
(y). $p \cap r < q \cap r .=. \sim P .p \cap r \cap \sim q.$
(z). $\vdash p < q .<. p \cap r < q \cap r.$
(aa). If $\vdash \sim P \sim p$, then $\vdash q < p \cap q.$

Ex. 4. Let C be the class of all integers which divide 216, i.e. $C = \{1, 2, 3, 4, 6, 8, 9, 12, 18, 24, 27, 36, 54, 72, 108, 216\}$. Let "$\alpha \cap \beta$" denote the greatest common divisor of α and β, and let

$$\alpha' = \begin{cases} 6\alpha & \text{if neither 8 nor 27 divides } \alpha, \\ 3/8\ \alpha & \text{if 8 divides } \alpha \text{ but not 27,} \\ 2/27\ \alpha & \text{if 27 divides } \alpha \text{ but not 8,} \\ 1 & \text{if } \alpha = 216. \end{cases}$$

Verify that $(C, \cap, ')$ is a four-valued Post algebra.

Ex. 5. Let C be the class of all divisors of 30, and let $\mathfrak{T} = \{1, 2\}$. Let $\alpha \cap \beta$ be the least common multiple of α and β, let $\alpha' = 30/\alpha$, and let $P\alpha = 1$ except in the cases $\alpha = 6$, 15, and 30, when $P\alpha = 3$, 5, and 15, respectively. Verify that postulates L0–L11 are satisfied but that $3 < 6 \;.\!<\!.\; P3 < P6$ is not in $\mathfrak{T}$. Explain the significance of this result.

Chapter III

THE LOGIC OF PROPOSITIONAL FUNCTIONS

SECTION 1 INFORMAL INTRODUCTION

Heretofore we have constructed logical systems which formalize reasoning on classes and on propositions as wholes. We shall now attempt to construct systems dealing with those general forms of reasoning which depend upon the inner structure of propositions. In this section we shall proceed informally on the basis of naive intuition in order to give the general ideas and also in order to exhibit the difficulties into which this naive intuition leads us.

The fundamental idea is that of a propositional function. In mathematics a *function* is a relation R whereby to each object there is at most one object y such that x has the relation R to y. Thus the relation holding between x and y if and only if x and y are numbers and $y = x^2$ is a function. The object y is called the *value* of the function for the argument x and is denoted by "$R(x)$", or if there is no danger of ambiguity, by "Rx". The class of all x's such that Rx exists, i.e. there exists a y such that x has the relation R to y, is called the *domain* of the function R, and the class of values y is called the *range* of R. By a *propositional function* we mean a function whose values are propositions. A propositional function is denoted by a *sentential function*, and a sentential function is usually denoted by a sentence-form such as "x is a man". This is not a sentence itself, but if a name of an object is substituted for "x", we obtain a sentence, which denotes a proposition; of course, this proposition may be either true or false. For example, if we substitute "Dewey" for "x" (i.e. we substitute a name of a certain object, namely, the man Dewey), we obtain the sentence "Dewey is a man", which expresses the true proposition that Dewey is a man. If we substitute "Pittsburgh" for "x", we obtain a sentence expressing the false proposition that Pittsburgh is a man. We shall say that a sentence-form expresses a propositional function; for example, the sentence-form "x is a man" expresses the propositional function that x is a man. The letter x will be called a variable occurring in this sentence-form. If names are substituted for the variables in a sentence-form, we obtain a sentence expressing a proposition, which is the corresponding value of the propositional function denoted by the sentence form. These distinctions may seem pedantic, but they are actually needed in order to avoid some of the common confusions in the treatment of propositional functions.

We shall denote properties by capital Latin letters. If A is a property, then the sentence-form "Ax" shall denote the propositional function that x has the property A. Thus if "α" is a name, then $A\alpha$ is a proposition, and the sentence "$A\alpha$" is its name. For example, if A is the property of being a man, then ADewey is the proposition that Dewey is a man, and "ADewey" is a sentence expressing this proposition. If "$\ldots x \ldots$" is a sentence form, then "$(x)(\ldots x \ldots)$" shall denote the proposition that for all x, $\ldots x \ldots$, and "$(\exists x)(\ldots x \ldots)$" shall denote the proposition that there is an x such that $\ldots x \ldots$. If A is the property of being a man, then $(x)(Ax)$ is the false proposition that for all x, x is a man, and $(\exists x)(Ax)$ is the true proposition that there is an x such that x is a man; in brief, "$(x)(Ax)$" says that everything is a man, while "$(\exists x)(Ax)$" says that there are men. The symbol "(x)" is called the *universal quantifier* on the variable "x", and "$(\exists x)$" is called the *existential quantifier* on that variable.

If "$\ldots x \ldots$" is a sentence-form, then "$x \ni (\ldots x \ldots)$" shall denote the class of all x's such that $\ldots x \ldots$. Hence in the above example $x \ni (Ax)$ is the class of men. The universe may be defined as $x \ni (x = x)$, and the null class as $x \ni (\sim(x = x))$.

We should expect that

$$a \in x \ni (\ldots x \ldots) \equiv \ldots a \ldots$$

is always a true proposition. We should also like to use classes as arguments, and thus to be able to make general statements about classes, classes of classes, etc. For example, we may define the class whose only member is a by

$$\iota(a) = x \ni (x = a),$$

and the integer 1 by

$$1 = \alpha \ni ((\exists x) .\alpha = \iota(x)).$$

This definition turns out to be satisfactory from many points of view. We then have the true proposition that

$$(\alpha)(x)(y) :. \alpha \in 1 \wedge x \in \alpha \wedge y \in \alpha :\supset: x = y.$$

This means, in ordinary language, that for all α, x, and y, if α is a unit class, i.e. $\alpha = \iota(z)$ for some z, and if x and y are members of α, then x is the same as y. We may define the ordered pair of x and y thus:

$$\langle x, y\rangle = \iota(\iota(x)) \cup \iota(\iota(x) \cup \iota(y)),$$

that is $\langle x, y\rangle$ is the class whose members are the classes $\iota(x)$ and $\iota(x) \cup \iota(y)$. It is easy to see that

$$\langle x, y\rangle = \langle u, v\rangle :\equiv: x = u \wedge y = v.$$

The trouble is that this naive point of view leads to contradiction. Consider the class of all men. It is itself not a man. On the other hand, the class of all classes is itself a class. This suggests the study of $\alpha \ni (\sim(\alpha \in \alpha))$, i.e. the class of all classes which are not members of themselves. Let us denote this class by "ρ", so that

$$\rho = \alpha \ni (\sim(\alpha \in \alpha)),$$

$$\text{i.e.} \vdash (\alpha) :\alpha \in \rho .\equiv. \sim(\alpha \in \alpha).$$

We raise the question, is ρ a member of ρ or not? We have

$$\vdash \rho \in \rho .\equiv. \sim(\rho \in \rho),$$

in words, if ρ is a member of ρ, then ρ is not a member of ρ, and conversely. This is, of course, a contradiction by Chapter II, section 2, Ex. 1(b). This paradox, due to Russell in the present modern form, shows that the naive application of the ideas outlined here leads to contradiction. This contradiction arises from a straightforward application of principles which are ordinarily accepted as intuitively correct. Furthermore, reasoning very similar to this is commonly used in important mathematical proofs.

We see, then, that in order to obtain a consistent logic it is essential to make certain restrictions and to forbid certain arguments which naive intuition permits. Most of the modern work on logic has been directed toward the construction and the study of formal systems which avoid these paradoxes. These systems differ considerably in the restrictions on intuitive logic which they introduce, and much controversy has arisen as to which of them is most acceptable on intuitive, philosophical, or mathematical grounds. Some of these systems are adequate for mathematics or a large portion thereof, but these have not been proved consistent, and in view of an important theorem of Gödel, are not likely to be proved consistent by methods which are universally acceptable. Furthermore, no such system can be categorical, according to another theorem of Gödel. By using a method based on transfinite induction Gentzen has proved the consistency of a system which is adequate for arithmetic, but the reasoning of Gentzen cannot be expressed in the object language itself. As A. Weil has said, God exists since mathematics is consistent, and the Devil exists since we cannot prove it. The consistency proofs of Gentzen and others for systems adequate for large parts of mathematics, even though they are based on methods which are under fire, for example, by the intuitionists, are convincing to the extent that no one seems to try seriously to construct counterexamples to results proved in this way. The margin between what can actually be proved by constructive methods and what is required for a proof of the consistency of arithmetic is, according to the work of Gentzen himself, Bernays, and Goodstein, very narrow but yet essential. We may say that they have confined the Devil to a dwelling place of almost vanishing, but still not negligible, dimensions.

A number of systems have been constructed which are adequate for much of arithmetic and other branches of mathematics, and Church has proved one of these to be consistent. Some advocates of these systems demand that those parts of mathematics which cannot be developed by their methods be abandoned. Brouwer and his disciples have been attempting the reconstruction of mathematics in the effort to develop as much as possible by intuitionist methods. Nevertheless, many of the important properties of real numbers which are used in everyday mathematical practice cannot be developed on such a basis, and their intuitionist analogues are probably too complicated to be considered as adequate substitutes. On the other hand, the work of Gödel, Kleene, and Nelson on intuitionist arithmetic provides a certain justification for that point of view and makes it seem less dogmatic and more plausible. The result of Gödel that every formula provable in the arithmetic based on a Boolean propositional logic can be translated into one provable in the arithmetic based on intuitionist propositional logic, shows that as far as arithmetic goes, the intuitionist logic is as powerful as the classical one, and also that if the intuitionist arithmetic is consistent, then so is the classical arithmetic. We repeat that the work of the intuitionists is valuable even for those who do not accept their philosophy, since a constructive proof often carries with it important additional information which is not yielded by a non-constructive proof.

EXERCISES

Ex. 1. Interpret, in ordinary language, the following strings of symbols:

(a). $\alpha \ni (\alpha \subset \beta)$.

(b). $x \ni ((\exists \alpha) . x \in \alpha \wedge \alpha \in A)$.

(c). $x \ni ((\alpha) . \alpha \in A \supset x \in \alpha)$.

(d). $(\alpha)(\beta) : \alpha \in \mathfrak{J} \wedge \beta \in \mathfrak{J} .\supset. \alpha \cap \beta \in \mathfrak{J}$.

(e). $\gamma \in \mathfrak{B} :\equiv: (\exists x)(\exists y) .\gamma = \langle x, y \rangle \wedge x \in a \wedge y \in a$.

(f). $\langle x, z\rangle \in \gamma :\equiv: (\exists y). \langle x, y\rangle \in \alpha \wedge \langle y, z\rangle \in \beta$.

Ex. 2. Give strings of symbols translating the following English phrases and sentences:

(a). The class α is included in the class β. (p. 3)

(b). The class α is the same as the class β.

(c). The common part of α and β.

(d). The union of α and β.

(e). The class of x's which are in α but not in β.

(f). $\mathfrak{J}$ is an ideal in the algebra of classes.

(g). K is a product system in the algebra of classes.

(h). α is a class containing exactly two members.

(i). α is a non-empty class containing at most three members.

(j). α is the class of all ordered pairs $\langle x, y\rangle$, where x is in β and y is in γ.

(k). The class of all classes β which contain α.

Ex. 3. Show that the "class" $\sigma = \alpha \ni ((\beta) .\sim. \alpha \in \beta \wedge \beta \in \alpha)$ leads to a contradiction.

SECTION 2 THE FUNCTIONAL LOGIC OF THE FIRST ORDER

We shall first set up the simplest of all functional logics, the first order logic of monadic functions. Our primitive notions are four classes of objects $\mathfrak{P}$, $\mathfrak{T}$, $\mathfrak{F}_1$, and $\mathfrak{J}$, two unary operations $\sim$ and $\prod$, and two binary operations $\supset$ and *application*, denoted by juxtaposition. The desired interpretation is:

$\mathfrak{P}$	is the class of propositions;
$\mathfrak{T}$	is the class of true propositions;
$\mathfrak{F}_1$	is the class of properties;
$\mathfrak{J}$	is the class of individuals;
$p \supset q$	is the proposition that if p, then q;
$\sim p$	is the proposition that it is false that p;
$A\alpha$	is the proposition that α has the property A;
$\prod A$	is the proposition that for all α, $A\alpha$.

We shall retain our earlier conventions as to the use of parentheses and dots, and we use the definitions and notations of II2.

As a mnemonic device we shall use small Latin letters except "i", "j", "k", "m", "n", "x", "y", and "z" to denote elements of $\mathfrak{P}$, capital Latin letters to denote elements of $\mathfrak{F}_1$, and small Greek letters to denote elements of $\mathfrak{I}$. The letters x, y, and z, with or without subscripts, are reserved for a special use as described below.

Our postulates are as follows:

A1″–A7″ as on p. 31.

$F_1 1$. If A is in $\mathfrak{F}_1$ and α is in $\mathfrak{I}$, then $A\alpha$ and $\prod A$ are uniquely determined elements of $\mathfrak{P}$.

$F_1 2$. If A is in $\mathfrak{F}_1$ and $\vdash A\alpha$ for all α in $\mathfrak{I}$, then $\vdash \prod A$.

By a *sentence-form in* x we mean a string of signs built up from "x", names of elements of $\mathfrak{P}$, $\mathfrak{F}_1$, and $\mathfrak{I}$, and the names "$\supset$" and "$\sim$" of the fundamental operations in $\mathfrak{P}$, and parentheses by means of a finite number of applications of the following rules:

(a). If A is in $\mathfrak{F}_1$, then "(Ax)" is a sentence-form in x.

(b). If p is in $\mathfrak{P}$, then "p" is a sentence-form in x.

(c). If A and B are sentence-forms in x, then "$(A \supset B)$" and "$(\sim A)$" are sentence-forms in x.

In (c) the signs "$(A \supset B)$" and "$(\sim A)$" are to be understood as the strings obtained by putting for "A" and "B" the strings which those letters denote. To remind the reader of the letter x used in these constructions we shall use symbols such as "$\mathfrak{A}(x)$" to denote sentence-forms in x. As we have remarked before, sentence-forms express propositional functions. We define in a similar manner the notion of sentence-form in any other letter. We shall, however, reserve the letters x, y, and z, with or without subscripts, for this use.

We define the *value* of a sentence-form $\mathfrak{A}(x)$ for the argument α, where α is a member of $\mathfrak{I}$, by the following rules:

(a). If A is in $\mathfrak{F}_1$, and $\mathfrak{A}(x)$ is "(Ax)", then $\mathfrak{A}(\alpha)$ is $A\alpha$.

(b) If p is in $\mathfrak{P}$, and $\mathfrak{A}(x)$ is "p", then $\mathfrak{A}(\alpha)$ is p.

(c). If $\mathfrak{A}(x)$ is "$(\mathfrak{B}(x) \supset \mathfrak{C}(x))$", where $\mathfrak{B}(x)$ and $\mathfrak{C}(x)$ are sentence-forms in x, then $\mathfrak{A}(\alpha)$ is $\mathfrak{B}(\alpha) \supset \mathfrak{C}(\alpha)$.

(d). If $\mathfrak{A}(x)$ is "$(\sim\mathfrak{B}(x))$", where $\mathfrak{B}(x)$ is a sentence-form in x, the $\mathfrak{A}(\alpha)$ is $\sim\mathfrak{B}(\alpha)$.

It follows from A2″, A3″, and $F_1 1$, that if α is in $\mathfrak{J}$ and $\mathfrak{A}(x)$ is a sentence-form in x, then $\mathfrak{A}(\alpha)$ is a uniquely determined element of $\mathfrak{P}$.

$F_1 3$. If $\mathfrak{A}(x)$ is a sentence-form in x, then there is a unique element A in $\mathfrak{F}_1$ such that $\vdash A\alpha \,.\!\equiv\!.\, \mathfrak{A}(\alpha)$ for all α in $\mathfrak{J}$.

A sentence-form expresses a propositional function, and $F_1 3$ assures us that every propositional function determines a property A such that the proposition that $A\alpha$ is always equivalent to the value of the propositional function for the argument α. Of course, $F_1 3$ is to be understood as applying to sentence-forms in any letter.

We shall denote this uniquely determined property by $\hat{x}\mathfrak{A}(x)$.

D1. "$(x)\mathfrak{A}(x)$" for "$\prod \hat{x}\mathfrak{A}(x)$".

Note that if p is in $\mathfrak{P}$, the "p" is a formula in x, and

$$\vdash(\hat{x}p)\alpha \equiv p \qquad \text{for all } \alpha \text{ in } \mathfrak{J},$$

by condition (b) in the definition of "$\mathfrak{A}(\alpha)$".

$F_1 4$. If p is in $\mathfrak{P}$ and A is in $\mathfrak{F}_1$, then

$$\vdash(x)(p \supset Ax) \,.\!\supset\!.\, p \supset \prod A.$$

$F_1 5$. If A is in $\mathfrak{F}_1$ and α is in $\mathfrak{J}$, then $\vdash \prod A \supset A\alpha$.

$F_1 6$. $\mathfrak{P}$ and $\mathfrak{J}$ are non-empty.

In this formulation of the first order logic of monadic functions the letter x in the syntax language plays the role of a variable with values in $\mathfrak{J}$, i.e. for which names of members of $\mathfrak{J}$ may be substituted. It is also possible to give a formulation in which the variables are part of the object language; this carries with it simplifications of some parts of the theory and complications of other parts.

In the expressions "$\hat{x}\mathfrak{A}(x)$" and "$(x)\mathfrak{A}(x)$" the letter x is a *dummy symbol*, that is, it has nothing to do with the particular elements of $\mathfrak{F}_1$ and $\mathfrak{P}$ here denoted. For this reason, in expressions of this type "x" is called an *apparent* variable or a *bound* variable. Such apparent variables are very convenient to work with, but the concepts of "variable" and "apparent variable" are quite difficult to analyze precisely; the detailed discussion of these notions is consequently deferred to a later section.

We can eliminate the complicated notions of "apparent variable" and sentence-form by a very simple device, at the cost of several extra postulates and primitives. The extra primitives and postulates amount to a real economy since they are equivalent to the assumption of $F_1 3$ for three very special sentence forms. The idea is that $\hat{x}p$ is the "constant" propositional function whose value is the proposition p for any argument α, and similarly $\hat{x}(\sim Ax)$ and $\hat{x}(Ax \wedge Bx)$ are the properties which correspond to A' and $A \cap B$ in the algebra of classes. An examination of the definition of "sentence-form in x" shows that these suffice for the construction of the properties corresponding to arbitrary sentence-forms.

We are thus led to adjoin two new primitive unary operations K, $'$, and a binary operation $\cap$, and the following postulates, replacing $F_1 3$ and $F_1 4$, to the primitive frame:

$F_1 7$. If p is in $\mathfrak{P}$, then Kp is a uniquely determined element of $\mathfrak{F}_1$.

$F_1 8$. If A and B are in $\mathfrak{F}_1$, then A' and $A \cap B$ are uniquely determined elements of $\mathfrak{F}_1$.

$F_1 9$. If p is in $\mathfrak{P}$, and α is in $\mathfrak{I}$, then $\vdash Kp\alpha \equiv p$.

$F_1 10$. If A is in $\mathfrak{F}_1$ and α is in $\mathfrak{I}$, then $\vdash A'\alpha \equiv \sim A\alpha$.

$F_1 11$. If A and B are in $\mathfrak{F}_1$ and α is in $\mathfrak{I}$, then $\vdash (A \cap B)\alpha \equiv A\alpha \wedge B\alpha$.

$F_1 12$. If p is in $\mathfrak{P}$ and A is in $\mathfrak{F}_1$, then $\vdash Kp \subset A \mathbin{.\supset.} p \supset \prod A$.

D2. "$A \subset B$" for "$\prod((A \cap B')')$".

We could have achieved greater elegance had we worked with the combination "$(A \cap B')'$" instead of "$\cap$", or had we formulated the propositional logic in terms of "$\sim$" and "$\wedge$". Postulate $F_1 12$ could be replaced by

$F_1 12'$. If p is in $\mathfrak{P}$ and A is in $\mathfrak{F}_1$, then $\vdash \prod(Kp \cap A) .\supset. p \wedge \prod A$.

We chose the present form to facilitate comparison with the postulates $F_1 1$–$F_1 5$ and with some logics introduced later.

It is now only an exercise for the reader to prove $F_1 3$ and $F_1 4$ from A1″–A7″, $F_1 1$, $F_1 2$, $F_1 5$–$F_1 12$. We leave the rest of this alternative development for him to work out for himself.

We return now to the postulates A1″–A7″, $F_1 1$–$F_1 5$, and their consequences. We shall denote the statement in the syntax language that A and B are the same element of $\mathfrak{F}_1$ by "$A = B$".

T1. *If* $\vdash A\alpha \equiv B\alpha$ *for all* α *in* $\mathfrak{I}$, *then* $A = B$.

Proof. "(Bx)" is a sentence form in x. Hence, by $F_1 3$, there is a unique element C in $\mathfrak{F}_1$ such that

$$\vdash C\alpha \equiv B\alpha$$

for all α in $\mathfrak{I}$. But A and B are such elements, so that they must be the same.

Corollary 1a. *If* A *is in* $\mathfrak{F}_1$, *then* $A = \hat{x}(Ax)$.

Corollary 1b. *If* $\mathfrak{A}(x)$ *is a sentence-form in* x, *and* $\mathfrak{A}(y)$ *is the result of substituting* "y" *for* "x" *in* $\mathfrak{A}(x)$, *then* $\hat{x}\mathfrak{A}(x) = \hat{y}\mathfrak{A}(y)$ *and* $\vdash (x)\mathfrak{A}(x) \equiv (y)\mathfrak{A}(y)$.

This follows from $F_1 3$, T2.2.28, and T1.

Corollary 1c. *If* $\mathfrak{A}(x)$ *and* $\mathfrak{B}(x)$ *are sentence forms in* x, *and* $\vdash \mathfrak{A}(\alpha) \equiv \mathfrak{B}(\alpha)$ *for all* α *in* $\mathfrak{I}$, *then* $\hat{x}\mathfrak{A}(x) = \hat{x}\mathfrak{B}(x)$.

Corollary 1b justifies our assertion that "x" is a dummy symbol in "$\hat{x}\mathfrak{A}(x)$" and "$(x)\mathfrak{A}(x)$".

T2. *If* $\mathfrak{A}(x)$ *is a sentence-form in* x *and* α *is in* $\mathfrak{I}$, *then* $\vdash (x)\mathfrak{A}(x) .\supset. \mathfrak{A}(\alpha)$. ($F_1 5$, $F_1 3$).

T3. *If* $\mathfrak{A}(x)$ *is a sentence-form in* x *and* $\vdash \mathfrak{A}(\alpha)$ *for all* α *in* $\mathfrak{I}$, $\vdash (x)\mathfrak{A}(x)$.

T4. *The set of postulates* A1″–A7″, $F_1 1$–$F_1 6$ *is consistent.*

Proof. Let $\mathfrak{P}$ be the two-element Boolean algebra with $\sim$ and

$\supset$ defined as in II1, identifying t with 1 and f with 0, let $\mathfrak{F}_1$ contain two elements V and Λ, and $\mathfrak{J}$ contain only one element α; let application and $\prod$ be defined by the tables

A	$A\alpha$	$\prod A$
V	1	1
Λ	0	0

Then the postulates are obviously satisfied. For the verification of $F_1 3$, note that if $\mathfrak{A}(x)$ is an arbitrary sentence-form, then $\mathfrak{A}(\alpha) = 0$ or $\mathfrak{A}(\alpha) = 1$, so that

$$\vdash \mathfrak{A}(\alpha) \equiv \Lambda\alpha \qquad \text{or} \vdash \mathfrak{A}(\alpha) \equiv \mathrm{V}\alpha$$

in the respective cases.

Essentially, our proof of consistency is the verification that the postulates hold in a universe of one individual.

D3. "$(\exists x)\mathfrak{A}(x)$" for "$\sim(x) . \sim\mathfrak{A}(x)$", i.e. "$(\exists x)\mathfrak{A}(x)$" is an abbreviation for "$\sim\prod\hat{x}(\sim\mathfrak{A}(x))$", where $\mathfrak{A}(x)$ is a sentence-form in x. The letter "x" is, of course, a dummy symbol in "$(\exists x)\mathfrak{A}(x)$". If A is in $\mathfrak{F}_1$ and α is in $\mathfrak{J}$, then $\vdash A\alpha . \supset .(\exists x)Ax$.

More generally, if $\mathfrak{A}(x)$ is a sentence-form in x and α is in $\mathfrak{J}$, then

$$\vdash \mathfrak{A}(\alpha) . \supset . (\exists x)\mathfrak{A}(x).$$

Proof. $\vdash (x) . \sim\mathfrak{A}(x) :\supset: \sim\mathfrak{A}(\alpha)$. (T2). Now apply T2.2.9, A7″, and D2.

T6. *If* $\mathfrak{A}(x)$ *is a sentence-form in* x, *then*

$$\vdash (x)\mathfrak{A}(x) . \supset . (\exists x)\mathfrak{A}(x).$$

Proof. Let α be in $\mathfrak{J}$ ($F_1 6$). Then T2 and T5 yield the conclusion.

Note that we needed in T6 the assumption that there are individuals. In some formulations where the notion of "variable" is used rather freely, T6 is proved without this assumption, but the deduction, while formally correct, smacks of sleight of hand.

One may doubt that a formal system in which such a deduction is valid is a correct representation of our admittedly vague intuitive ideas of what constitutes a valid inference.

T7. *If* $\mathfrak{A}(x)$ *and* $\mathfrak{B}(x)$ *are sentence-forms in* x, *then*

$$\vdash (x) . \mathfrak{A}(x) \supset \mathfrak{B}(x) : \supset : (x)\mathfrak{A}(x) . \supset (x)\mathfrak{B}(x).$$

Proof. Let α be in $\mathfrak{J}$. Take $(x) . \mathfrak{A}(x) \supset \mathfrak{B}(x)$ and $(x)\mathfrak{A}(x)$ as hypotheses. Then

$$(x)\mathfrak{A}(x) . \supset \mathfrak{A}(\alpha), \qquad \text{(T2)}$$
$$(x)\mathfrak{A}(x),$$
$$\mathfrak{A}(\alpha),$$
$$(x) . \mathfrak{A}(x) \supset \mathfrak{B}(x) : \supset : \mathfrak{A}(\alpha) \supset \mathfrak{B}(\alpha), \qquad \text{(T2)}$$
$$\mathfrak{A}(\alpha) \supset \mathfrak{B}(\alpha),$$

and

$$\mathfrak{B}(\alpha)$$

constitute a proof of $\mathfrak{B}(\alpha)$ from the hypotheses. By the deduction theorem (T2.3.3a),

(1) $\vdash (x) . \mathfrak{A}(x) \supset \mathfrak{B}(x) : \supset : (x)\mathfrak{A}(x) . \supset \mathfrak{B}(\alpha).$

By T3,

(2) $\vdash (x) :. (x) . \mathfrak{A}(x) \supset \mathfrak{B}(x) : \supset : (x)\mathfrak{A}(x) . \supset \mathfrak{B}(x).$

The conclusion follows by two applications of $F_1 4$ and A7$''$.

Note that in (1) and (2), $(x) . \mathfrak{A}(x) \supset \mathfrak{B}(x)$ and $(x)\mathfrak{A}(x)$ are elements of $\mathfrak{P}$. The inference is perhaps more obvious if we denote these elements by "p" and "q", respectively, thus:

$$\vdash p \supset . q \supset \mathfrak{B}(\alpha),$$
$$\vdash (x) : p \supset . q \supset \mathfrak{B}(x), \text{ etc.}$$

The quantifiers have "killed" the variable x, so that being "dead", it has no significance in the rest of the argument.

Corollary 7a. $\vdash (x) . \mathfrak{A}(x) \supset \mathfrak{B}(x) : \supset : (\exists x)\mathfrak{A}(x) \supset (\exists x)\mathfrak{B}(x).$

T8. *If* p *is in* $\mathfrak{P}$, *and* $\mathfrak{A}(x)$ *is a sentence-form in* x, *then*

$$\vdash (x) . \mathfrak{A}(x) \supset p : \supset : (\exists x)\mathfrak{A}(x) . \supset . p$$

Proof. Let α be in $\mathfrak{J}$, and take $(x) \,.\mathfrak{A}(x) \supset p$ and $\sim p$ as hypotheses. Then

$$(x) \,.\mathfrak{A}(x) \supset p,$$
$$(x) \,.\mathfrak{A}(x) \supset p :\supset: \mathfrak{A}(\alpha) \supset p, \qquad \text{(T2)}$$
$$\mathfrak{A}(\alpha) \supset p,$$
$$\mathfrak{A}(\alpha) \supset p \,.\supset.\, \sim p \supset \sim\mathfrak{A}(\alpha), \qquad \text{(T2.2.11)}$$
$$\sim p \supset \sim\mathfrak{A}(\alpha),$$
$$\sim p,$$
$$\sim\mathfrak{A}(\alpha)$$

is a proof of $\sim\mathfrak{A}(\alpha)$ from the hypotheses. Then

$$\vdash (x) \,.\mathfrak{A}(x) \supset p :\supset: \sim p \supset \sim\mathfrak{A}(\alpha)$$

for all α in $\mathfrak{J}$. Now T3, two applications $F_1 4$, T2.2.2, A6″, and A7″, and finally D3 yield the conclusion.

T9. $\vdash (x) \,.\mathfrak{A}(x) \equiv \mathfrak{B}(x) :\supset: (x)\mathfrak{A}(x) \equiv .(x)\mathfrak{B}(x)$.

Proof. If α is in $\mathfrak{J}$, then by D2.2.3 and T2.2.15, $\vdash \mathfrak{A}(\alpha) \equiv \mathfrak{B}(\alpha) \supset .\mathfrak{A}(\alpha) \supset \mathfrak{B}(\alpha)$. Hence, by T3 $\vdash (x) :\mathfrak{A}(x) \equiv \mathfrak{B}(x) \,.\supset.\, \mathfrak{A}(x) \supset \mathfrak{B}(x)$. Now T7 and A7″ yield $\vdash (x) \,.\mathfrak{A}(x) \equiv \mathfrak{B}(x) :\supset: (x) \,.\mathfrak{A}(x) \supset \mathfrak{B}(x)$, and the same theorems together with T2.2.2 give

$$\vdash (x) \,.\mathfrak{A}(x) \equiv \mathfrak{B}(x) :\supset: (x)\mathfrak{A}(x) \,.\supset.\, (x)\mathfrak{B}(x).$$

If in the first step we use T2.2.16, then by the same reasoning we arrive at

$$\vdash (x) \,.\mathfrak{A}(x) \equiv \mathfrak{B}(x) :\supset: (x)\mathfrak{B}(x) \,.\supset.\, (x)\mathfrak{A}(x),$$

and the conclusion now follows from T2.2.24, A7″, and D2.2.3.

T10. $\vdash (x) .\mathfrak{A}(x) \equiv \mathfrak{B}(x) :\supset: (\exists x)\mathfrak{A}(x) \,.\equiv.\, (\exists x)\mathfrak{B}(x)$.

Proof. If α is in $\mathfrak{J}$, then $\vdash \mathfrak{A}(\alpha) \equiv \mathfrak{B}(\alpha) \,.\supset.\, \sim\mathfrak{A}(\alpha) \equiv \sim\mathfrak{B}(\alpha)$ (T2.2.21). The conclusion follows by $F_1 2$, T7, A7″, and T2.2.21 again.

T11. $\vdash p \supset (x)\mathfrak{A}(x) :\equiv: (x) \,.p \supset \mathfrak{A}(x)$.

Proof. $\vdash (x) . p \supset \mathfrak{A}(x) :\supset: p \supset (x)\mathfrak{A}(x)$ ($F_1 4$, let $A = \hat{x}(\mathfrak{A}(x))$).
Here we use the fact that

$$\vdash p \supset \mathrm{A}\alpha \,.\equiv.\, p \supset \mathfrak{A}(\alpha)$$

for all α in $\mathfrak{I}$, and T3.1d. Let α be in $\mathfrak{I}$, and take $p \supset (x)\mathfrak{A}(x)$ and p as hypotheses. Then

$$p,$$
$$p \supset (x)\mathfrak{A}(x),$$
$$(x)\mathfrak{A}(x),$$
$$(x)\mathfrak{A}(x) \,.\supset.\, \mathfrak{A}(\alpha), \qquad \text{(T2)}$$
and
$$\mathfrak{A}(\alpha)$$

are a proof of $\mathfrak{A}(\alpha)$ from the hypotheses. Hence

$$\vdash p \supset (x)\mathfrak{A}(x) \,.\supset.\, p \supset \mathfrak{A}(\alpha).$$

Now $F_1 2$, $F_1 4$, and A7″ yield the other half of the equivalence, and T2.2.14 and A7″ complete the proof.

The proofs of the following are left as exercises for the reader.

T12. $\vdash (\exists x)\mathfrak{A}(x) \,.\supset.\, p :\equiv: (x) . \mathfrak{A}(x) \supset p.$
T13. $\vdash (x) . \mathfrak{A}(x) \wedge p :\equiv: (x)\mathfrak{A}(x) \,.\wedge.\, p.$
T14. $\vdash (x) . \mathfrak{A}(x) \vee p :\equiv: (x)\mathfrak{A}(x) \,.\vee.\, p.$
T15. $\vdash (\exists x) . \mathfrak{A}(x) \wedge p :\equiv: (\exists x)\mathfrak{A}(x) \,.\wedge.\, p.$
T16. $\vdash (\exists x) . \mathfrak{A}(x) \vee p :\equiv: (\exists x) . \mathfrak{A}(x) \,.\vee. p.$
T17. $\vdash (x)\mathfrak{A}(x) \,.\supset.\, p :\equiv: (\exists x) . \mathfrak{A}(x) \supset p.$
T18. $\vdash p \supset (\exists x)\mathfrak{A}(x) :\equiv: (\exists x) . p \supset \mathfrak{A}(x).$
T19. $\vdash (x) . \mathfrak{A}(x) \vee \mathfrak{B}(x) :\supset: (x)\mathfrak{A}(x) \,.\vee.\, (\exists x)\mathfrak{B}(x).$
T20. $\vdash (x) : \mathfrak{A}(x) \wedge \mathfrak{B}(x) .:\equiv:. (x)\mathfrak{A}(x) \,.\wedge.\, (x)\mathfrak{B}(x).$

In order to construct a logic for polyadic propositional functions, that is, intuitively, functions of several variables with propositions as values, we must introduce some new primitives. We proceed with the following intuitive idea in mind. The diadic function that x is bigger than y may be thought of as a function of the one individual variable x whose value, corresponding to an argument α, is a monadic function of y. Thus "2 is bigger than y" and "Spain is bigger than y" express monadic propositional functions and are regarded as the values of the previous function for the arguments 2 and Spain, respectively. If A^2 is a diadic propositional function and α is an individual, then $A^2\alpha$ is to be the monadic propositional function obtained as a value when the first argument of A^2 is α. Thus $A^2\alpha$ will be a member of $\mathfrak{F}_1$ and $A^2\alpha\beta$ will be a proposition, i.e. a member of $\mathfrak{P}$. We might have written instead $(A^2\alpha)\beta$, but the use of simple juxtaposition to denote the application of a function to an individual will not lead to any ambiguity. We shall also need an extension of the universal quantifier. To this end we regard $\prod$ as an operation which transforms diadic functions into monadic functions, triadic functions into diadic functions, and so on, in accordance with the rules

$$\vdash(\prod A^2)\alpha \equiv (x)A^2x\alpha,$$
$$\vdash(\prod A^3)\alpha\beta \equiv (x)A^3x\alpha\beta, \text{ etc.}$$

(Here A^n is an n-adic function.) Thus if "A^2xy" is the sentence-form "x is bigger than y", then "$(\prod A^2)\alpha$" will denote "for all x, x is bigger than α". We now proceed to a precise formulation of these ideas.

We take as primitive notions classes $\mathfrak{P}$, $\mathfrak{T}$, $\mathfrak{I}$, $\mathfrak{F}_1$, $\mathfrak{F}_2$, $\cdots$, $\mathfrak{F}_n$, $\cdots$, unary operations $\sim$ and $\prod$, and binary operations $\supset$ and application, the latter denoted by juxtaposition. Here $\mathfrak{P}$, $\mathfrak{T}$, $\mathfrak{I}$, $\mathfrak{F}_1$, $\sim$ and $\supset$ are to be interpreted as before, and for each n, $\mathfrak{F}_n$ is to be conceived as the class of n-adic propositional functions. We shall use capital Latin letters with the superscript "n" to denote members of $\mathfrak{F}_n$, and shall otherwise continue to use the notational conventions previously explained. By a sentence-form in x_1, x_2, $\cdots$, x_k we shall mean a string of signs built up from the letters x_1, $\cdots$, x_k, names of elements of $\mathfrak{P}$, $\mathfrak{I}$, $\mathfrak{F}_1$, $\cdots$, $\mathfrak{F}_n$, $\cdots$, and of the primitive operations, and parentheses, in accordance with the following rules:

if A^n is in $\mathfrak{F}_n$, then "$A^n \cdots$" is a sentence-form in x_1, $\cdots$, x_k, where "$\cdots$" denotes a string of n signs, each of which is "x_i" for some i or a name of an element of $\mathfrak{I}$;
if p is in $\mathfrak{P}$, then "p" is a sentence-form in x_1, $\cdots$, x_k;
if $\mathfrak{B}$ and $\mathfrak{C}$ are sentence-forms in x_1, $\cdots$, x_k, then "$(\mathfrak{B} \supset \mathfrak{C})$" and "$(\sim\mathfrak{B})$" are sentence-forms in x_1, $\cdots$, x_k.

A sign such as "$\mathfrak{A}(x_1, \cdots, x_k)$" shall denote a sentence-form in $x_1, \cdots, x_k$. If $\mathfrak{A}(x_1, \cdots, x_k)$ is a sentence-form in $x_1, \cdots, x_k$, then "$\mathfrak{A}(\alpha_1, \cdots, \alpha_k)$" shall denote the result of substituting "α_i" for "x_i", $i = 1, \cdots, k$, and is a name of a uniquely determined member of $\mathfrak{P}$. (See p. 75 for an explicit definition in the case of one letter.)

Our postulates are as follows:

A1″–A7″ and $F_1$1–$F_1$6 as before.

F_n1. *If A^n is in $\mathfrak{F}_n$ and α is in $\mathfrak{I}$, then $A^n\alpha$ and $\prod A^n$ are uniquely determined elements of F_{n-1}.*

F_n2. *If A^n is in $\mathfrak{F}_n$ and $\alpha_2, \cdots, \alpha_n$ are in $\mathfrak{I}$, then*

$$\vdash \prod A^n\alpha_2 \cdots \alpha_n \equiv (x)A^n x\alpha_2 \cdots \alpha_n .$$

F_n3. *If $\mathfrak{A}(x_1, \cdots, x_n)$ is a sentence-form in $x_1, \cdots, x_n$, then there is a unique element A^n in $\mathfrak{F}_n$ such that $\vdash A^n\alpha_1 \cdots \alpha_n \equiv \mathfrak{A}(\alpha_1, \cdots, \alpha_n)$ for all $\alpha_1, \cdots, \alpha_n$ in $\mathfrak{I}$.*

D4. *If $\mathfrak{A}(x_1, \cdots, x_n)$ is a sentence-form in $x_1, \cdots, x_n$, then we shall denote the element A^n of $\mathfrak{F}_n$ whose existence and uniqueness is postulated in F_n3 by $\hat{x}_1 \hat{x}_2 \cdots \hat{x}_n\mathfrak{A}(x_1, \cdots, x_n)$.*

Thus

$$\vdash \hat{x}_1 \cdots \hat{x}_n \mathfrak{A}(x_1, \cdots, x_n)\alpha_1 \cdots \alpha_n \equiv \mathfrak{A}(\alpha_1, \cdots, \alpha_n)$$

for all $\alpha_1, \cdots, \alpha_n$ in $\mathfrak{I}$.

D5. $(x_1)\mathfrak{A}(x_1, \cdots, x_n) =$
$(\prod \hat{x}_1 \cdots \hat{x}_n\mathfrak{A}(x_1, \cdots, x_n))x_2 \cdots x_n$.

Note that the uniqueness guaranteed in F_n3 assures us that "x_1", $\cdots$, and "x_n" are dummy symbols in "$\hat{x}_1 \cdots \hat{x}_n\mathfrak{A}(x_1, \cdots, x_n)$", e.g.

$$\hat{x}_1 \cdots \hat{x}_n\mathfrak{A}(x_1, \cdots, x_n) = \hat{y}_1 \cdots \hat{y}_n\mathfrak{A}(y_1, \cdots, y_n)$$

and similarly for any other string of n distinct letters. The *order* of the letters in the prefix is, however, essential, for

$$\vdash \hat{x}_1\hat{x}_2\mathfrak{A}(x_1, x_2)\alpha_1\alpha_2 \equiv \mathfrak{A}(\alpha_1, \alpha_2),$$

while

$$\vdash \hat{x}_2\hat{x}_1\mathfrak{A}(x_1, x_2)\alpha_1\alpha_2 \equiv \mathfrak{A}(\alpha_2, \alpha_1).$$

In D5 note that $\hat{x}_1 \cdots \hat{x}_n \mathfrak{A}(x_1, \cdots, x_n)$ is in F_n, so that $\prod \hat{x}_1 \cdots \hat{x}_n \mathfrak{A}(x_1, \cdots, x_n)$ is in $\mathfrak{F}_{n-1}$, and "x_1", $\cdots$, "x_n" are dummy symbols in this string, and therefore

$$(x_1)\mathfrak{A}(x_1, \cdots, x_n)$$

is a sentence-form in $x_2, \cdots, x_n$. We can, then, apply the quantification operation to the latter string and obtain

$$(x_2)(x_1)\mathfrak{A}(x_1, x_2, \cdots, x_n), \text{ etc.}$$

T21. $\prod A^n = \hat{x}_2 \cdots \hat{x}_n((x_1)A^n x_1 x_2 \cdots x_n)$.

Proof. For all $\alpha_2, \cdots, \alpha_n$ in $\mathfrak{J}$, we have

$$\begin{aligned} \vdash \prod A^n \alpha_2 \cdots \alpha_n &\equiv (x_1)A x_1 \alpha_2 \cdots \alpha_n \\ &\equiv \hat{x}_2 \cdots \hat{x}_n((x_1)A^n x_1 x_2 \cdots x_n)\alpha_2 \cdots \alpha_n, \end{aligned}$$

and the theorem follows from the uniqueness asserted in F_n3.

T22. $\vdash (x)(y)\mathfrak{A}(x, y) \equiv .(y)(x)\mathfrak{A}(x, y)$.

Proof. Let $A^2 = \hat{x}\hat{y}\mathfrak{A}(x, y)$, $B^2 = \hat{y}\hat{x}\mathfrak{A}(x, y)$. Then $(x)\mathfrak{A}(x, y) = (\prod A^2)y$, and $(y)(x)\mathfrak{A}(x, y) = \prod(\prod A^2)$, and similarly $(x)(y)\mathfrak{A}(x, y) = \prod(\prod B^2)$. Now take $(x)(y)\mathfrak{A}(x, y)$ as hypothesis, and let α, β be in $\mathfrak{J}$. Then

$$\begin{aligned} &\prod(\prod B^2), \\ &\prod(\prod B^2) \supset (\prod B^2)\alpha, \\ &(\prod B^2)\alpha, \\ &(\prod B^2)\alpha \supset B^2\beta\alpha, \qquad (F_n2) \\ &B^2\beta\alpha, \\ &B^2\beta\alpha \supset \mathfrak{A}(\alpha, \beta), \\ &\mathfrak{A}(\alpha, \beta), \\ &\mathfrak{A}(\alpha, \beta) \supset A^2\alpha\beta, \\ &A^2\alpha\beta \end{aligned}$$

form a proof of $A^2\alpha\beta$ from the hypothesis. Hence $\vdash \prod(\prod B^2) \supset A^2\alpha\beta$. Since this holds for all β in $\mathfrak{J}$, then $\vdash \prod(\prod B^2) \supset (\prod A^2)\beta$, by $F_1 2$, $F_1 4$, and A7″. Applying these postulates again, we obtain

$$\vdash \prod(\prod B^2) \supset \prod(\prod A^2).$$

By symmetry, $\vdash \prod(\prod A^2) \supset \prod(\prod B^2)$ and consequently the theorem holds by T2.2.14 and A7″.

COROLLARY 22a. *If* $i_1, \cdots, i_n$ *is any permutation of the integers* $1, \cdots, n$, *then* $\vdash (x_{i_1}) \cdots (x_{i_n})\mathfrak{A}(x_1, \cdots, x_n) \equiv (x_1) \cdots (x_n) \mathfrak{A}(x_1, \cdots, x_n)$.

D6. $(x_1, \cdots, x_n)\mathfrak{A}(x_1, \cdots, x_n) =$
$(x_1) \cdots (x_n)\mathfrak{A}(x_1, \cdots, x_n)$

D7. $(\exists x_1, \cdots, x_n)\mathfrak{A}(x_1, \cdots, x_n) =$
$(\exists x_1) \cdots (\exists x_n)\mathfrak{A}(x_1, \cdots, x_n)$

T24. *If* $i_1, \cdots, i_n$ *is a permutation of* $1, \cdots, n$, *then*
$\vdash (\exists x_{i_1}, \cdots, x_{i_n})\mathfrak{A}(x_1, \cdots, x_n) \equiv$
$(\exists x_1, \cdots, x_n)\mathfrak{A})x_1, \cdots, x_n)$.

A good deal of mathematics can be built up on the basis of the postulates of this section. For example, much of arithmetic can be developed if we adjoin to those already given the following primitives and postulates:

primitive	interpretation
N^1	("$N^1\alpha$" shall mean "α is a positive integer")
S^2	("$S^2\alpha\beta$" shall mean "$\beta = \alpha + 1$")
E^2	("$E^2\alpha\beta$" shall mean "$\alpha = \beta$")
1	(the integer one)

P0. N^1 *is in* $\mathfrak{F}_1$, *and* S^2, E^2 *are in* $\mathfrak{F}_2$, *and* 1 *is in* $\mathfrak{I}$.
P1. $\vdash N^1 1$.
P2. $\vdash (x, y) : N^1x \wedge S^2xy \,.\supset.\, N^1y$.
P3. $\vdash (x, y, z) : S^2xy \wedge S^2xz \,.\supset.\, E^2yz$.
P4. $\vdash (x) . N^1x \supset (\exists y)S^2xy$.
P5. $\vdash (x) \sim S^2x1$.
P6. $\vdash (x, y, z) : S^2xz \wedge S^2yz \,.\supset.\, E^2xy$.
P7. $\vdash (x)E^2xx$.
P8. $\vdash (x, y) .E^2xy \equiv E^2yx$.
P9. $\vdash (x, y, z) :E^2xy \wedge E^2yz \,.\supset.\, E^2xz$.
P10. *If* A^1 *is in* $\mathfrak{F}_1$, *then* $\vdash (x, y) : E^2xy \,.\supset.\, A^1x \equiv A^1y$.
P11. *If* A^1 *is in* $\mathfrak{F}_1$, *then* $\vdash A^1 1 \,.\wedge.\, (x, y):.\, A^1x \wedge S^2xy :\supset: A^1y ::\supset:: (x) .N^1x \supset A^1x$.

In words, P1 says that 1 is a positive integer, P2 that the successor of an integer is an integer, P3 that an integer can have at most one successor, P4 that every integer has at least one successor, P5 that 1 has no predecessor, P6 that integers with the same successor are the same, P7–P10 are the usual properties of equality, and P11 is the postulate of mathematical induction. P1–P5 and P11 are essentially Peano's postulates for arithmetic.

The main defect of the logic just constructed is illustrated by P10 and P11. A statement about all members of $\mathfrak{F}_1$ can be made in the syntax language but not in the object language. We have no machinery for applying quantifiers to letters representing elements of $\mathfrak{F}_1$. We can, of course, introduce a new primitive class $\mathfrak{F}_{1,1}$ and postulates of the type:

If A^1 is in $\mathfrak{F}_1$, and Γ is in $\mathfrak{F}_{1,1}$, then ΓA^1 is in $\mathfrak{P}$, $\prod \Gamma$ is in $\mathfrak{P}$.
If A^1 is in $\mathfrak{F}_1$, and Γ is in $\mathfrak{F}_{1,1}$, then $\vdash \prod \Gamma \supset \Gamma A^1$, etc.

Then we should also need to deal with sentence-forms in variables representing elements of $\mathfrak{F}_1 , \cdots , \mathfrak{F}_n , \cdots$, and also $\mathfrak{F}_{1,1}$; we should wish to apply quantifiers to letters representing elements of $\mathfrak{F}_{1,1}$, and similarly for $\mathfrak{F}_n$, etc. The manifold complications of such a system, not to speak of its inelegance, forces us to look for a better system. We shall discuss two ways of overcoming these difficulties. The first depends upon the construction of a very expressive object language without regard to any interpretation. We distinguish between various types of strings of symbols, and give rules for operation on these strings. It is only later that we interpret these strings as names of objects.

In the second approach, we note that F_n3 can be replaced by simpler assumptions at the cost of multiplying the primitive notions. For example, we may adjoin the operator K and two others C and W to the primitives, and such postulates as

F_nK. *If A^{n-1} is in $\mathfrak{F}_{n-1}$ and $\alpha_1 , \cdots , \alpha_n$ are in $\mathfrak{I}$, then KA^{n-1} is a uniquely determined element of $\mathfrak{F}_n$ and*
$\vdash KA^{n-1}\alpha_1\alpha_2 \cdots \alpha_n \equiv A^{n-1}\alpha_2 \cdots \alpha_n$.

F_nC. *If A^n is in $\mathfrak{F}_n$ and $\alpha_1 , \cdots , \alpha_n$ are in $\mathfrak{I}$, then CA^n is a uniquely determined element of $\mathfrak{F}_n$ and*
$\vdash CA^n\alpha_1\alpha_2\alpha_3 \cdots \alpha_n \equiv A^n\alpha_2\alpha_1\alpha_3 \cdots \alpha_n$.

F_nW. If A^{n+1} is in $\mathfrak{F}_{n+1}$ and $\alpha_1, \cdots, \alpha_n$ are in $\mathfrak{I}$, then WA^{n+1} is a uniquely determined element of $\mathfrak{F}_n$ and
$$\vdash WA^{n+1}\alpha_1\alpha_2 \cdots \alpha_n \equiv A^{n+1}\alpha_1\alpha_1\alpha_2 \cdots \alpha_n .$$

In section III4 we shall make an independent systematic study of such operators and shall show how they may be employed in constructing systems of logic.

EXERCISES

Ex. 1. Prove the following from A1″–A7″, F_11–F_16.

(a). If p is in $\mathfrak{P}$, then $\vdash p \equiv (x)p$.

(b). $\vdash (\exists x) . \mathfrak{A}(x) \supset \mathfrak{B}(x) :\equiv: (x)\mathfrak{A}(x) .\supset. (\exists x)\mathfrak{B}(x)$.

(c). $\vdash (\exists x)\mathfrak{A}(x) .\supset. (x)\mathfrak{B}(x) :\supset: (x) . \mathfrak{A}(x) \supset \mathfrak{B}(x)$.

Ex. 2. Prove the following from A1″–A7″, F_11–F_16, F1–F3.

(a). $\vdash (x)(y) . \mathfrak{A}(x) \wedge \mathfrak{B}(y) :\equiv: (x)\mathfrak{A}(x) .\wedge. (y)\mathfrak{B}(y)$.

(b). $\vdash (x)(y)\mathfrak{A}(x, y) .\supset. (x) . \mathfrak{B}(x) \supset (\exists y)\mathfrak{C}(x, y) :\equiv: (\exists x)(\exists y)(z)(\exists u) . \sim\mathfrak{A}(x, y) \vee \sim\mathfrak{B}(z) \vee \mathfrak{C}(z, u)$.

(c). $\vdash (x)(y)\mathfrak{A}(x, y) .\supset. (x) . \mathfrak{B}(x) \supset (\exists y)\mathfrak{C}(x, y) :\equiv: (x)(\exists y)(\exists z) . \sim\mathfrak{A}(y, z) \vee \sim\mathfrak{B}(x) \vee \mathfrak{C}(x, z)$.

(d). $\vdash (x) \sim\mathfrak{A}(x, x) :\wedge: (x)(y)(z) . \mathfrak{A}(x, y) \wedge \mathfrak{A}(y, z) \supset \mathfrak{A}(x, z) :\wedge: (x)(\exists y)\mathfrak{A}(x, y) .:\equiv:. (x)(y)(z)(\exists u) : \sim\mathfrak{A}(x, x) .\wedge. \sim\mathfrak{A}(x, y) \vee \sim\mathfrak{A}(y, z) \vee \mathfrak{A}(x, z) .\wedge. \mathfrak{A}(x, u)$.

(e). $\vdash (x) \sim\mathfrak{A}(x, x) :\wedge: (x)(y)(z) . \mathfrak{A}(x, y) \wedge \mathfrak{A}(y, z) \supset \mathfrak{A}(x, z) .:\supset:. (x)(y) . \mathfrak{A}(x, y) \supset \sim\mathfrak{A}(y, x)$.

(f). $\vdash (\exists x)\mathfrak{A}(x) .\supset. (x)\mathfrak{B}(x) :\equiv: (x)(y) . \mathfrak{A}(x) \supset \mathfrak{B}(y)$.

Ex. 3. Prove F_13 and F_14 from A1″–A7″, F_11, F_12, F_15–F_112.

Ex. 4. Define the notion of a sentence-form in $x_1, \cdots, x_k, X_1^1, \cdots, X_{k_1}^1, X_1^2, \cdots, X_{k_2}^2, \cdots, X_1^m, \cdots, X_{k_m}^m$. By a *prenex sentence form* in $X_1^1, \cdots, X_{k_1}^1, \cdots, X_1^m, \cdots, X_{k_m}^m$, we mean one of the form "$(Qx_1) \cdots (Qx_k)\mathfrak{A}(x_1, \cdots, x_k, X_1^1, \cdots, X_{k_m}^m)$", where "$(Qx_i)$" is either "$(x_i)$" or "$(\exists x_i)$" and $\mathfrak{A}$ is a sentence-form with no quantifiers. Prove that every sentence-form with only bound variables is equivalent to a prenex sentence-form. (See Ex. 2(b, c, e) above.)

Ex. 5. (a). Prove that if $\mathfrak{A}(X_1^1, \cdots, X_k^1)$ is a sentence-form in $X_1^1, \cdots, X_k^1$ with only bound variables, then $\mathfrak{A}$ is equivalent to a Boolean function $\mathfrak{C}$ of the following 2^k sentence-forms:

$$(\exists x) .\mathfrak{B}_1(x) \vee \cdots \vee \mathfrak{B}_k(x),$$

where $\mathfrak{B}_i(x)$ is either X_i^1x or $\sim X_i^1x$.

(b). Prove that if $\mathfrak{C}$ is not a theorem in the Boolean propositional logic, then there is a model of A1″–A7″, $F_1$1–$F_1$5, in which $\mathfrak{I}$ has 2^k members and in which $\mathfrak{C}$ is invalid.

(c). Prove that if $\mathfrak{A}(X_1^1, \cdots, X_k^1)$ is a sentence-form in the first order logic of monadic functions, then either

(1) "if $A_1^1, \cdots, A_k^1$ are in $\mathfrak{F}_1$, then $\vdash \mathfrak{A}(A_1^1, \cdots, A_k^1)$"

is a theorem, or there is a finite model (i.e. where $\mathfrak{I}$ contains only a finite number of elements) in which (1) is invalid.

Ex. 6. (a). Prove that if $\mathfrak{I}$ is finite, then for all A^2 in $\mathfrak{F}_2$

$$(2) \vdash \sim .: (x) \ \sim A^2xx :\wedge: (x)(y)(z) \ .A^2xy \wedge A^2yz \supset A^2xz :\wedge: (x)(\exists y)A^2xy.$$

(b). Prove that if arithmetic is consistent, then (2) is not a consequence of A1″–A7″, $F_1$1–$F_1$6, F_n1–F_n3. (Hint: take $\mathfrak{I}$ to be the class of positive integers and interpret "A^2xy" as "x is less than y".)

(c). A formula in the first order logic of monadic functions is either universally valid and provable, or is refutable in some finite model. This is not true in the logic of polyadic functions.

Ex. 7. (a). If $\mathfrak{A}(x, X_1^1, \cdots, X_k^1)$ is a sentence-form in x, $X_1^1, \cdots, X_k^1$, and if $A_1^1, \cdots, A_k^1$ are in $\mathfrak{F}_1$, then there are elements $p_1, \cdots, p_n$ in $\mathfrak{P}$ and Boolean functions $\mathfrak{B}_1(x), \cdots, \mathfrak{B}_n(x)$, of $A^1_1x, \cdots, A^1_kx$ such that

(3) $\vdash (x) \sim .\mathfrak{B}_i(x) \wedge \mathfrak{B}_j(x)\ (i, j = 1, \cdots, n; i \neq j)$, and $\vdash \mathfrak{A}(\alpha, A^1_1, \cdots, A^1_k) .\equiv. p_1 \wedge \mathfrak{B}_1(\alpha) .\vee. p_2 \wedge \mathfrak{B}_2(\alpha) .\vee. \cdots .\vee. p_n \wedge \mathfrak{B}_n(\alpha)$.

(b). If $\mathfrak{A}(x, y, X^1_1, \cdots, X^1_k)$ is a sentence-form in $x, y, X^1_1, \cdots, X^1_k$, and if $A^1_1, \cdots, A^1_k$ are in $\mathfrak{F}_1$, then there are elements p_{ij}, $i, j = 1, \cdots, n$, in $\mathfrak{P}$ and Boolean functions $\mathfrak{B}_1(x), \cdots, \mathfrak{B}_n(x)$ as in 7(a) such that (3) holds and $\vdash \mathfrak{A}(\alpha, \beta, A^1_1, \cdots, A^1_k) .\equiv. p_{11} \wedge \mathfrak{B}_1(\alpha) \wedge \mathfrak{B}_1(\beta) .\vee. p_{12} \wedge \mathfrak{B}_1(\alpha) \wedge \mathfrak{B}_2(\beta) .\vee. \cdots .\vee. p_{nn} \wedge \mathfrak{B}_n(\alpha) \wedge \mathfrak{B}_n(\beta)$.

Ex. 8. Let $\mathfrak{J}$ be the class of real numbers, which we may interpret geometrically as points on a line. To every element A^1 of $\mathfrak{F}_1$ there corresponds the class of all points x such that A^1x. Similarly, to every element A^2 of $\mathfrak{F}_2$ there corresponds the class of all points (x, y) in the plane such that A^2xy. Now take $\mathfrak{F}_1$ to be the class of all monadic properties of the form "$\hat{x}(a < x)$" or "$\hat{x}(x < a)$", i.e. the class of all half-lines, together with all others obtainable from these by the use of the postulates A1″–A7″, F_11–F_16.

(a). Prove that a property A^1 is in $\mathfrak{F}_1$ if and only if it corresponds to the sum of a finite number of disjoint intervals. (An interval is taken in the widest sense, i.e. with or without either or both endpoints, and it may degenerate to a single point, or it may be a half-line or the whole line in extreme cases.)

(b). Prove that if $\mathfrak{A}(x, y)$ is a sentence-form in x, y, the corresponding class of points (x, y) in the plane such that $\mathfrak{A}(x, y)$ is an "elementary figure", i.e. a sum of a finite number of disjoint rectangles, quarter-planes, half-planes, etc., with sides parallel to the axes.

(c). Conversely, to every elementary figure in the

plane there corresponds such a sentence-form $\mathfrak{A}(x, y)$.

Thus the class of polyadic propositional functions definable in terms of monadic functions alone is extremely restricted. On the other hand, essentially all of mathematics can be expressed in terms of diadic functions. (See Löwenheim [171]9, Kalmár [384]5, 6, 8.)

SECTION 3 SOME VERY EXPRESSIVE LANGUAGES

We shall now describe several languages which have been proposed and shall show how the difficulties of the last section can be eliminated. In section 5 we shall show how these languages are adequate for expressing much of mathematics. The problem of defining precisely what is meant by an interpretation of a language is not yet completely solved. For the present we shall content ourselves with intuitive interpretations which are at best vague.

We shall first construct the "pure" functional calculus of the first order. In general we shall follow the exposition of Church [X]19, with certain modifications to avoid an alphabet of infinitely many signs. Our alphabet consists of the signs 0, 1, a, f, (,), $\supset$, and $\sim$. By a *string* we shall mean a finite sequence of these signs. Sometimes we shall exhibit strings explicitly; more often we shall use special symbols as abbreviations for certain strings. In any context such a symbol may, of course, be replaced by the string which it abbreviates. We shall use capital Latin letters as names of strings. Two strings are said to be the same if they have the same length l, i.e. the number of signs in each is the same, and if for each k, $1 \leq k \leq l$, the k-th sign of each is the same. If A and B are strings then "AB" shall denote the string consisting of A followed by B. We shall introduce abbreviations thus:

$$\cdots \text{ for } A,$$

where it is to be understood that $\cdots$ is an abbreviation for the string A.

D1. A *string in the signs* $a_1, \cdots, a_k$ is a non-null string each of whose signs is one of "a_1", $\cdots$, "a_k". The class of such strings is denoted by $\mathfrak{S}(a_1, \cdots, a_k)$. This definition will apply to all languages here constructed.

D2. An *individual* is a string of the form "aA", where A is a $\mathfrak{S}(0)$.

D3. If n is a $\mathfrak{S}(1)$, then a *function of degree n* is a string of the form "fnA", where A is a $\mathfrak{S}(0)$.

We identify the strings in 1 with the positive integers for the sake of the exposition. This could be avoided at the cost of complicating the following definitions.

D4. A sentence is a string formed according to the following rules:

(a). If F is a function of degree n and $x_1, \cdots, x_n$ are individuals, then $Fx_1x_2 \cdots x_n$ is a sentence.

(b). If p and q are sentences, then $\sim p$ and $(p \supset q)$ are sentences.

(c). If p is a sentence and x is an individual, then $(x)p$ is a sentence.

In the intuitive interpretation the "individuals" will be either names of individuals in the ordinary sense or variables ranging over the class of individuals. We use the term "individual" here instead of the more suggestive term "individual variable" for the sake of brevity. Actually our language is so framed that the only true sentences are generally true sentences, i.e. those which are valid for all individuals. A function of degree n will express a propositional function of n individuals such as ". . . gives . . . to . . .". If this is denoted by "F" and b, c, and d are individuals, then the sentence "$Fbcd$" shall express the proposition that b gives c to d. If p is a sentence, then the sentence "$(x)p$" shall express the proposition that for all individuals x, p. We shall often denote individuals by "x", "y", "z", $\cdots$, sentences by "p", "q", $\cdots$, and functions of degrees n by "F_n", "G_n", $\cdots$.

It will be convenient to make use of the "null" string, denoted by "Λ", consisting of no signs at all. Thus ΛA and $A\Lambda$ shall be the same as A for any string A.

D5. $(A_1, \cdots, A_k)$ is a *partition* of B if B is $A_1A_2 \cdots A_k$.

D6. A is *part* of B if there are strings C and D (either of which may be null) such that B is CAD.

If C is null, then A is called a *head* of B.

If D is null, then A is called a *tail* of B.

D7. If x is an individual, and (C, x, D) is a partition of B, and "0" is not a head of D, then (C, x, D) is called an *occurrence* of x in B.

D8. If x is an individual and (C, x, D) is an occurrence of x in B, and if there exists a sentence p and strings C_1 and D_1 such that C_1xD_1 is $(x)p$ and C_1 is a tail of C and D_1 is a head of D, then (C, x, D) is called *bound*. Otherwise (C, x, D) is called *free*.

D9. If $x_1, \cdots, x_n$ are distinct individuals and p is a sentence, and if $(C_1, x_{i_1}, C_2x_{i_2} \cdots C_{k+1}), \cdots, (C_1x_{i_1} \cdots C_k, x_{i_k}, C_{k+1})$ are all the free occurrences of these individuals in p, then $Sb\{x_1, \cdots, x_n, p\}(y_1, \cdots, y_n)$ is the string $C_1y_{i_1}C_2 \cdots C_ky_{i_k}C_{k+1}$. This latter string is thus the result of substituting "y_i" for "x_i" ($i = 1, \cdots, n$) in all free occurrences of the x's in p.

D10. $(\exists x)p$ for $\sim(x)\sim p$.

D11. $p \supset_x q$ for $(x)(p \supset q)$.

D12. $p \supset_{x,y} q$ for $(x)(y)(p \supset q)$.

D13. $p \equiv_x q$ for $(x)(p \equiv q)$.

D14. $p \equiv_{x,y} q$ for $(x)(y)(p \equiv q)$.

In D13 and D14 and throughout this section we shall use the definitions and conventions of II2.

We shall now define a subclass of sentences called *true* sentences and shall denote the proposition that p is a true sentence by "$\vdash p$".

D15. A sentence s is said to be *true* (i.e. $\vdash s$) if and only if its being so follows from the following rules:

FI. If $\vdash p$ and $\vdash(p \supset q)$, then $\vdash q$.

FII. If $\vdash p$, then $\vdash(x)p$, where x is any individual.

FIII. If p, q, and r are sentences, then

$$\vdash p \supset .q \supset r. \supset .p \supset q \supset .p \supset r.$$

FIV. If p and q are sentences, then $\vdash p \supset . q \supset p$.
FV. If p and q are sentences, then $\vdash \sim p \supset \sim q \supset . q \supset p$.
FVI. If p and q are sentences and x is an individual with no free occurrences in p, then

$$\vdash p \supset_x q . \supset . p \supset (x)q.$$

FVII. If p is a sentence and x and y are individuals, and there are no strings C, C_1, D, D_1 such that (C, x, D) is a free occurrence of x in p, C_1 is a tail of C, D_1 is a head of D, and $C_1 x D_1$ is $(y)q$ for some sentence q, then

$$\vdash (x)p \supset Sb\{x, p\}(y).$$

In D15 the phase "follows from $\cdots$" is not clearly defined. We remedy this in

D16. The sequence $p_1, \cdots, p_n$ of sentences is called a *proof* of q if p_n is q and for each i, $1 \leq i \leq n$, either
(a). p_i has one of the forms described in FIII–FVII, or
(b). there are j and $k < i$ such that p_k is $(p_j \supset p_i)$, or
(c). there is a $j < i$ such that p_i is $(x)p_j$, where x is an individual.

A sentence q is said to be true if there is a proof of q. The language whose construction is embodied in the preceding definitions will be called L_1.

It is now easy to show that L_1 is essentially equivalent to the object language of the previous section. It is slightly weaker because of the absence of any analogue to F_n3 (p. 84). This postulate, introduced partly for the sake of the theory of quantification as developed there, says that $\mathfrak{F}_n$ is complete with respect to elementary propositions, i.e. that any sentence-form in $x_1, \cdots, x_n$ corresponds to an element of $\mathfrak{F}_n$, so that relations may be defined impredicatively. Otherwise the deductive power of these two systems is the same. The main difference is that previously we had an object language which communicated something, namely certain properties and relations involving the elements of $\mathfrak{P}$, $\mathfrak{F}_1$, $\mathfrak{I}$, etc. The center of interest was just the properties of and relations between the elements of these classes, and the object language was merely a convenient tool for expressing these matters. In the exposition the syntax of the object language was an automatic affair since we gave rules for determining what a given string denotes (e.g. $F_1 1$) and these enable us to decide whether a string is meaningful or not. There is no obscurity in the problem of interpretation, for if we are given certain classes of objects, $\mathfrak{P}$, $\mathfrak{T}$, $\mathfrak{J}$, $\mathfrak{F}_1$, etc., and operations $\sim$, $\supset$, $\prod$, etc. defined upon them, then the question of whether these constitute an example of the deductive science there considered simply requires an examination of these classes and operations, and a verification of the postulates. If the classes $\mathfrak{P}$, $\mathfrak{T}$, $\mathfrak{J}$, $\mathfrak{F}_1$, $\cdots$, $\mathfrak{F}_n$ and the operations are given concretely, then this verification of the postulates involving only these classes is a matter of direct observation. On the other hand, in this section we have constructed an object language without any reference at all to the denotations of the signs and strings. Our rules for the classification of strings as individuals, functions, and sentences, and true sentences may be considered merely as rules for a game played with these signs. The problem of consistency may be thought of as the problem of whether the game is loaded against us or fair, i.e. whether every sentence is true or not. The game is interesting insofar as the proposed intuitive interpretation is acceptable, i.e. as our mental habits agree with the rules of the game when the signs and strings are interpreted in that way. This is unsatisfactory mathematically since there is no effective way of determining exactly what our mental habits, i.e. yours and mine and the other fellow's, are, and of communicating them with complete precision to others, or even to ourselves. (In the latter respect the situation is analogous to that of the indeterminancy principle in quantum mechanics; the very act of observing our own thought processes changes the phenomena observed.) Thus the most interesting and important interpretation of our object language is unfortunately one whose acceptability we cannot test, and therefore is unavailable to us in a rigorous theory. In this way the problem of defining the notion of an interpretation of a language becomes of fundamental importance when a language is constructed syntactically, i.e. without any reference to what its strings denote. This has been neglected by a number of otherwise competent authors who construct languages (or as they sometimes call them, calculi) independently of an interpretation and content themselves with giving untestable intuitive interpretations. Such practices have given rise to the view that mathematics consists of a game played with meaningless signs according to certain prescribed rules, and to the charge that this way of approaching logic and mathematics is not mathematics at all since the latter is not such a conventional game. It must be said that many writers who attack mathematical logic on this basis insist on some mystical virtues of ordinary language as compared to a precisely constructed language of the sort under consideration, and forget that words are also symbols, and that ordinary language merely differs from these other symbolic languages in that its rules of syntax are very complicated and never stated precisely and explicitly. (It is true that there are countries like France and Sweden which have official agencies, their academies, which formulate canons of correct usage, but an examination of these formulations and a comparison with those of logicians show that the last statement holds without exception.)

We observe, however, that the study of an object language for its own sake without reference to an interpretation is often fruitful and has led to results of fundamental importance. We shall, ourselves, make use of this procedure. But we emphasize that a language must have an interpretation in order for it to serve as a language, namely as a tool for communication, and that those who neglect this, and those who dogmatically insist that the study of a language independently of its meaning is the only rigorous procedure, are wrong. This statement is itself somewhat dogmatic; it is difficult not to be dogmatic when one feels strongly about something.

The language L_1 is adequate for much of mathematics but suffers as indicated at the end of the preceding section, from the defect of lacking an apparatus for applying quantifiers to functions. We shall now consider some proposed remedies of this situation. A device due to Wiener, and later simplified by Kuratowski, enables us to develop the theory of polyadic functions from that of monadic functions, or alternatively from the theory of classes. We shall adopt this procedure. In this section we shall restrict ourselves to the construction of various languages and shall discuss in section 5 their adequacy for mathematics.

We shall first construct a language L_2 due originally to Russell and Whitehead, simplified by the aid of the device of Wiener and Kuratowski, and formulated in a precise manner by Tarski. The following exposition is due essentially to Quine. Our alphabet consists of the signs (,), $\in$, $\sim$, $\supset$, a, b, and v.

D17. A *variable of type n*, where n is a $\mathfrak{S}(b)$, is a string of the form "vnA" where A is a $\mathfrak{S}(a)$.

D18. A *sentence* is a string built up according to the following rules:

(a) If x is a variable of type n and y is a variable of type nb, then $(x \in y)$ is a sentence.

(b) If p and q are sentences, then $\sim p$ and $(p \supset q)$ are sentences.

(c) If p is a sentence and x is a variable (of any type), then $(x)p$ is a sentence.

A string is a sentence if and only if its being so follows from these rules.

In the intuitive interpretation a variable of type b will be an individual variable, a variable of type bb will denote a variable whose values are classes of individuals, a variable of type bbb will denote a variable whose values are classes of classes of individuals, etc. Other strings will be assigned interpretations in a manner analogous to that of the previous language (see p. 92). The paradoxes will be avoided since strings of the form "$(x \in x)$" are not sentences, by condition (a) in D18, and hence the rules for the construction of true sentences do not apply to them.

Definitions D5–D14 are taken over with the change that "individual" is to be replaced by "variable" in D7–D9.

D19. $(x \subset_z y)$ for $(z)((z \in x) \supset (z \in y))$.

If z is a variable of type n and x and y are variables of type nb, then $(x \subset_z y)$ is a sentence. Of course, z will turn out to be a dummy symbol in D19.

D20. A sentence s is said to be *true* (i.e. $\vdash s$) if and only if its being so follows from the following rules:

FI–FVII with "individual" replaced by "variable". In FVII add to the hypothesis that y is a variable of the same type as x.

FVIII. If z is a variable of type n, and x and y are variables of type nb, and u is a variable of type nbb, then

$$\vdash ((z)((z \in x) \equiv (z \in y)) \supset ((x \in u) \supset (y \in u))).$$

FIX. If p is a sentence containing no free occurrence of the variable x, and y is a variable of type n, and x is a variable of type nb, then

$$\vdash (\exists x)(y)((y \in x) \equiv p).$$

FIX is a form of the "Axiom of reducibility" of Whitehead and Russell, stated in a simple and precise manner. Intuitively, it guarantees the existence of the class of all y's such that p, in other words it justifies the definition of a class by abstraction from a propositional function. FVIII says, intuitively, that if the classes x and y have the same members, then y is a member of any class containing x. Since, by FIX, every property defines a class, it follows that y has every property which x has, so that x and y are identical in the intuitive meaning of the word.

Although the system L_2 is already adequate for practically all of mathematics, it is convenient to introduce an abstraction operator. In order to maintain our convention of writing strings in linear order, we shall denote this by "$x \ni$" instead of "$\hat{x}$" as before. Thus we adjoin to the alphabet the sign $\ni$ and make the following modifications of the previous definitions, and replace D18 and D20 by D21 and D22.

D21. We define "*term*" and "*sentence*" simultaneously:

(a). If x is a variable of type n, then x is a term of type n.

(b). If x and y are terms of type n and nb respectively, then $(x \in y)$ is a sentence.
(c). (b) and (c) as in D18.
(d). If p is a sentence and x is a variable of type n, then $x \ni p$ is a term of type nb.

A string is a term or a sentence respectively, if and only if its being so follows from these rules. In D8 the occurrence (C, x, D) in B will also be called bound if C_1xD_1 is $x \ni p$.

D22. The definition of a true sentence is the same as in D20 except for the following changes.
(a). In FVII y may be an arbitrary term of the same type as x. If y is a variable, then after the phrase "C_1xD_1 is $(y)q$" add "or $y \ni q$".
(b). Add the rules

FX. If p is a sentence, and x and y are variables of type n, and z is a variable of type nb which has no free occurrence in p, then

$$\vdash y \in x \ni p \,.{:}{\equiv}{:}.\, (\exists z) : y \in z \,.\wedge.\, (x)((x \in z) \equiv p).$$

FXI. If p is a sentence, and z is a variable of type nb, and y is a variable of type nbb, and x is a variable of type n, and there is no occurrence of z in p, then

$$\vdash x \ni p \in y \,.{:}{\equiv}{:}.\, (\exists z) : z \in y \,.\wedge.\, (x)((x \in z) \equiv p).$$

The language obtained from L_2 by means of D21 and D22 will be called L_2'.

We use here and shall continue to use dots for parentheses according to the conventions explained before. It can easily be shown (see Hailperin ([IX]1)) that we can set up a correspondence whereby to each sentence p in L_2' there corresponds a uniquely determined sentence q in L_2 such that

(1). $\vdash p \equiv q$ in L_2',
(2). $\vdash p$ in L_2', if and only if $\vdash q$ in L_2,
(3). if p is a sentence in L_2, then $\vdash p$ in L_2' if and only if $\vdash p$ in L_2. This shows that the system L_2' is essentially equivalent to L_2. L_2' is what we call in the next chapter a conservative exten-

sion of L_2 . It is, however, technically easier to manage. The following applies to either system, but for the sake of technical convenience L_2' will be the one actually used.

In Principia Mathematica Whitehead and Russell showed in great detail how practically all of mathematics can be developed within a system of which L_2' is a simplified version. On the other hand, Tarski has pointed out that this simplified version is already adequate for Principia Mathematica. Thus the present language is adequate for practically all mathematical reasoning. All we lack is a consistency proof. But by Gödel's theorem, if the system is consistent, then any consistency proof must involve methods of reasoning which cannot be formulated in the system. To this extent a proof of consistency seems hopeless. This cannot be considered as a reason for rejecting the system since Gödel's theorem applies to every adequate system so far proposed. It means, however, that the system can be accepted only as a working hypothesis as long as no contradiction is discovered in it. From this point of view this system is one of the best which have been constructed up to now.

While the language L_2' satisfies reasonable demands of adequacy, it has certain technical defects which cause many to consider it unsatisfactory. To illustrate this let us try to define the universal class (the "1" of Chapter I). The simplest way is to choose a sentence p which is universally true, i.e. such that $\vdash(x)p$, and to define the universal class as the class of all x such that p, i.e. as $x \ni p$. Thus we are led to the following definition:

$$V \text{ for } x \ni (y)((x \in y) \supset (x \in y)).$$

But if the definiens is to be a term, and x is a variable of type n, then y must be a variable of type nb. Consequently V is a term of type nb. The particular choice of the variables x and y is immaterial since they can easily be shown to be dummy symbols. It is now easy to prove that $\vdash(x \in V)$ for every term x of type n. If x is not a term of type n, then $(x \in V)$ is not even a sentence. Hence V denotes the class of all terms of type n, and for the sake of precision we must indicate this, and modify the definition in the following way:

$$V_n \text{ for } x \ni (y)((x \in y) \supset (x \in y)),$$

where x is a variable of type n and y is a variable of type nb. We have, then, not a single universal class, but infinitely many, one for each type. The same phenomenon arises in connection with all other mathematical concepts. There is an integer 3 for each type, an arithmetic for each type, and so on. To each true sentence involving terms of one type there corresponds an exactly analogous true sentence in each higher type. We have an infinite reduplication of logical principals on the various type levels. To put it in another way, we can in the object language L_2' express propositions about all classes of individuals, or about all classes of classes of individuals, etc., but we cannot express propositions about all classes, for example.

Whitehead and Russell get around this difficulty by their convention of typical ambiguity. In the theorems and proofs they do not indicate the types of the terms which occur except in the rare cases where the neglect of the type distinctions would cause trouble. It is tacitly assumed that the variables are always chosen in such a way that the rules of D21 are observed.

Another objection which has been raised is that the theory of types is artificial. It is contended that such statements as "the class of all classes is a class" or "the class of all men is a man" ought to be considered as meaningful, and should therefore be reckoned as sentences. Hence it is concluded that a theory such as the theory of types, wherein it is impossible to express such propositions, does not jibe with our intuitions. There are, however, also very plausible philosophical arguments to the effect that the type restrictions are natural. We shall not, however, digress at this point and enter into the dangerous quicksand of philosophical controversy.

Some authors have dismissed the theory of types as an ad hoc device, i.e. one invented for the sole purpose of avoiding the paradoxes. Historically this is surely the case, but is not in itself a serious objection. For in attacking a problem we often hit upon a device that works, and then discover, upon reflection, that the device was an obvious and natural one after all.

Quine ([II]86) has proposed a system which eliminates the

technical difficulties involved in the theory of types without leading to any known contradiction. We shall call the language now under construction L_3. The alphabet shall be the same as in L_2'. The definitions up to D21, including the new version of D8, are retained except that all phrases of the form "of type n" in D17 and D21 are omitted. The same applies to D22 except for FVII and FIX. FVII is taken as in L_2 rather than L_2' so that the substitution of a term of the form "$z \ni r$" for "y" is not directly possible. In order to explain how FIX is to be altered we must introduce the important concept of stratification.

D23. If (C, q, D) is a partition of p and (C_1, x, D_1) is an occurrence of the variable x in q, then (CC_1, x, D_1D) is called the (C, q, D)-extension of (C_1, x, D_1).

D24. If p is a sentence and $[\mathfrak{K}_1, \cdots, \mathfrak{K}_n]$ is a division of the occurrences of the variables in p into a finite number of disjoint classes, then $[\mathfrak{K}_1, \cdots, \mathfrak{K}_n]$ will be called a *stratification* of p if and only if the following conditions are satisfied:

(a). If x is a variable, q is a sentence, and (C, q, D) is a partition of p, then all (C, q, D)-extensions of free occurrences of x in q belong to the same class.

(b). If there are free occurrences of the variable x in the sentence q, and $(C, (x)q, D)$ is a partition of p, then $(C(, x,)\ qD)$ belongs to the same class as the $(C, (x)q, D)$-extensions of all free occurrences of x in q.

(c). The analogue of (b) with "$x \ni q$" instead of "$(x)q$".

(d). If $(C, (x \in y), D)$ is a partition of p, and x and y are variables, and if $(C(, x, \in y)D)$ is in $\mathfrak{K}_i$, then $1 \leq i < n$ and $(C(x \in, y,)D)$ is in $\mathfrak{K}_{i+1}$.

(e). The analogues of (d) with "$(x \in y \ni q)$", "$(x \ni r \in y)$", and "$(x \ni r \in y \ni q)$", respectively, instead of "$(x \in y)$". In the respective conclusions the class of the corresponding occurrence of y is $\mathfrak{K}_i$, $\mathfrak{K}_{i+2}$, and $\mathfrak{K}_{i+1}$.

Note that the class of $(C(, x,)qD)$ according to (b) need not be the same as that of other occurrences of x in p of the form "$(C_1(, x,)qD_1)$" or of free occurrences of x in p.

If an occurrence of a variable in p belongs to $\mathfrak{L}_i$, we shall say that its *level* is i (in this stratification).

D25. The sentence p will be called stratified if and only if there is a stratification of p.

We can now explain the desired modification of FIX:

FIX′. If p is a stratified sentence containing no free occurrence of the variable x, and y is a variable, then

$$\vdash(\exists x)(y)((y \in x) \equiv p).$$

This makes it possible to substitute for "y" in FVII a term of the form "$z \ni r$" whenever r is stratified.

The system L_3 just constructed could have been slightly simplified in that we no longer need the sign "b" in the alphabet since its only use in L_2' was in providing the distinctions of type. We have not done this in order to make the transition from L_2' to L_3 slightly easier. The former procedure would, of course, be preferable in an independent construction of L_3.

The infinite reduplication of logical principles in L_2' now disappears. For example, we can define the universe V as follows:

$$V \text{ for } x \ni ((x \in y) \supset_y (x \in y)),$$

where y is any variable different from x. The sentence "$(x \in y \supset_y x \in y)$", or "$(y)((x \in y) \supset (x \in y))$" in its unabbreviated form, is stratified by taking $\mathfrak{L}_1$ as the class of all occurrences of x and $\mathfrak{L}_2$ as the class of all occurrences of y.

By FIX′, we have

$$\vdash(\exists z)(x)(x \in z \,.\!\equiv\!.\, x \in y \supset_y x \in y),$$

which provides a justification for the definition of V.

If x is a variable, then $\sim(x \in x)$ is a sentence in L_3, in contrast to L_2'. It is, however, impossible to prove by FIX′ that

(1) $$\vdash(\exists z)(x)(x \in z \,.\!\equiv\!.\, \sim(x \in x)),$$

so that Russell's paradox is avoided. Postulate FX yields only

$$(2)\quad \vdash x \in y \ni \sim(y \in y)$$
$$.:\equiv:.\ (\exists z) : x \in z \ .\wedge.\ (y)((y \in z) \equiv \sim(y \in y)),$$

which no longer leads to contradiction by the substitution of "$y \ni \sim(y \in y)$" for "x" by FII, FVII, and FI. If we had omitted the condition that p be stratified in FIX′, then (1) would be a true sentence.

Now

$$\vdash (x)(x \in z \ .\equiv.\ \sim(x \in x)) \ :\supset:\ z \in z \ .\equiv.\ \sim(z \in z)$$

by FVII.

But $\vdash \sim(z \in z \ .\equiv.\ \sim(z \in z))$ (Ex. 2.2.1b).
Hence $\vdash \sim(x)(x \in z \ .\equiv.\ \sim(x \in x))$ (T2.2.11, FI),
so that $\vdash (z) \sim(x)(x \in z \ .\equiv.\ \sim(x \in x))$ (FII),
and consequently $\vdash \sim(\exists z)(x)(x \in z \ .\equiv.\ \sim(x \in x))$ (D10, T2.2.5, FI),
which contradicts (1).

The same reasoning applied to (2) would yield only

$$\vdash (x) \sim(x \in y \ni \sim(y \in y)),$$

which simply says that $y \ni \sim(y \in y)$ is the null class.

Rosser ([IV]15) reports the results of his unsuccessful attempts to find an inconsistency in L_3. This language is probably the most flexible language so far proposed which leads to no known contradiction. We shall in the next section discuss the work of Curry which indicates that he may have found a still more flexible system which is demonstrably consistent.

The language L_3 avoids almost all the objections which have been advanced to the theory of types. The condition of stratification may, of course, be criticized as artificial. It is, however, the weakest restriction on our intuitive reasoning so far proposed which is not known to lead to contradiction. One weakening of the stratification restriction in L_3 which Quine proposed later ([V]163) was shown by Lyndon and Rosser ([VII]1) to lead to the Burali-Forti paradox. Hailperin ([IX]1) has shown that FIX′ may be replaced by a finite number of similar postulates involving only special forms of "p" instead of a general stratified sentence. A more serious defect of L_3 is that there are certain simple and natural arguments which are correct intuitively and which can be translated into L_3, but whose validity is not provable in L_3. These arguments are so plausible that we should probably condemn L_3 as a formalization of logic if the stronger system obtained by postulating the validity of these arguments is inconsistent. Rosser ([IV]15) did not succeed in finding an inconsistency in this stronger system. By Gödel's theorem, we could not hope to incorporate all consistent and intuitively valid methods of reasoning into the system.

Other systems have been proposed which avoid the known paradoxes in a somewhat different way. The first of these was proposed by Zermelo ([125]3), and later formulated more precisely by Skolem ([247]5). As we have seen, the origin of the paradoxes is the intuitive process of constructing the class of all x's which have a certain property. Quine's improvement over Russell's solution of the problem is to restrict oneself to properties expressed by stratified sentences. Zermelo's idea is that it is unreasonable to demand that one gather together from the *whole* universe those objects which have a given property. He considers it reasonable to pick out from an already known class the objects which have the given property. This leads to the replacement of FIX′ by

FIX″. If x, y, and z are distinct variables and p is a sentence containing no free occurrence of x, then

$$\vdash (\exists x)(y)(y \in x :\equiv: y \in z \wedge p).$$

The resulting language will be called L_z. Zermelo adds certain postulates providing for the existence of classes constructed from given classes according to some simple rules. For example, the following guarantees the existence of the class of all subclasses of a given class:

FXII. If x, y, z, and u are distinct variables, then

$$\vdash (\exists x)(y)(y \in x .\equiv. y \subset_z u).$$

Quine ([I]45) has shown, however, that L_z without such additional postulates as FXII (and with a slight alteration of FVIII) is already adequate for standard methematics as measured, for example, by L_2'. He does this by constructing within L_z a model of L_2'. With Zermelo's additional postulates the system becomes almost as manageable technically as L_3.

An interesting alternative has been suggested by Quine ([VI]135). As L_z stands without FXII and the like, we are not only unable to prove the existence of a class corresponding to an arbitrarily given property, but we are also unable to prove that an arbitrarily given object is a member of some class. We may, then, weaken the restrictions on those properties which define classes and impose instead restrictions on which objects may be members of classes. In this way we can eliminate Russell's paradox not by denying the existence of the class of x's such that $\sim(x \in x)$, but by denying that this class can be a member of any class, in particular itself. Formally this can be done by adding to L_z the postulate

FXIII. If x, y, and z are distinct variables, then

$$\vdash(\exists y)(x)(x \in y \,.\!\equiv\!.\, (\exists z)(x \in z)).$$

This guarantees the existence of a class which contains everything which is a member of something. This class plays the role of V in L_3. It is easy to show that FXIII and FIX″ together are equivalent to

FIX‴. If x, y, and z are distinct variables, and p is a sentence containing no free occurrence of x, then

$$\vdash(\exists x)(y)(y \in x :\equiv: (\exists z)(y \in z) \,.\wedge.\, p).$$

Let us call an object an *element* if it is a member of some class. Then FIX‴ guarantees the existence of the class of all elements which have a given property. It now becomes desirable to add postulates which guarantee that certain entities are elements. In other words, we may supplement L_z either with postulates of class existence or of elementhood. Both yield plausible systems.

It is still too early to decide which of these is the most convenient.

We call attention to the detailed development by Bernays ([II]65) of a system which is essentially the same as L_z with FIX″ replaced by FIX‴ with an additional restriction on p, and with supplementary postulates of class existence. He shows how classical mathematical analysis can be developed on this basis. In his epoch making memoir on the continuum hypothesis Gödel ([VI]112) made use of this system.

EXERCISES

Ex. 1. Interpret in English the following sentences in L_1 :
(a). $((a0)f10a0 \supset f10a00)$.
(b). $((a0)f10a0 \supset \sim(a0) \sim f10a0)$.
(c). $((a0)(a00)f110a0a00 \supset (a00)(a0)f110a0a00)$.
(d). $(a0)(f110a0a00 \supset \sim f110a0a0)$.
(e). $\sim(a0)(a00)(f110a0a00 \supset f1100a00a0)$.
(f). $((a0)(f10a0 \supset f100a0) \supset (f10a0 \supset f100a0))$.

Ex. 2. Identify the occurrences of the individuals in the above sentences. Which are free and which are bound?

Ex. 3. Translate the sentences of Ex. 1, 2, p. 88, into L_1 .

Ex. 4. Define the notion of consequence (see p. 45 in L_1). Show that q is a consequence of the sentences $r_1, \cdots, r_n$ if and only if $\vdash \bar{r}_1 \wedge \bar{r}_2 \wedge \cdots \wedge \bar{r}_n \supset q$, where $\bar{r}_k$ is $(x_1) \cdots (x_m)r_k$ and $x_1, \cdots, x_m$ are all the individuals which occur free in r_k .

Ex. 5. Interpret the following strings in L_2 and L_2' :
(a). $((vba)((vba \in vbba) \supset (vba \in vbbaa)) \supset$
$((vba)((vba \in vbbaa) \supset (vba \in vbbaaa)) \supset$
$(vba)(vba \in vbba) \supset (vba \in vbbaaa))))$.
(b). $((vba)(vba \in vbba) \supset (vbaa \in vbba))$.
(c). $(\exists vbba)(vba)((vba \in vbba) \equiv \sim(vba \in vbbaa))$.
(d). $vba \ni (\exists vbba)((vba \in vbba) \wedge (vbba \in vbbba))$.
(e). $((vba \in vba \ni (vbba)((vba \in vbba) \supset (vba \in vbba))) \equiv (\exists vbba)((vba \in vbba) \wedge (vba)((vba \in vbba) \equiv (vbba)((vba \in vbba) \supset (vba \in vbba)))))$.
(f). $vbbaa \ni (vba)((vba \in vbba) \equiv (vba \in vbbaa))$.

Ex. 6. Give suitable definitions in L_2' for the following concepts:

(a). The null class of type *bb*.

(b). The union of α and β, where α and β are terms of type *bbb*.

(c). The join of α and β, where α and β are terms of type *bb*.

(d). The common part of all members of a class of type *bbb*.

(e). The class of all ideals in the Boolean algebra of all terms of the type *bb*.

Ex. 7. Translate the following English sentences into L_3 .

(a). Every member of α is a member of β.

(b). x is in α if and only if x is in β but not in γ.

(c). For all x, y, and z, if x and y are in α, then x is in z if and only if y is in z.

(d). β has a member in common with each member of α.

(e). For all x and y, if x and y are in α, then x and y have no common members.

(f). There is a class α containing all members of members of β.

(g). The members of α are linearly ordered with respect to inclusion. (See p. 20)

(h). There is a member of β which is included in all members of α.

Ex. 8. Tell which of the following sentences are stratified, and give stratifications of those which are:

(a). $\sim(vba) \sim(vba \in vbaa)$

(b). $\sim(vba \in vba)$

(c). $(\exists vba)((vbaaa)((vba \in vbaaa) \supset (vbba \in vbaaa)) \supset (vba \in vbba))$

(d). $\sim(vbaa)((vba \in vbaa) \supset \sim(vbaa \in vbaaa))$

Ex. 9. (a). Prove FIX‴ from FIX″ and FXIII.

(b). Prove FIX″ and FXIII from FIX‴.

SECTION 4 COMBINATORY LOGICS

We have already emphasized (p. 95) the striking contrast between the systems just described and the logical systems treated before. The root of the difficulty of interpretation lies in the use of variables and in the process of substitution. In ordinary mathematical usage a variable is not the name of an entity but rather a letter used in building up "word-forms" or "sentence-forms" such that when the name of an entity in an appropriate category is substituted for the variable, a word or a sentence, i.e. a name of something, results. Thus "$x + 1 = 1 + x$" is not a sentence, and does not express a proposition, but if the name of an integer, say "3", is substituted for "x", a sentence, expressing in this case a true proposition, results. It makes sense to substitute "Dewey" for "x" in "x is disappointed", but it is nonsense to substitute the man Dewey for "x" in the "proposition" that x is disappointed. The use of variables is convenient because of the rule of substitution, which is expressed in L_3 by FII and FVII, whereby we may substitute, in a sentence-form whose values express true propositions, word-forms for the variables occurring free, and the result is again a sentence-form whose values express true propositions. The precise definition of the process of substitution, and the correct statement and justification of the rule, are nasty enough when the variables represent entities of only one category, as in sections II2, III2, and III3. It becomes much worse when we have several categories of entities, as would be the case in III2 if we had considered also sentence-forms in variables representing elements of $\mathfrak{F}_n$ as well as $\mathfrak{I}$. The situation becomes almost intolerably complex when we must allow for bound or apparent variables, for which substitution must be forbidden. Thus the statements of this rule in such standard works as Hilbert-Ackermann ([365]1), ([III]83), Hilbert-Bernays ([507]1), Quine ([458]5), Gödel ([418]14) are all incorrect; for a correct statement see Church ([359]9), ([X]19). From our analysis of the process of substitution in the very simple language of II2 we see that it is essentially a complicated matter, and no real short-cut is to be expected.

Also from another point of view the use of variables, though convenient, seems unnatural. For in a sentence like

"for all integers x, $x + 1 = 1 + x$",

the variable "x" has nothing at all to do with the assertion. The sentence is really about the constants $+$, 1, $=$, and the class of integers. The letter "x" is used merely as a tool in communicating a certain proposition, but only apparently appears in it. In the language L_3 it would be expressed by the sentence

$$((x)(x \in N . \supset . x + 1 = 1 + x)),$$

where N is the class of integers, and the fact that "x" doesn't really enter into the meaning of this proposition is shown by the analogue in L_3 of T3.2.1b, whereby "x" is a dummy symbol. In the system of section III2 this proposition is expressed without variables thus:

$$\prod A^1,$$

where A^1 is the element of $\mathfrak{F}_1$ such that

$$\vdash A^1\alpha :\equiv: N^1\alpha . \supset . E^2(\alpha + 1)(1 + \alpha), \text{ for all } \alpha \text{ in } \mathfrak{J},$$

assuming that addition has already been defined. We know, however, that this formalism is inadequate from the remarks on p. 87. It thus appears that the notion of a variable is a linguistic, rather than a logical, concept, and similarly, that a rule of substitution is a linguistic, rather than a logical, law, amounting to the observation that in certain languages only generally true propositions can be deduced, so that what is provable about one object of a certain category is provable about all. This view is substantiated by Lindenbaum and Tarski ([I]115).

This raises the question: can a system of logic be constructed in which the signs of the object language have denotations, which is adequate for at least a large part of mathematics, and which deals only with constants? Can we make the system adequate for all the ordinary uses of variables and the process of substitution, so that the convenience of variables as tools in communication is not lost? This problem has been solved by Curry, partly on the basis of previous work by Schönfinkel, and simplifications of Curry's work have been made by Rosser and Curry himself. Kleene and Rosser have shown the close connection between Curry's theory and that developed independently by Church. They also found a serious inconsistency in the systems originally proposed by Curry and Church.

We shall attempt here to give an idea of the work of these authors, but for lack of space we shall be forced to limit ourselves to a brief, and perhaps inadequate, sketch. Our first task is to set up an independent theory of operators, the so-called "combinators", of the sort introduced on p. 87.

We start with a primitive frame consisting of a class $\mathfrak{E}$ of objects called *entities*, two special entities A and K, a binary operation $|$ called *application*, and a binary relation $=$ between entities. If a and b are entities then "$|ab$" shall denote the application of a to b. We may conceive of the entities as operators or functions, and $|ab$ as the result of operating on b with a.

By writing the stroke before the names of the entities combined by means of the indicated operation we avoid the need of parentheses, and also simplify considerably the syntax of the object language. We define the *rank* of a string of names of entities and strokes as the number of strokes minus the number of letters, i.e. names of entities. A string is a *word*, i.e. a name of an entity, if and only if its rank is -1 and the rank of each proper head (a head which is not the whole string) is non-negative. To each sign in a word there corresponds a unique part which is a word beginning with that sign. These syntactical theorems will be proved for more general languages in the next chapter (Theorem 4.1.1.)

For example, the string $||A|K|AAK$ is a word. The word beginning with the third stroke is "$|K|AA$". If we had denoted the fundamental operation by "$a|b$" and used parentheses, then this word would have been written "$(A|(K|(A|A)))|K$". After a little practice in the use of the above criteria this notation is much simpler to read than the ordinary parentheses notation, especially when the formulae are rather complicated. For convenience and economy, we shall omit writing the strokes on the extreme left of a word occurring alone. Thus this word will be written "$A|K|AAK$"; by the use of the above criteria we see that two strokes must be written to the left in order to obtain a string of rank -1, and therefore an unabbreviated word in the "official" notation.

The assumptions are:

R. If a and b are in $\mathfrak{E}$, then $|ab$ is a uniquely determined member of $\mathfrak{E}$.
E1. If a is in $\mathfrak{E}$, then $a = a$.
E2. If $a = b$, then $b = a$.
E3. If $a = b$ and $b = c$, then $a = c$.
E4. If $a = b$ and $c = d$, then $|ac = |bd$.
E5. If a and b are in $\mathfrak{E}$, and $|ac = |bc$ for all c in $\mathfrak{E}$, then $a = b$.

This means that a and b are the same operator if and only if they always yield the same result when applied to an arbitrary entity c. E5 may be called a postulate of "extensionality" in analogy to FVIII (p. 98).

C0. A and K are in $\mathfrak{E}$.
C1. If a, b, and c are in $\mathfrak{E}$, then $Aabc = ac|bc$.
C2. If a and b are in $\mathfrak{E}$, then $Kab = a$.

Thus K is a "constancy" operator, generalizing the notion introduced in F_nK (p. 87). The entity $|Ka$ is an operator which, when applied to an arbitrary entity b, yields the constant result a. The entity A is a certain "substitution" operator. If a is an operator which, when applied to arbitrary integers m and n, yields the integer $2m^3 + n + 1$ while b is an operator which, when applied to an arbitrary integer n, yields n^2, then Aab is an operator which, when applied to an arbitrary integer n, yields the integer $2n^3 + n^2 + 1$. If f is a function of two variables and g is a function of one variable, then Afg is the function h whose value, for an arbitrary argument c, would be expressed in the usual notation by $h(c) = f(c, g(c))$.

The following definitions are very useful:

D1. "I" for "AKK".
D2. "B" for "$A|KAK$".

D3. "W" for "$AA|AK$".
D4. "D" for "BB".
D5. "C" for "$A|DA|KK$".
D6. "T" for "CI".

The following elementary theorems exhibit the nature of these operators, and illustrate the use of these postulates. In the following, the small Latin letters a, b, c, d, and e denote arbitrary members of $\mathfrak{E}$.

T1. $Ia = a$.
Proof. $Ia = AKKa = Ka|Ka = a$. (D1, C1, C2).

T2. $Ba = A|Ka$.
Proof. $Ba = A|KAKa = KAa|Ka = A|Ka$.

T3. $Babc = a|bc$.
Proof. $Babc = A|Kabc = Kac|bc = a|bc$.

T4. $Wab = abb$.
Proof. $Wab = AA|AKab = Aa||AKab = ab|||AKab$
$= ab||Kb|ab = abb$.

T5. $Dabcd = ab|cd$.
Proof. $Dabcd = BBabcd = B|abcd = ab|cd$.

T6. $Cabc = acb$.
Proof. $Cabc = A|DA|KKabc = DAa||KKabc$
$= DAaKbc = Aa|Kbc = ac||Kbc = acb$.

T7. $Tab = ba$.
Proof. $Tab = CIab = Iba = ba$.

Thus I is the identity operator, which leaves each entity unchanged. If f and g are functions of one variable, then Bfg is the function whose value, for an arbitrary argument c, is expressed in the usual notation by $f(g(c))$. If f is a function of two variables, then Cf is the function h whose value, for arbitrary arguments b and c, is expressed by $h(b, c) = f(c, b)$, and Wf is the function φ such that $\varphi(c) = f(c, c)$, for an arbitrary argument c. See also p. 87.

T8. $A|KaI = a$.

Proof. If b is in $\mathfrak{C}$, then $A|KaIb = Kab|Ib = a|Ib = ab$. Since b is an arbitrary element of $\mathfrak{C}$, the theorem follows by E5.

COROLLARY T8a. $AB|KI = I$.

Proof. $AB|KIa = Ba||KIa = BaI = A|KaI = a = Ia$. Again we apply E5 to obtain the desired result.

T9. $A||A|KKab = a$.

Proof. If c is in $\mathfrak{C}$, then $A||A|KKabc = A|KKac|bc = KKc|ac|bc = K|ac|bc = ac$. (E5).

COROLLARY T9a. $BA|BK = K$.

Proof. $BA|BKab = A||BKab = A||A|KKab = a = Kab$. (E5).

T10. $A|Ka|Kb = K|ab$.

Proof. $A|Ka|Kbc = Kac||Kbc = ab = K|abc$. (E5).

T11. $A|DB|KK = B|BKI$.

Proof. $A|DB|KKab = DBa||KKab = DBaKb = Ba|Kb = A|Ka|Kb$.
$B|BKIab = BK|Iab = BKab = K|ab$. (E5).

T12. $A||Aac||Abc = A||A||BAabc$.

Proof. $A||Aac||Abcd = Aacd|||Abcd = ad|cd||bd|cd$.
$A||A||BAabcd = A||BAabd|cd = BAad|bd|cd = A|ad|bd|cd$. (C1, E5).

T13. $A|D||BA||B|BAA|KA = B|BA||WI|BA$.

Proof. $A|D||BA||B|BAA|KAabc$
$= D||BA||B|BAAa||KAabc$
$= D||BA||B|BAAaAbc = BA||B|BAAa|Abc$
$= A|||B|BAAa|Abc = A||BA|Aa|Abc$
$= BA|Aac||Abc = A||Aac||Abc$.
$B|BA||WI|BAabc = BA|||WI|BAabc$
$= A||||WI|BAabc = A||||I|BA|BAabc$
$= A||||BA|BAabc = A|A||BAabc$. (E5).

These theorems all have very simple meanings, namely that two operators always have the same effect. Thus T13 says that we can construct the entity $ad|cd||bd|cd$ from four arbitrarily given ones, a, b, c, and d, in two ways, either by forming $Aacd$ and $Abcd$, applying C1, and combining, or by applying the operator A to the entities ad, bd, and cd.

We shall show later that T8a, T9a, T11, and T13 are sufficient for the whole theory in that two words in "A" and "K" can be proved equal from R, E1–5, C0–2 if and only if they can be proved equal from R, E1–4, C0–2 and these equations. This is important in the "metatheory", i.e. the theory of the structure of the system, since the hypothesis of E5 requires infinitely many premises, so that it is a simplification to replace E5 by a finite number of equations. On the other hand, the proofs are much simpler on the present basis.

Curry took B, C, W, and K as primitive notions and gave another system of postulates in terms of these operations. Rosser gave a set of postulates for a weaker system without a constancy operator, and Fitch studied a still weaker one without a W operator. We give below Curry's "combinatory axioms" and indicate how they are proved by showing the steps where E5 is applied. The details may be left to the reader as an exercise.

T14. $BI = I$.
Proof. $BIab = ab = Iab$.

T15. $C||BB||BBBB = B|BBB$.
Proof. $C||BB||BBBBabcd = a|b|cd = B|BBBabcd$.

T16. $C||BB||BBBC = B|BC||BBB$.
Proof. $C||BB||BBBCabcd = a||bdc = B|BC||BBBabcd$.

T17. $C||BBBW = B|BW||BBB$.
Proof. $C||BBBWabc = a||bcc = B|BW||BBBabc$.

T18. $C||BBBK = B|BKI$.
Proof. $C||BBBKabc = ab = B|BKIabc$.

T19. $CBI = I$.
Proof. $CBIab = ab = Iab$.

T20. $B||B|BCC|BB = BBC$.
Proof. $B||B|BCC|BBabcd = ad|bc = BBCabcd$.

T21. $B|B||B||B|BWW|BC|B|BBB = BBW$.
Proof. $B|B||B||B|BWW|BC|B|BBBabc = a|bd|bd$
$= BBWabc$.

T22. $BBK = BKK$.
Proof. $BBKabc = a = BKKabc$.

T23. $BCC = I$.
Proof. $BCCabc = abc = Iabc$.

T24. $B||B|BCC|BC = B||BC|BCC$.
Proof. $B||B|BCC|BCabcd = adcb = B||BC|BCCabcd$.

T25. $B||B|BWC|BC = BCW$.
Proof. $B||B|BWC|BCabc = accb = BCWabc$.

T26. $BCK = BK$.
Proof. $BCKabc = ab = BKabc$.

T27. $BWC = W$.
Proof. $BWCab = abb = Wab$.

T28. $BW|BW = BWW$.
Proof. $BW|BWab = abbb = BWWab$.

T29. $BWK = I$.
Proof. $BWKab = ab = Iab$.

We shall now prove that our system is functionally complete. In order to do this we shall need some syntactical concepts. We adjoin to the object language an infinite list of letters x, y, z, x_1, y_1, z_1, x_2, y_2, z_2, $\cdots$, which shall be called *variables*. We define a *word* as a string built up from names of entities, variables, and the strokes, according to the following rules:

(a). If $\mathfrak{A}$ is a variable or a name of an entity, then $\mathfrak{A}$ is a word.

(b). If $\mathfrak{A}$ and $\mathfrak{B}$ are words, then $|\mathfrak{A}\mathfrak{B}$ is a word. Here "$|\mathfrak{A}\mathfrak{B}$" denotes the string consisting of "|", followed by the signs of $\mathfrak{A}$, followed by the signs of $\mathfrak{B}$. By a word in the variables x_1, x_2, $\cdots$, x_k we mean a word in which these, or some of these, are the only variables; thus "x" does not necessarily occur in a word in x. We shall denote a word in $x_1, \cdots, x_k$ by some such symbol as "$\mathfrak{A}(x_1, \cdots, x_k)$". If $\mathfrak{A}(x)$ is a word in x and "a" is a name of an entity, then "$\mathfrak{A}(a)$" shall denote the result of substituting "a" for "x" in $\mathfrak{A}(x)$, and similarly for words in several variables or for substitution of words for the variables occurring in another word. If no variables other than "x" occur in $\mathfrak{A}(x)$, then $\mathfrak{A}(a)$ is a name of a uniquely determined entity. Thus if $\mathfrak{A}(x, y)$ is "$|x|yx$" then $\mathfrak{A}(|AK, B)$ is "$||AK|B|AK$", so that $\mathfrak{A}(|AK, B)$ is the name of a definite entity, while $\mathfrak{A}(|AK, z)$ is "$||AK|z|AK$" which is merely another word. We shall use such symbols as "$\mathfrak{A}(a)$" to denote the entities of which they are the names.

We aim to prove that if $\mathfrak{A}(x)$ is a word in x, then there is a uniquely determined entity F such that $Fa = \mathfrak{A}(a)$ for all entities a. To do this we introduce a new sign, "λ", and establish a correspondence between words and entities by means of the following rules:

(a). If $\mathfrak{A}(x)$ is a name of an entity, then $\lambda x\mathfrak{A}(x)$ is $|K\mathfrak{A}(x)$.
(b). If $\mathfrak{A}(x)$ is "x", then $\lambda x\mathfrak{A}(x)$ is I.
(c). If $\mathfrak{A}(x)$ is $|\mathfrak{B}(x)\mathfrak{C}(x)$, then $\lambda x\mathfrak{A}(x)$ is $||A\lambda x\mathfrak{B}(x)\lambda x\mathfrak{C}(x)$.

For example,

$$\lambda x||A|KxI = ||A\lambda x|A|Kx\lambda xI = ||A||A\lambda xA\lambda x|Kx|KI$$
$$= ||A||A|KA||A\lambda xK\lambda xx|KI = ||A||A|KA||A|KKI|KI.$$

For ease in reading, we mention that "$\lambda x\mathfrak{A}(x)$", where $\mathfrak{A}(x)$ is a word in x, is also a word. If we define the rank of "λ" as $+1$ and that of a variable as -1, then the previous criterion that a string be a word still applies, with the restriction that "λ" must always be immediately followed by a variable. Note that if a is an arbitrary entity, then

$$|\lambda x||A|KxIa = |||A||A|KA||A|KKI|KIa$$
$$= A|KA||A|KKIa||KIa = KAa|||A|KKIaI$$
$$= A|||KKa|IaI = A|KaI,$$

so that in this case $\lambda x||A|KxI$ is the entity F such that $Fa = A|KaI$ for all a in $\mathfrak{E}$. We shall now prove this in general. Until further notice we shall not use E5, but shall instead rely on T8a, T9a, T11, T13 and the other assumptions.

T30. $|\lambda x\mathfrak{A}(x)a = \mathfrak{A}(a)$.

Proof. If $\mathfrak{A}(x)$ is a name of an entity, then

$$|\lambda x\mathfrak{A}(x)a = ||K\mathfrak{A}(x)a = \mathfrak{A}(x) = \mathfrak{A}(a).$$

If $\mathfrak{A}(x)$ is "x", then $|\lambda x\mathfrak{A}(x)a = |Ia = a = \mathfrak{A}(a)$. If $\mathfrak{A}(x)$ is $|\mathfrak{B}(x)\mathfrak{C}(x)$, and the theorem is true for all words shorter than $\mathfrak{A}(x)$, then

$$|\lambda x\mathfrak{A}(x)a = |||A\lambda x\mathfrak{B}(x)\lambda x\mathfrak{C}(x)a = ||\lambda x\mathfrak{B}(x)a|\lambda x\mathfrak{C}(x)a$$
$$= |\mathfrak{B}(a)\mathfrak{C}(a) = \mathfrak{A}(a).$$

We now supplement the above definition of "$\lambda x\mathfrak{A}$" by the following rule:

(d). If $\mathfrak{A}$ is a variable different from "x", then $\lambda x\mathfrak{A}$ is $|K\mathfrak{A}$, and we assume E0–4, C0–2, T8a, T9a, T11, and T13 for arbitrary strings. In this way, if $\mathfrak{A}$ is a word in any number of variables, then $\lambda x\mathfrak{A}$ is a word in which x no longer occurs. T30 still holds, with the remark that "$\mathfrak{A}(a)$" means the result of substituting "a" for "x" in $\mathfrak{A}$, leaving the other variables untouched. In this way we can construct words like "$\lambda x\lambda y\mathfrak{A}(x, y)$", "$\lambda x\lambda y\lambda z\mathfrak{A}(x, y, z)$", etc.

T30a. $||\lambda x\lambda y\mathfrak{A}(x, y)ab = \mathfrak{A}(a, b)$; $|||\lambda x\lambda y\lambda z\mathfrak{A}(x, y, z)abc = \mathfrak{A}(a, b, c)$, etc.

For example,

$$\lambda x\lambda y||xyy = \lambda x||A\lambda y|xy\lambda yy = \lambda x||A||A\lambda yx\lambda yyI$$
$$= \lambda x||A||A|KxII = ||A\lambda x|A||A|KxI\lambda xI$$
$$= ||A||A\lambda xA\lambda x||A|KxI|KI = ||A||A|KA||A\lambda x|A|Kx\lambda xI|KI$$
$$= ||A||A|KA||A||A\lambda xA\lambda x|Kx|KI|KI$$
$$= ||A||A|KA||A||A|KA||A\lambda xK\lambda xx|KI|KI$$
$$= ||A||A|KA||A||A|KA||A|KKI|KI|KI.$$

Of course, this entity is equal to W.

It is useful to note that T8 follows from T8a, T9 follows from T9a, T10 follows from T11, and T12 follows from T13, as is seen from the above proofs.

T31. *If "x" does not occur in the word* $\mathfrak{A}$, *then* $\lambda x\mathfrak{A} = |K\mathfrak{A}$.

Proof. If $\mathfrak{A}$ is a single sign, then the conclusion follows from parts (a) and (d) of the definition of "$\lambda x\mathfrak{A}$". If $\mathfrak{A}$ is $|\mathfrak{B}\mathfrak{C}$, and the theorem is true for all words shorter than $\mathfrak{A}$, then

$\lambda x\mathfrak{A} = \lambda x|\mathfrak{B}\mathfrak{C} = ||A\lambda x\mathfrak{B}\lambda x\mathfrak{C} = A|K\mathfrak{B}|K\mathfrak{C}$
$= K|\mathfrak{B}\mathfrak{C}$, by T10.

T32. *If "x" does not occur in the word* $\mathfrak{A}$, *then* $\lambda x|\mathfrak{A}x = \mathfrak{A}$.

Proof. $\lambda x|\mathfrak{A}x = ||A\lambda x\mathfrak{A}\lambda xx = A|K\mathfrak{A}I = \mathfrak{A}$, by T8.

T33. *If* $\mathfrak{A}$, $\mathfrak{B}$, *and* $\mathfrak{C}$ *are words, then* $\lambda x|||A\mathfrak{A}\mathfrak{B}\mathfrak{C} = \lambda x||\mathfrak{A}\mathfrak{C}|\mathfrak{B}.\mathfrak{C}$

Proof. $\lambda x|||A\mathfrak{A}\mathfrak{B}\mathfrak{C} = ||A\lambda x||A\mathfrak{A}\mathfrak{B}\lambda x\mathfrak{C}$
$= A||A\lambda x|A\mathfrak{A}\lambda x\mathfrak{B}\lambda x\mathfrak{C} = A||A||A\lambda xA\lambda x\mathfrak{A}\lambda x\mathfrak{B}\lambda x\mathfrak{C}$
$= A||A||A|KA\lambda x\mathfrak{A}\lambda x\mathfrak{B}\lambda x\mathfrak{C}$
$= A||A\lambda x\mathfrak{A}\lambda x\mathfrak{C}||A\lambda x\mathfrak{B}\lambda x\mathfrak{C}$, by T12,
and $\lambda x||\mathfrak{A}\mathfrak{C}|\mathfrak{B}\mathfrak{C} = ||A\lambda x|\mathfrak{A}\mathfrak{C}\lambda x|\mathfrak{B}\mathfrak{C}$
$= A||A\lambda x\mathfrak{A}\lambda x\mathfrak{C}||A\lambda x\mathfrak{B}\lambda x\mathfrak{C}$.

T34. *If* $\mathfrak{A}$ *and* $\mathfrak{B}$ *are words, then* $\lambda x||K\mathfrak{A}\mathfrak{B} = \lambda x\mathfrak{A}$.

Proof. $\lambda x||K\mathfrak{A}\mathfrak{B} = ||A\lambda x|K\mathfrak{A}\lambda x\mathfrak{B} = A||A\lambda xK\lambda x\mathfrak{A}\lambda x\mathfrak{B}$
$= A||A|KK\lambda x\mathfrak{A}\lambda x\mathfrak{B} = \lambda x\mathfrak{A}$, by T9.

T35. *If* $\lambda x\mathfrak{A} = \lambda x\mathfrak{B}$ *and* $\lambda x\mathfrak{C} = \lambda x\mathfrak{D}$, *then* $\lambda x|\mathfrak{A}\mathfrak{C} = \lambda x|\mathfrak{B}\mathfrak{D}$.

Proof. $\lambda x|\mathfrak{A}\mathfrak{C} = A\lambda x\mathfrak{A}\lambda x\mathfrak{C} = A\lambda x\mathfrak{B}\lambda x\mathfrak{D} = \lambda x|\mathfrak{B}\mathfrak{D}$.

T36. *If* $\mathfrak{A}$ *and* $\mathfrak{B}$ *are words, and* "$\mathfrak{A} = \mathfrak{B}$" *follows from R*, E1–4, C0–2, T8a, T9a, T11, *and* T13, *then so does* "$\lambda x\mathfrak{A} = \lambda x\mathfrak{B}$".

Proof. Each of T8a, $\cdots$, T13 is of the form "$\mathfrak{A}_1 = \mathfrak{B}_1$", where x does not occur in $\mathfrak{A}_1$ or $\mathfrak{B}_1$. Then $\lambda x\mathfrak{A}_1 = K\mathfrak{A}_1 = K\mathfrak{B}_1 = \lambda x\mathfrak{B}_1$ (T31). Thus the desired conclusion holds for these four equations. Now if "$\mathfrak{A}$" and "$\mathfrak{B}$" are arbitrary words, and if, in the proof that $\mathfrak{A} = \mathfrak{B}$, we replace each application of E4 by T35, of C1 by T33, of C2 by T34, and of T8a, $\cdots$, T13, by the corresponding equation of the form "$\lambda x\mathfrak{A}_1 = \lambda x\mathfrak{B}_1$", then we obtain a proof that $\lambda x\mathfrak{A} = \lambda x\mathfrak{B}$.

Corollary 36a. If "$\mathfrak{A}$" and "$\mathfrak{B}$" are words, and if "x" does not occur in either, and if "$|\mathfrak{A}x = |\mathfrak{B}x$" follows from R, $\cdots$, T13, then so does "$\mathfrak{A} = \mathfrak{B}$".

For $\mathfrak{A} = \lambda x|\mathfrak{A}x = \lambda x|\mathfrak{B}x = \mathfrak{B}$, by T32 and T36.

These last two results show that E5 may be replaced by T8a, $\cdots$, T13 without any change in the theorems.

It is instructive to work out the proof of $BI = I$ by this method. In the above proof we first showed that $BIab = ab = Iab$ for arbitrary entities a and b, and then applied E5 twice. Now we parallel the proof in accordance with T36. The following steps should be compared with the original proof, beginning with $BI = A|KI$.

We first prove that $A|KIx = x$ by applying the method of T36 to the proof that $A|KIxy = Ixy$. We note that $A|KIx = \lambda y|I|xy = \lambda y|||AKK|xy$ by T32, which suggests the following steps:

$$\begin{aligned} A|KIx &= A|K||AKKx = A||A|K|AK|KKx && \text{(T10)} \\ &= A||A||A|KA|KK|KKx && \text{(T10)} \\ &= A||A|KKx||A|KKx && \text{(T12)} \\ &= x && \text{(T9)}. \end{aligned}$$

We now apply the method of T36 to this proof to obtain the result that $A|KI = I$, remembering that $\lambda x||A|KIx = A|KI$, by T32. Thus

$$\begin{aligned} A|KI &= A|K|A|KII && \text{(T8)} \\ &= A|K|A|K||AKKI = A|K|A||A|K|AK|KKI && \text{(T10)} \\ &= A|K|A||A||A|KA|KK|KKI && \text{(T10)} \\ &= A|K||A||A|KA|A|KK|A|KKI && \text{(T13)} \\ &= A|K||AK|A|KKI && \text{(T9a)} \\ &= A||A||A|KA|KK|K|A|KKI && \text{(T10)} \\ &= A||A|KKI||A|K|A|KKI && \text{(T12)} \\ &= I && \text{(T9)}. \end{aligned}$$

Of course, once we have found a proof by a direct application of T36, we may often construct a much simpler one, but in any case T36 shows one universally applicable method of dispensing with E5. We now return to the free use of E5.

We can construct a sequence of entities which have a remarkable analogy to the (non-negative) integers, and may, for our present purposes, be identified with them. The idea behind this correspondence is that the integer n may be considered as an operator which, when applied to any other operator a, yields the n-th iterate of a. Thus $|na$ is the operator which, when applied to an arbitrary entity b, yields the same result as a applied n times to b. For example,

$$2ab = a|ab, \qquad 3ab = a|a|ab, \qquad \text{etc.}$$

In particular, $1a$ must be the same as a; it is convenient to consider $0a$ as the "operation" of not applying any operator, so that it leaves every entity b unchanged. This leads to the equations

$$0ab = b$$
$$1ab = ab.$$

By E5, we have the following equations:

$$0 = \lambda x \lambda yy = \lambda xI = KI,$$
$$1 = \lambda x \lambda y|xy = I,$$
$$2 = \lambda x \lambda y|x|xy = ABI,$$
$$3 = \lambda x \lambda y|x||2xy = A||BAK2, \text{ etc.}$$

In general, the successor of n (i.e. $n + 1$), denoted by "Sn", may be identified as the operator such that

$$Snab = a||nab,$$

i.e. Sna consists in applying a n times and then applying a to the result. This leads us to the definition

$$S = \lambda x \lambda y \lambda z|y||xyz = A||BAK.$$

It is easy to check that $1 = S0$, $2 = S1$, $3 = S2$, etc. We may now define $\mathfrak{N}$, the class of non-negative integers, as the common part of all classes $\mathfrak{M}$ such that 0 is in $\mathfrak{M}$ and if n is in $\mathfrak{M}$, then Sn

is in $\mathfrak{M}$. We intend $\mathfrak{N}$ to be the class of all entities obtained by operating with S on 0 a finite number of times, but must employ some dodge to avoid the vicious circle of using the concept of number in the definition of $\mathfrak{N}$.

The elementary arithmetic operations are easy to define. Thus the m-th iterate of the n-th iterate of the operator a is the $(m \times n)$-th iterate of a, i.e.

$$(m \times n)a = m|na = Bmna,$$

so that

$$m \times n = Bmn.$$

Similarly, the m-th iterate of a applied after the n-th iterate of a yields the $(m + n)$-th iterate of a, i.e.

$$(m + n)ab = ma||nab,$$

so that

$$(m + n) = \lambda xy||mx||nxy = A||BBmn = A|Dmn.$$

Finally,

$$n^2a = (n \times n)a = n|na = 2na,$$
$$n^3a = (n \times n^2)a = n|n^2a = n||2na = 3na, \text{ etc.},$$

which leads to the simple definition

$$n^m = mn.$$

The entity mn occurring here is not to be confused with $(m \times n)$, which is $||Bmn$.

We might also define an operator $+$ such that $+ab = (a + b)$ for all entities a and b, i.e.

$$+ = \lambda x\lambda y(x + y) = \lambda x\lambda y||A||BBxy = A|KA|BB = BAD.$$

Then parentheses would be unnecessary, and $+$ would be an entity itself. The corresponding entity for multiplication is B, and for exponentiation is T. An alternative definition of addition is discussed in the exercises below.

We can now derive most of the important properties of integers. With the definitions just given, some of these properties hold for all entities. We give some examples.

T37. *If a, b, and c are in* $\mathfrak{E}$, *then* $(a \times b) \times c = a \times (b \times c)$.

Proof. Let d be an arbitrary entity. Then
$((a \times b) \times c)d = B||Babcd = Bab|cd = a|b|cd$,
while
$(a \times (b \times c))d = Ba||Bbcd = a|||Bbcd = a|b|cd$.
The conclusion follows by E5.

T38. *If a, b, and c are in* $\mathfrak{E}$, *then* $(a + b) + c = a + (b + c)$.

Proof. Let d and e be arbitrary entities. Then
$((a + b) + c)de = (a + b)d||cde = ad||bd||cde$,
while
$(a + (b + c))de = ad||(b + c)de = ad||bd||cde$.
Now apply E5.

These theorems hold for all entities. The next one is more characteristic of the members of $\mathfrak{N}$.

T39. *If n is in* $\mathfrak{N}$, *then* $Sn = n + 1 = 1 + n$.

Proof. We note that $Sa = 1 + a$ for all entities a, for if b and c are arbitrary entities then
$Sabc = b||abc = 1b||abc = (1 + a)bc$.
Let $\mathfrak{M}$ be the class of all entities a such that $Sa = a + 1$. Then 0 is in $\mathfrak{M}$. For
$S0 = 1$, and $(0 + 1)ab = 0a||1ab = Iab = 1ab$,
so that $S0 = 0 + 1 = 1$. If a is in $\mathfrak{M}$, then $Sa = a + 1$, so that
$S(Sa) = 1 + (Sa) = 1 + (a + 1) = (1 + a) + 1$
$= (Sa) + 1$,
which shows that Sa is in $\mathfrak{M}$. Hence all members of $\mathfrak{N}$ are in $\mathfrak{M}$, which proves the theorem.

Church has developed a system of logic with an apparently completely different approach. We take as primitive an infinite list of signs x_1, x_2, $\cdots$, called *variables*, the stroke, and the symbol λ. By a *word* we mean a string formed according to the following rules:

(a) If $\mathfrak{A}$ is a variable, then $\mathfrak{A}$ is a word.
(b) If $\mathfrak{A}$ and $\mathfrak{B}$ are words, then $|\mathfrak{A}\mathfrak{B}$ is a word.
(c) If $\mathfrak{A}$ is a word and "x" is a variable, then $\lambda x \mathfrak{A}$ is a word.

All occurrences of a variable "x" in parts of a word $\mathfrak{A}$ of the form "$\lambda x \mathfrak{A}_1$", where $\mathfrak{A}_1$ is a word, are called *bound*; all other occurrences of "x" in $\mathfrak{A}$ are called *free.* The precise definitions of *occurrence, part, bound,* and *free* occurrence, as given in III3, D17–19, are to be modified in the obvious way to apply to the present object language. A word in the variables $x_1, \cdots, x_k$ is one in which no other variable occurs free; all of these variables do not necessarily occur in the word. As before, we shall denote a word in $x_1, \cdots, x_k$ by some such symbol as "$\mathfrak{A}(x_1, \cdots, x_k)$". If $\mathfrak{A}(x)$ is a word in x, and $\mathfrak{B}$ is a word, then "$\mathfrak{A}(\mathfrak{B})$" shall denote the result of substituting "$\mathfrak{B}$" for "x" in all free occurrences of "x" in $\mathfrak{A}(x)$, and similarly if $\mathfrak{A}$ is a word in several variables.

A relation $\rightarrow$ (read "produces") between words is defined by the following rules:

I. If $\mathfrak{A}$ is a word, and "x" is a variable which does not occur free in $\mathfrak{A}$, while "y" does not occur at all in $\mathfrak{A}$, and if $\mathfrak{B}$ is the result of substituting "y" for "x" throughout $\mathfrak{A}$, then $\mathfrak{A} \rightarrow \mathfrak{B}$.

II. If $\mathfrak{A}(x_1, \cdots, x_k)$ is a word in the variables $x_1, \cdots, x_k$, and $\mathfrak{B}$ is a word, then $|\lambda x_1 \mathfrak{A}(x_1, \cdots, x_k)\mathfrak{B} \rightarrow \mathfrak{A}(\mathfrak{B}, x_2, \cdots, x_k)$.

III. Under the hypotheses of II, $\mathfrak{A}(\mathfrak{B}, x_2, \cdots, x_k) \rightarrow |\lambda x_1 \mathfrak{A}(x_1, \cdots, x_k)\mathfrak{B}$.

IV. If $\mathfrak{A} \rightarrow \mathfrak{B}$, $\mathfrak{C}$ is a word, and "x" is a variable, then $|\mathfrak{A}\mathfrak{C} \rightarrow |\mathfrak{B}\mathfrak{C}$, $|\mathfrak{C}\mathfrak{A} \rightarrow |\mathfrak{C}\mathfrak{B}$, and $\lambda x \mathfrak{A} \rightarrow \lambda x \mathfrak{B}$.

V. If the variable "x" does not occur in the word $\mathfrak{A}$, then $\lambda x|\mathfrak{A}x \rightarrow \mathfrak{A}$ and $\mathfrak{A} \rightarrow \lambda x|\mathfrak{A}x$.

If $\mathfrak{A}$ and $\mathfrak{B}$ are words, then $\mathfrak{A}$ is said to be convertible to $\mathfrak{B}$, denoted by "$\mathfrak{A}$ conv $\mathfrak{B}$", if and only if there is a sequence of words $\mathfrak{A}_1, \cdots, \mathfrak{A}_n$ such that $\mathfrak{A}$ is $\mathfrak{A}_1$, $\mathfrak{B}$ is $\mathfrak{A}_n$, and $\mathfrak{A}_i \rightarrow \mathfrak{A}_{i+1}$ $(i = 1, \cdots, n-1)$.

We can define A and K as the following words:

"A" for "$\lambda x \lambda y \lambda z||xz|yz$",

and "K" for "$\lambda x \lambda y x$".

It is a remarkable fact, first proved for an analogous system by Rosser, that if $\mathfrak{A}(x_1, x_2)$ and $\mathfrak{B}(x_1, x_2)$ are words in x_1 and x_2, and do not contain the symbol "λ", then $\mathfrak{A}(A, K)$ conv $\mathfrak{B}(A, K)$ if and only if "$\mathfrak{A}(A, K) = \mathfrak{B}(A, K)$" can be proved from our assumptions. The proof is fairly easy on the basis of T36 and T36a.

We shall illustrate this system by proving a few elementary results on the basis of the definitions

$$I \text{ for } \lambda xx,$$
$$B \text{ for } \lambda x\lambda y\lambda z|x|yz,$$
$$\text{and } C \text{ for } \lambda x\lambda y\lambda z||xzy.$$

T40. AKK conv I.

Proof. AKK conv $\lambda x\lambda y\lambda z||xz|yzKK$ conv $\lambda z||Kz|Kz$. But $||Kz|Kz$ conv $||\lambda x\lambda yxz|Kz$ conv z, so that $\lambda z||Kz|Kz$ conv λzz conv λxx conv I.

T41. BI conv I.

Proof. BI conv $|\lambda x\lambda y\lambda z|x|yzI$ conv $\lambda y\lambda z|I|yz$. But $|I|yz$ conv $|\lambda xx|yz$ conv $|yz$, so that $\lambda y\lambda z|I|yz$ conv $\lambda y\lambda z|yz$ conv λyy conv λxx conv I.

T42. $A|Kx|Ky$ conv $K|xy$.

Proof. $A|Kx|Ky$ conv $\lambda z|||Kxz||Kyz$ conv $\lambda z|xy$ conv $\lambda u\lambda zu|xy$. But $\lambda u\lambda zu$ conv $\lambda x\lambda yx$ conv K, by rule I. Hence, by rule IV, $|\lambda u\lambda zu|xy$ conv $K|xy$.

These examples should suffice to illustrate the technique of conversion.

The theorem of Rosser, cited above, shows the essential equivalence of the theories of Curry and Church. Church and Rosser have also proved a consistency theorem which shows that such words as A and K are not convertible into each other. By the equivalence theorem, it follows that the system of Curry is also consistent.

On the basis of these results Church constructed, by the adjunction of another primitive notion, a system of logic whose consistency could be proved and which, though inadequate for extant mathematics, is undoubtedly adequate for all mathematics acceptable to the intuitionists. The system of Church escapes Gödel's theorem that logics are, in general, inadequate for the proof of their own consistency just through its inadequacy in another direction, namely that no universal quantifier exists in his system. There exist, indeed, better and better approximations to a universal quantifier, but it is impossible to express a proposition of the form "for all x, $\cdots$" within his object language. On the other hand, Curry has made certain suggestions, whose detailed development has not yet been published, but which promise to be more adequate for mathematics as actually practiced. We can only give the merest sketch of these ideas in this volume.

We take now as primitive notions a class $\mathfrak{E}$ of objects called entities, certain special entities A, K, Q, $\prod$, $\supset$, and P, a binary operation $|$, called application, and a subclass $\mathfrak{T}$ of entities, called *true*. As before, we shall denote that a is in $\mathfrak{T}$ by "$\vdash a$". The entity Q is to be an operator such that for any entities a and b, $||Qab$ is the proposition that a equals b. The entity P is an operator such that $|Pa$ is the proposition that a is a proposition. The operator $\supset$ is such that if a and b are propositions, then $||\supset ab$ is the proposition that if a, then b. A class is to be an entity a such that for certain entities b, $|ab$ is the proposition that b is a member of a, expressed in our former languages by "$b \in a$". Finally, if a is a class, then $\prod a$ is the proposition that for all x, $|ax$.

In stating the assumptions and definitions it will be convenient to use words and the symbol λ as before. The symbol λ can be eliminated by the definition on p. 117.

D7. "$a = b$" for "$\vdash ||Qab$".
R, D1–6, E1–4, C1–2, T8a, T9a, T11, T13, as before.
C0′. A, K, Q, $\prod$, $\supset$, and P are in $\mathfrak{E}$.
D8. "$a, \cdots, b \vdash c$" means that if $\vdash a, \cdots$, and $\vdash b$, then $\vdash c$.
C3. $a, ||Qab \vdash b$.
D9. "E" for "$|WQ$".
L1. $\prod A, Eb, \vdash |ab$.
L2. $a \vdash |Pa$.
L3. $Pa, Pb \vdash |P||\supset ab$.
D10. "P_1" for "$||BP\prod$".
D11. "f" for "$|\prod|QA$".

Q1. $\vdash\prod||B\prod||B|BPQ$.
Q2. $\vdash\prod||BP_1Q$.
F1. $a, ||\supset ab \vdash b$.
F2. If $\vdash|ab$ for all b in $\mathfrak{E}$, then $\vdash|\prod a$.
F3. $Pa, Pb, Pc \vdash||\supset||\supset ab||\supset||\supset bc||\supset ac$.
F4. $Pa, Pb \vdash||\supset||\supset||\supset abaa$.
F5. $Pa, Pb \vdash||\supset a||\supset ba$.
F6. $Pa \vdash||\supset fa$.
D12. "$\sim$" for "$\lambda x||\supset xf$" (i.e. $||C \supset f$).
D13. "Ξ" for "$\lambda x\lambda y|\prod\lambda z||\supset|xz|yz$" (i.e. $B|B\prod||BA|B \supset$).
F7. $P_1a \vdash|\prod\lambda x||\supset|\prod a|ax$ (i.e. $\vdash|\prod||B|\supset|\prod aa$).
F8. $Pa, P_1b \vdash||\supset||\Xi|Kab||\supset a|\prod b$.

In the old notation the postulates F3–6 have the forms

F3. If a, b, and c are in $\mathfrak{P}$, then $\vdash a \supset b . \supset . b \supset c \supset . a \supset c$.
F4. If a and b are in $\mathfrak{P}$, then $\vdash a \supset b \supset a \supset a$.
F5. If a and b are in $\mathfrak{P}$, then $\vdash a \supset . b \supset a$
F6. If a is in $\mathfrak{P}$, then $\vdash f \supset a$.

Now f is the proposition that every entity is equal to A, so that f may be taken as a typical false proposition. It can easily be shown that F1, L3, F3–F6 are an adequate set of postulates for a Boolean propositional logic. The assumptions L1, F2, F7 and F8 complete the assumptions for the logic of propositional functions as given in L_1 (III3). Assumptions Q1 and Q2 say that Qab and $\prod|Qa$ are propositions for all entities a and b. L2 says that every true entity is a proposition. C3 says that if $a = b$ and a is a proposition, then so is b. Some of the above postulates are superfluous, and Q may be defined satisfactorily in terms of the other primitives, but we shall not attempt to gain the utmost economy. We have taken "P_1" to mean the class of classes, i.e. a is a class if and only if $\prod a$ is a proposition.

A large part of mathematics can be derived from these assumptions, especially if we adjoin some postulates concerning class formation. There is reason to believe that these postulates are consistent, although a proof would be rather difficult.

In the original formulations of Curry and Church they postulated the properties of implication and quantification in full generality, i.e. for all entities, with no restriction that these entities be propositions, classes, etc. As might be expected, these systems turned out to be inconsistent. Kleene and Rosser showed that Richard's paradox (see III6) arose in these systems. Later Curry showed that in any system which is functionally complete in the sense of T30, and in which certain laws of the propositional logic hold for arbitrary entities, Russell's paradox arises. We may formulate this result in the following manner,

T43. *If, besides the above postulates, we assume that* $\vdash \| \supset aa$ *and* $\| \supset a \| \supset ab \vdash \| \supset ab$ *for all a and b in* $\mathfrak{E}$*, then* $\vdash d$ *for all d in* $\mathfrak{E}$.

Proof. We first construct an element a in $\mathfrak{E}$ such that $a = \| \supset ad$. Let $N = \| C \supset d$, $R = |W|BN$, and $a = |RR$. Thus we have

$$Nb = C \supset db = \supset bd \text{ for all } b \text{ in } \mathfrak{E},$$
$$Rc = W|BNc = BNcc = N|cc \text{ for all } c \text{ in } \mathfrak{E},$$

so that

$$a = RR = N|RR = Na = \supset ad.$$

Intuitively, if d is a false proposition, then "Nb" expresses the falsity of b, and if c is a class, then Rc is the proposition that c is not a member of c. Thus R is precisely the class which appears in Russell's paradox. We now obtain successively

$\vdash \| \supset aa$, $\vdash \| \supset a \| \supset ad$, $\vdash \| \supset ad$, $\vdash a$, and $\vdash d$, by C3 and F1.

Thus under the conditions of T43 every entity is asserted, which means that the system is inconsistent.

Curry proposes to avoid the difficulty by distinguishing a certain subclass $\mathfrak{C}$ of $\mathfrak{E}$, called the class of *canonical* entities, and by assuming such laws as *F*3–F6 only for members of $\mathfrak{C}$. The canonical entities may be thought of as generalizations of the notions of proposition and class. For certain systems of this type, which appear to be adequate for mathematics, Curry has announced the possession of a proof of consistency. It is to be hoped that he will publish the details of this work in the near future.

He has pointed out that much of the formal development can be simplified if one takes as a primitive the entity

$$F = \lambda x \lambda y \lambda z || \Xi x || Byz.$$

If a and b are classes and c is an arbitrary operator, then $Fabc$ is the proposition that if x is an arbitrary element of a, then $|cx$ is in b, so that c is a function on a to b. In terms of F we may define Ξ, $\prod$, and $\supset$ by the equations

$$\Xi = \lambda x \lambda y || FxyI = A||BAF|K|KI,$$
$$\prod = \Xi E,$$
and $$\supset = \lambda x \lambda y || \Xi |Kx|Ky = A||A|KB||B\Xi K|KK.$$

It may be noted that combinatory logics analyze the processes of reasoning into such "atomic" steps that the preliminary development needed in order to arrive at "real mathematics" is longer than with other approaches, but the single steps make much smaller demands on our intuition than is the case in other systems.

EXERCISES

Ex. 1. If "$||+ xy$" denotes $x + y$, "$||Pxy$" denotes xy, and "$|-x$" denotes $-x$, where x and y are numbers and these are the usual algebraic operations, then interpret the following operators:

(a). $B + |WP$.

(b). $A + ||BP| - 2$.

(c). $AP|WP$.

(d). $C||BB||BB ++$.

(e). $C||BB||BB + P$.

Ex. 2. Using the notations of Ex. 1, construct operators which, when applied to arbitrary numbers, yield the following results:

(a). $x^2 + y^2$.
(b). $x - y$.
(c). $2x - x^2$.
(d). $xy + xz$.
(e). $(x + y)(x + 2y)$.

Ex. 3. Eliminate "λ" from the following words:

(a). $[\; = \lambda x \lambda y \lambda z || z | Kyx$.
(b). $\alpha = \lambda x ||[| S | x0 | x0$.
(c). $\mathfrak{p} = \lambda x ||| x\alpha | K01$.
(d). $\beta = \lambda x \lambda y \lambda z \lambda w ||||[| Kx | y | \mathfrak{p} ww | z | \mathfrak{p} w$.
(e). $\Theta = \lambda x || W | Bx | W | Bx$.
(f). $R = \lambda x \lambda y | \Theta || \beta xy$.
(g). $\mu = \Theta \lambda x \lambda y \lambda z |||[z || xy | Sz | yz$.
(h). $\Lambda = \lambda x \lambda y ||| \mathfrak{p} y || B | \mu x S || \mu x 0$.
(i). $\lambda x_0 \lambda x_1 \cdots \lambda x_n | x_0 || \cdots | x_1 x_2 \cdots x_n$.
(j). $\lambda x \lambda y \lambda z || W | yx | zx$.
(k). $\lambda x \lambda y | \cdots | xyy \cdots y$, with n y's.
(m). $\lambda x_0 \lambda x_1 \cdots \lambda x_n x_0$.
(n). $\lambda x_0 \lambda x_1 \cdots \lambda x_n | \cdots | x_0 x_n x_1 \cdots x_{n-1}$.

Ex. 4. Prove the following in three ways, from R, E1–5, C0–2, using T8a, T9a, T11, and T13 instead of E5, and from I–V, p. 124:

(a). $B|ab = A||Ba|Kb$.
(b). $AK = KI$.
(c). $A||A||BBabc = Aa||Abc$.
(d). $A||BWab = A||Aabb$.
(e). $ADa = D||AIa$.
(f). $B0 = K0$.
(g). $A||BBa0 = a$.
(h). $A||BDab = D||Aab$.
(i). $A||A||A||BDabcd = A||Aab||Acd$.
(j). $A||A||BCabc = A||Aacb$.
(k). $A||BTab = Aba$.
(l). $BCCab = ab$.
(m). $B||Babc = Ba||Bbc$.
(n). $B|Ka = K|Ka$.
(o). $BBK = BKK$.

(p). $B||Bab = B|Ba|Bb.$

(q). $C||BBBK = BK.$

(r). $W||B|Bab = Ba|Wb.$

(s). $BA|A||BBa = B|B|AaA.$

Ex. 5. Using the notations of Ex. 3(a, $\cdots$, h), prove the following:

(a). $[ab0 = a.$

(b). $[ab|Sn = b.$

(c). If n is in $\mathfrak{N}$, then $n\alpha|K00 = n.$

(d). $\mathfrak{p}0 = 0.$

(e). If n is in $\mathfrak{N}$, then $\mathfrak{p}|Sn = n.$

(f). $\Theta a = a|\Theta a.$

(g). $\beta agf0 = a.$

(h). If n is in $\mathfrak{N}$, then $\beta agf|Sn = gn|fn.$

(i). If $f = Rag$, then $f = \beta agf$, and

$f0 = a,$

$f|Sn = gn|fn,$ for all n in $\mathfrak{N}$.

(j). $\mu an = [n||\mu a|Sn|an.$

(k). If $a0 = 0$, then $\mu a0 = 0.$

(l). If $a0$ is in $\mathfrak{N}$ but different from 0, then $\mu a0 = \mu a1.$

(m). If $an = 0$, then $\mu an = n.$

(n). If an is in $\mathfrak{N}$ but different from 0, then $\mu an = \mu a|Sn.$

(o). If there is an n in $\mathfrak{N}$ such that $an = 0$, then $\mu a0$ is the smallest such integer.

(p). If there is an integer $n \geq m$ such that $an = 0$, then μam is the smallest one.

(q). $\Lambda a1 = \mu a0.$

(r). $\Lambda a|S|Sn = \mu a|S||\Lambda a|Sn.$

(s). If the equation $am = 0$ has at least n solutions in non-negative integers, then Λan is the n-th solution in order of magnitude.

(t). $00 = 1$, $Sn0 = 0.$

Ex. 6. Using the results of Ex. 5, give definitions of entities satisfying the following conditions where m, n, etc. are in $\mathfrak{N}$:

(a). $\dot{-}mn = 0$ if $m \leq n$, $\dot{-}mn = m - n$ if $m > n.$

(b). $Mmn = \max(m, n)$.

(c). $M_1mn = \min(m, n)$.

(d). $\Delta mn = 1$ for $m = n$, $\Delta mn = 0$ for $m \neq n$.

(e). $!0 = 1$, $!|Sn = B|Sn!n$. (n factorial).

(f). $<mn = 0$ if $m \geq n$, $<mn = 1$ if $m < n$.

(g). $\div mn =$ the integral part of the fraction m/n where $n \neq 0$.

(h). $\rho mn =$ the remainder on division of m by n, where $n \neq 0$.

(i). $\delta mn = 1$ if m is divisible by n, 0 if m is not divisible by n.

(j). $\pi n = 1$ if n is a prime number, 0 if n is not a prime number.

(k). $\omega n =$ the n-th prime number.

(l). $\psi n =$ the integral part of $\sqrt{n}$.

(m). $\Psi n = 1$ if n is a perfect square, $\Psi n = 0$ if n is not a perfect square.

(n). $\tau n =$ the number of divisors of n.

(o). $\sigma n =$ the sum of the divisors of n.

(p). $\varphi_1 nxy =$ the smallest of the numbers $|x^n - y^n - z^n|$, as z ranges through the values $1, 2, \cdots$.

(q). $\varphi_2 nx =$ the smallest of the numbers $\varphi_1 nxy$ for $y = 1, 2, \cdots, x$.

(r). $\varphi_3 n =$ the smallest $x \geq 1$ such that the equation $x^n = y^n + z^n$ has a solution in positive integers y and z, if such exist.

(s). $\varphi_4 =$ the smallest integer $n \geq 3$ such that the equation $x^n = y^n + z^n$ has a solution in positive integers x, y, z, if such n's exist.

(t). $\gamma n =$ the smallest of the numbers $(\tau m) + (\tau(n + n - m))$ for $m = 2, 3, \cdots, n$.

(u). $\gamma_1 =$ the first $n \geq 2$ such that $\gamma n > 4$, if such exist.

(v). $\gamma_2 n =$ the number of integers m such that $2 \leq m \leq n$ and $\gamma m > 4$.

(w). $\sim 0 = 1$, $\sim 1 = 0$.

(x). $\vee 00 = 0, \quad \vee 01 = \vee 10 = \vee 11 = 1.$
(y). $\wedge 00 = \wedge 01 = \wedge 10 = 0, \quad \wedge 11 = 1.$
(z). $\supset 00 = \supset 01 = \supset 11 = 1, \quad \supset 10 = 0.$

SECTION 5 THE DEVELOPMENT OF MATHEMATICS WITHIN AN OBJECT LANGUAGE

We shall now sketch the formalization of mathematics within a language of the sort constructed in section 3. To fix the ideas, everything will be carried out in L_3, although similar developments are possible for the others except L_1. We shall make free use of the results of section 2, all of which can be derived in L_3, with trivial modifications in the statements and notations.

It will be useful, however, to state and prove some of the results again for L_3. We shall adopt the mnemonic device of using "u", "w", "x", "y", "z" for variables, "p", "q", "r", and "s" for sentences, and "α", "β", "γ", etc. for terms.

It will be convenient to begin with the following definitions:

D1. A string of the form "$(x)p$" or "$x \ni p$", where p is a sentence is called *x-bound.*

D2. The $(n + 1)$-tuple $(x_1, \cdots, x_n, p)$, where the x's are variables and p is a sentence, is said to be *adjusted* to $(\alpha_1, \cdots, \alpha_n)$ if for no i, $1 \leq i \leq n$, is there a variable y with a free occurrence in α_i such that there is a y-bound part C of p and a free occurrence of x_i in C.

The importance of $(x_1, \cdots, x_n, p)$ being adjusted to $(\alpha_1, \cdots, \alpha_n)$ is that when we form $Sb\{x_1, \cdots, x_n, p\}(\alpha_1, \cdots, \alpha_n)$ we do not wish free occurrences of variables in the α's to become bound after the substitution. In this terminology FVII can be stated more simply:

FVII. If p is a sentence and x and y are variables, and if (x, p) is adjusted to y, then

$$\vdash (x)p \,.\supset.\, Sb\{x, p\}(y).$$

We can now prove some useful analogues in L_3 to T3.2.1b and T3.2.1c.

T1. *If* (x, p) *is adjusted to* y, *and* q *is* $Sb\{x, p\}(y)$ *and* y *does not occur free in* p, *then* $\vdash (x)p \;.\equiv.\; (y)q$.

Proof. By FVII, $\vdash (x)p \;.\supset.\; q$.

By FII, $\vdash (x)p \;.\supset_y.\; q$.

Hence $\vdash (x)p \;.\supset.\; (y)q$. (FVI, FI).

By D2, (y, q) is adjusted to x, and p is $Sb\{y, q\}(x)$, and x does not occur free in q. By symmetry, we have

$$\vdash (y)q \;.\supset.\; (x)p.$$

The conclusion follows by T2.2.14 and FI.

This shows that "x" is a dummy symbol in "$(x)p$", i.e. "x" may be replaced throughout by any other variable y, which does not occur free in p and such that (x, p) is adjusted to y, and the result will be equivalent to $(x)p$. Thus in a definition where a variable bound by a universal quantifier appears in the definiens, it may be replaced by any other variable satisfying these conditions without affecting the notion defined, and therefore does not have to be indicated explicitly in the notation for that notion. These remarks will be used from now on without explicit mention. For example, D3.19 may be written as follows:

D3. $(\alpha \subset \beta)$ for $(z)((z \in \alpha) \supset (z \in \beta))$,

and "z" may be replaced by any variable which does not occur in α or β without affecting the result as far as equivalence is concerned.

We now define identity as follows:

D4. $(\alpha = \beta)$ for $(z \in \alpha \equiv_z z \in \beta)$.

In such definitions as D3 and D4 it is simplest to adopt the convention that z is chosen as a variable which does not occur in α or β, and analogously in all similar cases.

T2. *If* p, q, x, *and* y *are as in T1, then* $\vdash x \ni p = y \ni q$.

Proof. $\vdash (x)(x \in u \;.\equiv.\; p) \equiv (y)(y \in u \;.\equiv.\; q)$. (T1).

Hence $\vdash (\exists u) : z \in u \wedge (x)(x \in u .\equiv. p) .:\equiv:. (\exists u) : z \in u \wedge (y)(y \in u .\equiv. q)$ by T2.2.37, FII, T3.2.11, and FI. The conclusion follows by FX, T2.2.28, FII, and D4.

The comments to T1 apply also to T2. We shall use these observations from now on without explicit mention.

Postulate FVIII may be written in the following form:

FVIII. $\vdash x = y .\supset. x \in u \supset y \in u.$

The following theorems are almost trivial.

T3. $\vdash (x) . x = x.$

T4. $\vdash (x)(y) : x = y .\equiv. y = x.$

T5. $\vdash (x)(y)(z) :. x = y \wedge y = z :\supset: x = z.$

T6. $\vdash (x)(y)(z) :. x = y :\supset: x \in z .\equiv. y \in z.$

T7. $\vdash (x)(y)(z) :. x = y :\supset: z \in x .\equiv. z \in y.$

T8. $\vdash p \equiv_x q .\supset. (x \ni p) = (x \ni q).$

By repeated application of T6–T8 we can show that if $\vdash x = y$, the "x" may be replaced by "y" in any free occurrence of "x" without changing the result with respect to equivalence or identity, according as the substitution is performed on a sentence or a term. In fact, if p and q are sentences so related, and α and β are terms so related, then

$$\vdash x = y .\supset. p \equiv q,$$

and $\vdash x = y .\supset. \alpha = \beta.$

This is the principle of substitution of equals for equals.

It is convenient to introduce the null class:

D5. Λ for $x \ni \sim(x = x).$

T9. $\vdash (x) \sim (x \in \Lambda).$

Proof. $\vdash y \in \Lambda .:\equiv:. (\exists z) : y \in z \wedge (x)(x \in z \equiv \sim(x = x)).$ (FX).

$\vdash (x)(x \in z \equiv \sim(x = x)) .\supset. y \in z \equiv \sim(y = y)$ (FVII)

$.\supset. \sim(y \in z)$ (T3, T2.2.21, T2.2.15,

T2.2.7), and therefore

$\vdash \sim((y \in z) \wedge (x)(x \in z \equiv \sim(x = x)))$.

(D2.2.2, T2.2.5, T2.2.12). Hence

$\vdash (z) \sim ((y \in z) \wedge (x)(x \in z \equiv \sim(x = x)))$

(FII), and

$\vdash \sim(\exists z) : y \in z \wedge (x)(x \in z \equiv \sim(x = x))$

(D10, T2.2.5), so that

$\vdash \sim(y \in \Lambda)$. (T2.2.21, FI).

The notation of the second and third steps of this proof indicates that the conclusion of step (2) implies the conclusion of step (3), so that, by T2.2.8, the hypothesis of step (2) also implies the conclusion of step (3).

T10. *If p, q, x, and y are as in T1, and z is a variable which does not occur in either p or q, then*

$$\vdash (\exists z)(x)(x \in z \equiv p) :\supset: y \in x \ni p . \equiv . q.$$

This shows that if the property expressed by p corresponds to a class, then $x \ni p$ is that class.

Proof. $\vdash (x)(x \in z \equiv p) :\supset: y \in z \equiv q$ (FVII)

$:\supset: y \in z \wedge (x)(x \in z \equiv p)$

$. \equiv . q$ (Ex. 2.2.1g).

Hence $\vdash (\exists z)(x)(x \in z \equiv p) :\supset: y \in x \ni p$

$\equiv (\exists z)q$ (FII, T3.3.11).

Now it is trivial that $\vdash (\exists z)q . \equiv . q$, for

$\vdash (z)(q \supset q) :\supset: (\exists z)q . \supset . q$ (T3.3.9),

and $\vdash (z)(q \supset q) :\supset: q \supset (z)q$ (FVI),

$:\supset: q \supset (\exists z)q$ (T3.3.7).

Now apply T2.2.1 and FII.

Corollary T10a. $\vdash (x)(x \in z \equiv p) . \supset . z = (x \ni p)$.

T11. *If x, y, z, p, and q are as in* T10, *then*

$$\vdash y \in x \ni p :\supset: q \wedge (\exists z)(x)(x \in z . \equiv . p).$$

Proof. $\vdash y \in x \ni p .:\supset:. (\exists z) . y \in z$

$\wedge (x)(x \in z . \equiv . p)$: (FX).

$$\text{But} \vdash y \in z \wedge (x)(x \in z \equiv p)$$

$$:\supset: y \in z \,.\wedge.\, y \in z \equiv q \qquad \text{(FVII)}$$

$$.\supset. q. \qquad \text{(Ex. 2.2.1j)}$$

$$\text{Also} \vdash (\exists z) : y \in z \wedge (x)(x \in z \,.\!\equiv p)$$

$$.:\supset:. (\exists z)(x)(x \in z \equiv p).$$

(T2.2.18, T3.2.8a).

The conclusion is now obvious.

COROLLARY T11a. $\vdash \sim(\exists z)(x)(x \in z \,.\!\equiv\!.\, p)$
$.\supset. (y) \sim(y \in x \ni p)$.
$\vdash \sim(\exists z)(x)(x \in z \,.\!\equiv\!.\, p)$
$.\supset. x \ni p = \Lambda$.

Proof. The first part is an obvious consequence of the theorem. To prove the rest, we note that

$$\vdash \sim(y \in x \ni p) :\supset: y \in x \ni p \equiv . \sim(y = y) \qquad \text{(FX)}$$

$$\equiv y \in \Lambda. \qquad \text{(T9)}.$$

Thus if the property expressed by p does not correspond to a class, then $x \ni p$ is the null class. Hence if $x \ni p$ has any members at all, then it is the class of all x such that p. In particular, if p is stratified, then it automatically corresponds to a class, by FIX (and therefore $y \in x \ni p$ if and only if q, by T10), and $x \ni p$ is this class.

We can now define the operations of Boolean algebra:

D6. V for $x \ni (x = x)$.
D7. $\alpha \cup \beta$ for $x \ni (x \in \alpha \vee x \in \beta)$.
D8. $\alpha \cap \beta$ for $x \ni (x \in \alpha \wedge x \in \beta)$.
D9. α' for $x \ni \sim(x \in \alpha)$.

It is easy to show that classes form a Boolean algebra with respect to these operations, so that all the results of Chapter I hold in L_3.

We shall now explain the Wiener-Kuratowski method of developing the theory of polyadic propositional functions from the theory of classes. To fix the ideas let us consider diadic functions, or what comes to the same thing, binary relations. Suppose that we are able to define a notion of *ordered pair* so that

(1) $\vdash \langle x, y\rangle = \langle u, v\rangle :\equiv: x = u \wedge y = v;$

i.e. two ordered pairs are the same if and only if they consist of the same elements in the same order. Then to each relation R we can associate the class of all ordered pairs $\langle x, y\rangle$ such that xRy:

$$z = u \ni ((\exists x, y) : xRy \wedge u = \langle x, y\rangle).$$

In this way each relation corresponds to a uniquely determined class of ordered pairs, and conversely if z is a class of ordered pairs, then the sentence "$\langle x, y\rangle \in z$" expresses a relation between x and y. It is then a natural step to *define* a relation as a class of ordered pairs. For this we need only a definition of "ordered pair". This will be accomplished as soon as we have constructed a notion "$\langle x, y\rangle$" satisfying (1). Its exact nature is immaterial for mathematical purposes. This leads us to

D10. $(\iota\alpha)$ for $y \ni (\alpha = y)$.
D11. $\langle \alpha, \beta\rangle$ for $(\iota(\iota\alpha)) \cup \iota((\iota\alpha) \cup (\iota\beta))$.

Thus ιx is the "unit class" of x, the class whose only member is x. And $\langle x, y\rangle$ is the class whose only members are ιx and $\iota x \cup \iota y$. It is now easy to prove (1). We can therefore define the relation expressed by a given sentence:

D12. $xy \ni p$ for $z \ni ((\exists x, y)z = \langle x, y\rangle \wedge p)$, where z is a variable not occurring in p.

It is easy to see that if p is stratified and if the free occurrences of x and y in p (if there be any at all) have the same level in the stratification, then "$(\exists x, y) : z = \langle x, y\rangle \wedge p$" is stratified, so that

(2) $\vdash (\exists u)(z)(z \in u \,.:\equiv:.\, (\exists x, y) : z = \langle x, y\rangle \wedge p).$

If (2) does not hold, then $(xy \ni p) = \Lambda$. It is also easy to prove the following analogue of T10.

T12. *If* (x, y, p) *is adjusted* to (x_1, y_1), *and if* $q = Sb\{x, y, p\}\ (x_1, y_1)$ *and if neither* x_1 *nor* y_1 *occurs free in* p, *then* $\vdash (z)(z \in u \ .{:}{\equiv}{:}.\ (\exists x, y) : z = \langle x, y\rangle \wedge p)$ $:\supset: u = xy \ni p$.

We shall usually use capital Latin letters R, S, T, etc., for relations.

D12. "$(\alpha R\beta)$" for "$(\langle\alpha, \beta\rangle \in R)$."

The *converse* of the relation R is defined thus:

D13. $\breve{R}$ for $xy \ni (yRx)$.

Many important concepts can be defined in terms of relations. Thus a *function* is a relation R such that to each x there is at most one y such that xRy. The x's for which there is a y form the *domain* of the function. To each x in the domain of the function there is a unique y such that xRy. This y is the *value* of the function for the argument x. In the language L_3 we have

D14. $\text{Rel} = R \ni (z \in R \ .{\supset_z}.\ (\exists x, y)\ .z = \langle x, y\rangle)$.

D15. $\text{Fct} = R \ni (R \in \text{Rel} \ .{:}{\wedge}{:}.\ xRy \wedge xRz :\supset_{x,y,z}: y = z)$.

D16. $\text{Cor} = R \ni (R \in \text{Fct} \wedge \breve{R} \in \text{Fct})$.

Thus a relation is a class of ordered pairs. A function is a relation R such that if xRy and xRz, then $y = z$. And a *correspondence* is what we usually call a one-to-one correspondence. An example is the relation between a man x and his partner y at a dance in which there are no wallflowers.

D17. $D(R) = x \ni ((\exists y)xRy)$.
D18. $\text{Cl}(R) = D(\breve{R})$.

If R is a function, then $D(R)$ is its domain and $\text{Cl}(R)$ is its *range*, i.e. the class of values taken on by the function. We shall often denote functions by the letters f, g, h, φ, ψ, F, G, H, etc.

D19. $f(\alpha) = z \ni ((\exists y) :\alpha f y \wedge z \in y)$.

The notation here will be used principally in the case where

f is a function. Then if $\alpha \in D(f)$, there is only one y, anyway, such that $\alpha f y$. In the cases of interest to us, y will be a class, and will therefore be determined by its members. In this case $f(\alpha)$ will have the same members, so that $\vdash f(\alpha) = y$. In other cases $f(\alpha)$ also has an interesting interpretation, but we shall not digress now to discuss it.

It is more to the point to meditate on the proverbial process of counting noses. In order to understand more clearly the philosophy behind nose counting let

$$R = xy \ni (x \text{ is a nose of } y \ .\wedge.\ y \text{ is human and not a freak}).$$

Then R is a correspondence, since no nose belongs to different humans, and a human non-freak has exactly one nose. From this we conclude that we can determine the number of members in a class of normal humans by counting their noses. If "$Nc(\alpha)$" denotes the number of members of α, then

$$Nc(\alpha) = Nc(x \ni ((\exists y)\ .xRy \wedge y \in \alpha))$$

for any class α of normal humans. This leads us to a better idea of the notion of number. For we can now determine when two classes have the same number of members without counting them, simply by looking for a correspondence between their members. Two classes for which there exists such a correspondence will be called *similar*.

D20. $\text{sm} = xy \ni ((\exists R) : R \in \text{Cor} \wedge D(R) = x \wedge \text{Ɑ}(R) = y)$.

Thus "x sm y" will mean that there is a correspondence between the members of x and the members of y whereby to each z in x there corresponds a unique u in y and conversely. As nose counting teaches us, such a correspondence exists if and only if x and y have the same number of members.

We have thus been able to define the relation holding between two classes which have the same number of members, without using in the definition the concept of number. This was accomplished in a manner which may at first sight seem roundabout, but which really analyzes the concept of the equality of numbers into simpler notions. The process of counting can be explained now as follows. We have a standard class consisting of the words "one", "two", etc. To determine the number of members of an arbitrary class α we pair off the members of α with these words until the class α is exhausted. The last number-word used in constructing this correspondence is the name of the number of members of α.

Clearly we may use any class as a standard provided only that it has enough members for our purposes and that its members can be distinguished from each other. In particular, in our language L_3 we can construct many classes which could serve equally well as standard. Its members (or rather the corresponding strings in L_3) may be used as number-names just as "one", "two", $\cdots$, in ordinary discourse. One simple method is the following:

D21. $Nc(\alpha)$ for $x \ni (\alpha \text{ sm } x)$.
D22. Nc for $x \ni ((\exists y) \,.x = Nc(y))$.

Thus we *define* the number of members of α as the class of all classes similar to α, and a (cardinal) number as any x which is the number of members of some class y. These definitions yield concepts which are very easy to work with in the language L_3 .

We now show how the *finite* numbers may be distinguished from the rest. One of the characteristic properties of the finite numbers, or as we may also call them, the (non-negative) integers, is that expressed by the principle of mathematical induction. It turns out that this is very convenient to use as the *definition* of the class of integers. For this we need the special integers 0 and 1 and the concept of addition. (We could also define the successor of an integer directly, but it is more natural to proceed in the following way).

D23. 0 for $Nc(\Lambda)$.
D24. 1 for $x \ni ((\exists y) \,.x = \iota y)$.
D25. $u + v$ for $x \ni ((\exists y, z) : Nc(y) = u \,.\wedge.\, Nc(z) = v \,.\wedge.\, y \cap z = \Lambda \,.\wedge.\, x \text{ sm } (y \cup z))$.
D26. Fin for $x \ni (0 \in y \,.\wedge.\, z \in y \supset_z (z + 1) \in y \,:\supset_y:\, x \in y)$.

Thus 0 is the number of members of the null class, and 1 is the number of members of $\iota\alpha$ for any α. If u and v are cardinal numbers, and y and z are classes with no common members such that y has u members and z has v members, then $u + v$ is the number of members of $y \cup z$. A number x is finite if and only if it belongs to every class y which contains 0 and which contains $z + 1$ whenever it contains z.

We can now describe one of the intuitively valid arguments which cannot be formalized in L_3. It may very well happen that

(1) $\vdash Sb\{x, p\}(0), \quad \vdash Sb\{x, p\}(1), \quad \vdash Sb\{x, p\}(1 + 1), \quad \cdots$

are all provable without

(2) $$\vdash x \in \text{Fin} \supset_x p$$

being provable in L_3. For example,

$$\vdash 0 \neq \Lambda, \quad \vdash 1 \neq \Lambda, \quad \vdash 1 + 1 \neq \Lambda, \quad \cdots$$

are all provable in L_3, but there is no known proof that

(3) $$\vdash x \in \text{Fin} \supset_x x \neq \Lambda,$$

and it is very unlikely that (3) is provable at all in L_3. In other words, we may be able to prove that each particular integer has a certain property, and yet be unable to prove the sentence expressing the proposition that all integers have this property.

Rosser has proposed to adjoin to L_3 the rule FΩ. *If p is a sentence and if* $\vdash Sb\{x, p\}(0), \vdash Sb\{x, p\}(1), \vdash Sb\{x, p\}(1 + 1), \cdots$, *then* $\vdash x \in Fin \supset_x p$. If there should be an inconsistency in the language L_4 thus obtained, then we should probably reject L_3 as unacceptable intuitively. In the paper previously cited Rosser reports on his vain attempts to prove L_4 inconsistent.

We have now shown how many basic mathematical concepts can be defined in L_3, and have indicated briefly how their most important properties may be proved. Of course, our treatment was, of necessity, very sketchy. We have contented ourselves with these brief indications partly because of limitations of space, but mainly because we wish to emphasize the main tendency of modern work on logic, namely the study of the structure of a logical system as a whole, rather than the detailed development within the system. The latter is, nevertheless, necessary and important when one is either interested in the adequacy of the system or in the applications of the system.

EXERCISES

Ex. 1. Prove the following:

(a). $\vdash \sim(\exists z)(x)(x \in z \equiv (y) \sim((x \in y) \wedge (y \in x)))$.

(b). $\vdash \alpha \cap \beta = \beta \cap \alpha$.

(c). $\vdash(\alpha \cap \beta) \cap \gamma = \alpha \cap (\beta \cap \gamma)$.

(d). $\vdash \alpha \cap \beta' = \Lambda \equiv \alpha \subset \beta$.

(e). $\vdash \alpha \cap \beta = \alpha \equiv \alpha \subset \beta$.

(f). $\vdash \alpha \cap \alpha' = \Lambda$.

(g). T3–T8 above.

(h). $\vdash \langle x, y \rangle = \langle u, v \rangle \,.\!\equiv\!.\, x = u \wedge y = v$.

(i). $\vdash x \in \iota z \wedge y \in \iota z \supset x = y$.

(j). $\vdash x = y \ni (y \in x)$.

(k). $\vdash \breve{R} = R$.

(l). $\vdash \beta = x \ni (y)(y \in \alpha \supset x \in y) \wedge z \in \alpha \,.\!\supset\!.\, \beta \subset z$.

(m). $\vdash (z)(z \in \alpha \supset \beta \subset z) \supset \beta \subset x \ni (y)(y \in \alpha \supset x \in y)$.

(n). $\vdash \gamma = x \ni (\exists y)(y \in \alpha \wedge x \in y) \wedge z \in \alpha \,.\!\supset\!.\, z \subset \gamma$.

(o). $\vdash (z)(z \in \alpha \supset z \subset \gamma) \supset x \ni (\exists y)(y \in \alpha \wedge x \in y) \subset \gamma$.

(p). $\vdash \alpha \cap \beta = \Lambda \supset Nc(\alpha \cup \beta) = Nc(\alpha) + Nc(\beta)$.

(q). $\vdash 0 \neq \Lambda$.

(r). $\vdash 1 \neq \Lambda$.

(s). $\vdash n \in Nc \wedge n \neq \Lambda \wedge n \neq Nc(\mathrm{V}) \,.\!\supset\!.\, n + 1 \neq \Lambda$.

Ex. 2. Give suitable definitions for the following:

(a). The product of two cardinal numbers. (Hint: how many ordered pairs $\langle x, y \rangle$ are there with $x \in \alpha$ and $y \in \beta$?)

(b). The class of functions with a given domain and a given range.
(c). The relation "less than" between cardinal numbers.
(d). The class of equivalence relations.
(e). The class of transitive relations.
(f). The class of even integers.
(g). The relation between α and R which holds if and only if (α, R) is an ordered system.
(h). The class of sum ideals in the algebra of classes.

SECTION 6 THE PARADOXES

The restrictions on intuitive reasoning which are embodied in the languages constructed in section 3 were introduced in order to avoid the paradoxes into which our naive intuition leads us. The simplest of these paradoxes, namely Russell's, has already been discussed. We shall now describe some of the others.

One of the oldest is the so-called Epimenides paradox. Epimenides, the Cretan, said, "All Cretans always lie." It is supposed to be known that all other statements by Cretans are lies. Now if this statement is true, then the Cretan Epimenides spoke the truth for once, and Cretans do not always lie, so that the statement is really false. If, on the other hand, this statement is false, then *all* statements made by Cretans are false, so that Epimenides was speaking the truth, after all.

A simpler, but less picturesque, form of this paradox is

"The sentence quoted on this line is false."

This sentence is so framed as to refer to itself. That is, the phrase "the sentence quoted on this line" is a name of the whole sentence. Now if it is true, then it is false, and conversely.

It is not obvious how this can be formulated in any of the languages constructed here. What is needed is a sentence p of the form "$\sim q$", where "q" is also a name of p. In combinatory logic such a phenomenon seems possible if we adjoin a negation operator $\sim$. For if p is $W|B \sim |W|B\sim$, then we have

$$p = B \sim|W|B\sim |W|B\sim = \sim||W|B\sim |W|B\sim = \sim p.$$

The way out of the difficulty is to deny that "p" is a sentence, i.e. that p is a proposition. As we have mentioned before, in Curry's original system he postulated the properties of implication for all entities without restriction, so that the paradox did arise in his system. In such a language as L_3 we can formulate something similar to this paradox, using a method due to Gödel. We can construct a sentence p whose intuitive meaning is "$\sim p$ is provable in L_3". If L_3 is consistent, then the reasoning of this paradox shows that neither $\vdash p$ nor $\vdash \sim p$ in L_3. Thus the Epimenides paradox shows that if L_3 is consistent, then there is an undecidable sentence in L_3, so that L_3 is not categorical. The same argument holds for a large class of languages adequate for arithmetic.

The theory of types, as originally formulated by Russell, explains this paradox in another way. In his original version types were assigned to sentences as well as terms. A proposition about a sentence of one type is itself expressed by a sentence of the next higher type. Since every sentence has a definite type, the sentence " "p" is a false sentence" is a sentence of the next higher type than "p" and therefore "p" cannot be a name of the proposition here expressed. Hence a sentence of the form "I am now making a false statement of type n" is itself a false sentence of type $n + 1$, since no statement of type n is being asserted.

We have already discussed Russell's paradox. We only mention here that an essentially similar, but correct, argument is used by Cantor to prove that the class of subclasses of a given class α has more members than the class of all subclasses of α of the form "ιx", where $x \in \alpha$. Intuitively, the number of such subclasses is equal to the number of members of α. Propositions analogous to this can be proved in systems of the Zermelo type. In L_3 and similar systems a sentence expressing intuitively that R is the relation between x and y such that $xRy \equiv x \in y$ is not stratified, and does not define a relation by FIX.

Richard's paradox arises on considering the names of the integers in the English language. "The least integer not nameable in English in less than thirteen words" is itself the name of a definite integer, and is a name consisting of twelve words. In consistent languages which are adequate for arithmetic one can formulate sentences whose intuitive meaning is just this. This leads, however, not to contradiction but to a theorem of the Gödel type on undecidable sentences. In the systems originally proposed by Church and Curry the freedom of expression was so great that it allowed a paradox analogous to Richard's.

The paradox of Burali-Forti concerns ordinal numbers, and is beyond the scope of this book.

We observe that when a logical system has too weak restrictions on the means of expression or proof, there is always danger that the paradoxes of intuitive reasoning may creep in. On the other hand, the reasoning in each of these paradoxes contains a kernel of truth, and when performed within the frame of a suitable and precisely formulated language, leads to results of fundamental importance.

EXERCISES

Ex. 1. Prove in L_3 that $\vdash \sim(\exists x)(y)(yRx \equiv \sim(yRy))$. Relate this to Russell's paradox.

Ex. 2. Show that naive intuition leads to a paradoxical situation on consideration of the relation R which holds between the relations S and T when and only when S does not have the relation S to T. How is this paradox avoided in L_2 and in L_3? Show how this paradox could be formulated in combinatory logic if a negation operator is adjoined.

SECTION 7 THE AXIOM OF CHOICE

Zermelo, in 1904, proposed as an axiom a principle which has led to one of the most hotly contested controversies in the history of mathematics. Let β be a class of mutually disjoint nonempty classes. Zermelo postulates that there exists a class γ such that for each α in β, the class $\alpha \cap \gamma$ has exactly one member. This says, intuitively, that the class γ chooses one element out of each member α of the class β. We remark that Zermelo was, to some extent, anticipated by Peano in 1890 and Levi in 1902.

This principle had been used implicitly before Zermelo and has often been used without explicit mention since. Many objections to it have been raised by distinguished mathematicians and philosophers. The difficulty is that the existence of a class γ is postulated without any method for constructing such a class. There are many who deny that an object can meaningfully be said to exist unless a method is given for constructing it.

The underlying reasons for the controversy seem to be psychological rather than logical. Those who accept the axiom of choice are, in general, pragmatists or idealists (in the technical philosophical sense). The former accept it because it works, i.e. because we can draw so many useful and interesting consequences from it, and also because many of these consequences are obtainable without it. The idealists accept it because they are willing to conceive of something as existing even though they can't lay their hands on it or see it or otherwise ascertain just what it is. Sometimes the idealist approach smacks of theology and metaphysics.

Those who oppose the axiom of choice are usually empiricists or realists or members of some offshoot of these schools. They are like the man from Texas, who doesn't believe that something exists unless you put it in his hand. Obviously the intuitionists are strong opponents of the axiom of choice. Often these opponents profess not to understand the very meaning of existence without explicit construction.

Formerly the argument has often been voiced that there was danger of arriving at a contradiction by means of the axiom of choice. Since, however, Fraenkel has shown that if such languages as L_2, L_3, and L_z are consistent, then they remain consistent if either the axiom of choice or its negation is postulated, such arguments have lost their plausibility. It is to be observed that the axiom of choice is convincing at least to the extent that its opponents do not try to find counter-examples to results proved with its help. Nevertheless, some of its consequences are so amazing that they seem automatically to arouse distrust.

There are some who feel that Fraenkel's result is irrelevant. They say, "So what! It may very well happen that a given proposition doesn't lead to contradiction in spite of its being false. The axiom of choice is true or false in an absolute sense and this may be determined by examining the real world (or sometimes, the absolute laws of logic)." (This argument has some weight since, as is shown in Chapter IV, we may adjoin, without destroying consistency, to a language of a very general type a postulate which we can prove to be false by an argument outside the system. See also Gödel [XIII]116). As we have seen before, the very existence of controversies over the foundations of logic shows that our intuitions differ greatly from person to person, and make it extremely doubtful that there are any absolute laws of thought.

It may be useful to list here some of the most interesting propositions equivalent to the axiom of choice (see the comments which follow): (We use here L_3 as a shorthand for ordinary language.)

(1) There exists a function f such that

$$\vdash f(\alpha) \in \alpha \,.\equiv.\, (x) \,.x \in \alpha.$$

(2) If β is a class of non-empty classes, then there is a function f whose domain is β such that $\vdash f(\alpha) \in \alpha$ for all $\alpha \in \beta$.

(3) If α is a non-empty class, then there is a relation R such that

(a). $x \in \alpha \,.\supset_x.\, \sim(xRx)$.
(b). $xRy \wedge yRz \,:\supset_{x,y,z}:\, xRz$.
(c). $x, y \in \alpha \,.\supset_{x,y}.\, xRy \vee x = y \vee yRx$.
(d). $\gamma \subset \alpha \wedge \gamma \neq \Lambda \,.:\supset_\gamma:.\, (\exists x) \,:x \in \gamma \,.\wedge.$
$y \in \gamma \supset_y x = y \vee xRy$.

(4). If α and β are arbitrary classes, then either α is similar to a subclass of β or β is similar to a subclass of α. (p. 140, D3.5.20).

(5). If α is a class, and $\sim(Nc(\alpha) \in \text{Fin})$, and if β is the class of all ordered pairs $\langle x, y\rangle$ where $x \in \alpha \wedge y \in \alpha$, then β is similar to α.

(6). If R is a relation satisfying (3b) above, and if to every relation S satisfying (3b) and (3c) with $\alpha = D(S) \cup \mathrm{C\!I}(S)$ and also (e). $\vdash xSy \supset_{x,y} xRy$

there is an x such that $\vdash ySz \supset_{y,z} zSx$, then there is a u such that

$$\vdash u \in D(R) \cup \text{Cl}(R) . \wedge . uRx \supset_x xRu.$$

(7). Let β be a class of classes such that

$$\vdash x \in \beta .: \equiv_x :. y \subset x \wedge Nc(y) \in \text{Fin}. \supset_y . y \in \beta.$$

Then if γ is any class, one of whose subclasses belongs to β, there is a subclass δ of γ such that $\delta \in \beta$ and such that $\delta \subset x \subset \gamma . \wedge . x \in \beta : \supset_x : x = \delta$.

Proposition (1) means that there is a function f which to each class α assigns an object $f(\alpha)$ such that $f(\alpha) \in \alpha$ if and only if everything is in α. We may think of $f(\alpha)$ as a test case so that we can find out whether $\alpha = \text{V}$ simply by testing whether $f(\alpha)$ is in α. For example, some political observers, mostly Republicans, consider Mr. Truman such a test case when it comes to understanding political questions. Thus, according to these observers, if Truman can understand a given political question, then anyone can. The axiom of choice implies that we can always find a test case.

Proposition (2) says that given any class β of non-empty classes, then there is a function f which picks a member out of each member α of β.

Conditions 3a-3c mean that the members of α are ordered by the relation R in a series. This becomes clearer if we think of "xRy" as meaning "x precedes y". Condition (3d) signifies that every non-empty subclass γ of α has a first member in this ordering. If 3a-3d are satisfied then we usually say that the class α is *well ordered* by R. The axiom of choice implies that every class can be well ordered.

If α and β are classes and α is similar to a subclass of β, then we should say that $Nc(\alpha) \leq Nc(\beta)$. According to proposition (4), and therefore according to the axiom of choice, any two cardinal numbers are comparable in size. This can, of course, be proved without the axiom of choice in the case of finite cardinals.

If α is a finite class, then the number of ordered pairs of the form $\langle x, y \rangle$, where x and y are in α, is equal to n^2, where

$n = Nc(\alpha)$. If α is an arbitrary class and $\mu = Nc(\alpha)$, it is natural to define μ^2 as the number of these ordered pairs $\langle x, y\rangle$, where x and y are in α. The axiom of choice is equivalent to proposition (5), which states that if μ is not finite, then $\mu^2 = \mu$. If α is the class of positive integers, then the similarity can be proved by constructing the required correspondence explicitly. If R is the relation such that

$$kR\langle m, n\rangle \text{ if and only if } k = \frac{(m + n - 2)(m + n - 1)}{2} + m,$$

then R is a correspondence between α and the class of ordered pairs of positive integers; the pairs corresponding to 1, 2, 3, 4, 5, $\cdots$ are

$$\langle 1, 1\rangle, \quad \langle 1, 2\rangle, \quad \langle 2, 1\rangle, \quad \langle 1, 3\rangle, \quad \langle 2, 2\rangle, \quad \cdots,$$

respectively.

Proposition (6) is what we called Zorn's lemma on p. 21. (It was actually discovered independently by R. L. Moore and Kuratowski in 1923. Zorn rediscovered it in 1935, and shortly after Teichmüller did it again. The name "Zorn's lemma" was apparently coined by Bourbaki in ignorance of the literature, but became current because of the important applications which Bourbaki made of this result).

A class β of classes is said to be of *finite character* when a class x belongs to β if and only if every finite subclass of x belongs to β. By proposition (7), if β is of finite character, then every class γ, one of whose subclasses belongs to β, contains a maximal subclass δ belonging to β, i.e. no other subclass of γ contains δ and belongs to β.

In many applications, propositions (3), (6), and (7) are more directly useful than the axiom of choice itself.

Among the more astounding consequences of the axiom of choice is the theorem of Banach and Tarski (later refined by Robinson) that a sphere of radius 1 can be decomposed into 5 parts which can be put together again in such a way as to form two spheres of radius 1.

The axiom of choice is often used so casually that one often does not realize how much it pervades the most common reasoning processes in mathematical analysis. Whenever, in speaking of an infinite class α, we say, "Let $x_1, x_2, x_3, \cdots$ be a sequence of distinct members of α", we are using the axiom of choice in the form of proposition (2). For let β be the class of non-empty subclasses of α, and let f be a function whose existence is asserted in (2). Then $x_1, x_2, \cdots$ are obtained by the construction

$$x_1 = f(\alpha),\ x_2 = f(\alpha - \iota x_1),\ x_3 = f(\alpha - \iota x_1 - \iota x_2), \text{ etc.},$$

and the assumption that α is infinite implies that the process doesn't stop. The assumption that we can choose a sequence of distinct members of α is equivalent to the existence of such a function f.

It is for this reason, that the axiom of choice is so useful, and simplifies so much of mathematics, that opponents of this axiom, when not writing about the foundations of mathematics, often make free use of it.

It seems surprising, after all this controversy, that there has been no systematic study of the consequences of denying the axiom of choice, beyond some work on the consistency and independence of different forms of it. The only work in this direction, so far as we know, is a paper of Church [359]1. When one considers some of the complications in mathematical analysis if this axiom is not assumed, one may well expect consequences of its denial as paradoxical as the Banach-Tarski theorem. Denjoy [XIII] 144 gives some indications in this direction.

EXERCISES

Ex. 1. State the axiom of choice and the propositions (1)–(7) in the languages L_2 and L_3.

Ex. 2. Prove that (1) is equivalent to the axiom of choice.

Ex. 3. Prove the axiom of choice from Zorn's lemma. (Hint: consider the class Γ of all classes γ such that $\gamma \cap \alpha \neq \Lambda$ for all α in β. Let $\gamma_1 R \gamma_2$ mean that $\gamma_2 \subset \gamma_1$.)

Chapter IV

THE GENERAL SYNTAX OF LANGUAGE

SECTION 1 BASIC CONCEPTS SIMPLE LANGUAGES

We have, up to now, studied logic mostly as a deductive science, although we have indicated in II2 and III3 how one might approach logic by considering a language and its formal rules apart from any interpretation. As we have pointed out on p. 95, the second approach does not tell the whole story, but is a valuable tool just the same, which should be neither overestimated nor underestimated. In this chapter we shall attempt to describe some of the methods and results of this syntactical study of language. As we shall see, the deepest of these results could hardly have been obtained without syntactical methods.

A language consists of certain signs, and certain strings of these signs. Its syntax consists of rules for classifying and transforming these strings. The *alphabet* of a language consists of certain basic signs, usually in finite number. By a *string* we mean a finite sequence of signs. A string is exhibited by writing its signs in linear order from left to right. We shall denote strings by small Greek letters. If α and β are strings, then "$\alpha\beta$" shall denote the string consisting of the signs of β written in order after the signs of α. Two strings are said to be the same if they have the same length, and the same signs in corresponding places. We recall D3.3.1. The length of a string is, of course, the number of signs in it, repetitions counted. We shall denote the length of σ by "$l(\sigma)$".

The syntax of a language can be very simple or very complicated. We might define the English language as follows. The alphabet consists of the letters "*a*", "*b*", $\cdots$, "*z*", the usual punctuation marks, and a sign for the space between two consecutive words. A word is any string listed as a word in the Oxford English Dictionary. A sentence is any string which is formed according to the rules in some standard book of English grammar. We may alternatively construct the English language by taking as the alphabet the strings of letters already classified as words, together with the punctuation marks. Then a sentence is a string in this alphabet formed according to standard rules of sentence formation. We may then regard English sentences as "words" in this alphabet and the rules of formation of English sentences as rules of word formation (i.e. spelling) in this alphabet. This procedure of using the strings in one alphabet, or names of these strings, as letters in another alphabet, is very useful. As in all natural languages, including Esperanto, the rules of word and sentence formation in English are so complicated and full of irregularities and exceptions that it is almost impossible to get a general view of the structure of the language, and to make generally valid statements about the language. It is for this reason that mathematicians and logicians prefer to work with languages like L_3 with very simple and regular structures.

Among the languages suitable for mathematical purposes there are some whose rules are especially simple. The signs of the alphabet are classified as *letters* and *connectives*, and each connective has a certain *degree*, denoted by a positive integer. The main rule of word formation is:

W1. If α is a connective of degree n, and $\beta_1, \cdots, \beta_n$ are words, then $\alpha\beta_1 \cdots \beta_n$ is a word.

By formulating the rule so that a connective is written in front of the words which it connects we avoid the need of parentheses to indicate grouping.

Thus the language of II2 can be formulated as follows. The alphabet consists of the letters p and 1, the connective $\sim$ of degree 1, and the connective $\supset$ of degree 2. Besides rule W1 we have the rules:

A1. "p" is a word.
A2. If ν is a string in 1, then $p\nu$ is a word.

Thus "$\sim p1$" and "$\supset pp111$" are words. Then we have some rules classifying certain words as "true". For example, "$\supset p \supset p1p$" is a true word (A12^{IV}). A slightly different but equivalent and syntactically more convenient formulation is obtained by taking as the alphabet the connectives $\sim$ and $\supset$ as above, and the letters $p, p_1, p_{11}, \cdots$, where "p_ν" is a name of the string $p\nu$, and ν is a string in 1. Then the rules are W1 above and

W2. A string consisting of a single letter is a word.

As we shall see, the syntax of languages governed by rules W1 and W2 is especially simple.

We can formulate a part of arithmetic as a language in this sense. Our alphabet consists of the letter 1, the connective $-$ of degree 1, and the connective $+$ of degree 2. We take rules W1 and W2 as rules of word formation. Thus "$-+1+11$" is a word, and denotes what we usually would mean by "-3". We can classify a word as true if the integer denoted by it is zero. E.g. "$+1-1$" would be true. With this intuitive idea as a basis we can easily set up a system of rules of inference, and thus obtain a suitable language for arithmetic.

Before we go on to a discussion of the rules for sentence formation, and the classification of words or sentences as true, we wish to give a general theorem on word formation. We shall say that a language L is *simple* if its alphabet consists only of letters and connectives, and if W1 and W2 are the rules of word formation in L. We define the *rank* of a string as follows:

D1. (a). If σ is a letter, then $\rho(\sigma) = -1$.
(b). If σ is a connective of degree n, then $\rho(\sigma) = n - 1$.
(c). If σ is $\sigma_1\sigma_2$, and $l(\sigma_2) = 1$, then $\rho(\sigma) = \rho(\sigma_1) + \rho(\sigma_2)$.
(d). If σ is the null string, then $\rho(\sigma) = 0$.

Thus if σ is "$a_1a_2 \cdots a_k$", and "a_i" is a letter or a connective for each $i (i = 1, \cdots, k)$, then $\rho(\sigma) = \rho(a_1) + \rho(a_2) + \cdots + \rho(a_k)$. We recall D3.3.5 and D3.3.6.

THEOREM 1. *If L is a simple language, and σ is a string in L, then σ is a word in L if and only if*

(1). $\rho(\sigma) = -1$.
(2). *If* σ_1 *is any head of* σ, *and* $\sigma_1 \neq \sigma$, *then* $\rho(\sigma_1) \geq 0$.

We divide the proof of this theorem into four parts.

T2. *Under the hypothesis of* T1, *if* σ *is a word in L, then* (1) *and* (2) *hold.*

Proof. If $l(\sigma) = 1$, then the lemma is true by W2. If T2 is true for strings of length less than k, ($k > 1$), and if $l(\sigma) = k$, then, by W1, σ is $\alpha\beta_1 \cdots \beta_n$ where α is a connective of degree n and $\beta_1, \cdots, \beta_n$ are words. For convenience we denote α by "β_0". Let $l(\beta_i) = l_i$, $0 \leq i \leq n$. Now

$$\begin{aligned}\rho(\sigma) &= \rho(\beta_0) + \rho(\beta_1) + \cdots + \rho(\beta_n)\\ &= n - 1 + (-1) + \cdots + (-1)\\ &= -1,\end{aligned}$$

so that (1) holds. If σ_1 is a head of σ, and $\sigma_1 \neq \sigma$, then there is a unique integer j, $0 \leq j \leq n$, such that

$$l_0 + \cdots + l_j \leq l(\sigma_1) < l_0 + \cdots + l_{j+1}.$$

Then there is a string σ_2, possibly null, such that σ_1 is $\beta_0 \cdots \beta_j\sigma_2$. If σ_2 is not null, then it is a head of β_{j+1} and different from β_{j+1}. Hence, in any case, $\rho(\sigma_2) \geq 0$, by T2 applied to β_{j+1}. Therefore

$$\begin{aligned}\rho(\sigma_1) &= \rho(\beta_0) + \cdots + \rho(\beta_j) + \rho(\sigma_2)\\ &\geq n - 1 + (-1) + \cdots + (-1) + 0\\ &= n - 1 - j\\ &\geq 0,\end{aligned}$$

which proves (2).

T3. *If* σ *is a string in L satisfying* (1) *and* τ *is not null, then* $\sigma\tau$ *does not satisfy* (2).

For σ is a head of $\sigma\tau$ and $\rho(\sigma) = -1$, so that (2) does not hold for $\sigma\tau$.

T4. *Under the hypotheses of* T1, *if* σ *is a string satisfying* (1) *and* (2), *and* $\sigma = \sigma_1\sigma_2$, σ_2 *not null, then there is a unique string* τ *such that* τ *satisfies* (1) *and* (2) *and is a head of* σ_2 .

Proof. There cannot be more than one such string τ, by T3. Now

$$\rho(\sigma_2) = \rho(\sigma) - \rho(\sigma_1) = -1 - \rho(\sigma_1) < 0.$$

Let τ be the head of σ_2 of minimum length with negative rank. If τ_1 is any head of τ different from τ, then $\rho(\tau_1) \geq 0$. Let "a_i" be the last sign of τ, and let $\tau = \tau_2 a_i$. Then

$$0 > \rho(\tau) = \rho(\tau_2) + \rho(a_i) \geq \rho(a_i).$$

Hence "a_i" must be a letter, and $\rho(a_i) = -1$, and therefore $0 \leq \rho(\tau_2) < 1$, so that $\rho(\tau_2) = 0$, $\rho(\tau) = -1$.

T5. *Under the hypotheses of* T1, *if* σ *is a string satisfying* (1) *and* (2), *then* σ *is a word.*

Proof. If $l(\sigma) = 1$, the lemma is true by D1a. Suppose that T5 is true for all strings of length less than k, $k > 1$, and that $l(\sigma) = k$. If "a_1" is the first sign of σ, then $\rho(a_1) \geq 0$, by (2). Hence "a_1" is a connective of degree $n = 1 + \rho(a_1)$. Let σ be "$a_1 a_2 \cdots a_k$". There is a unique string β_1 such that β_1 is a head of "$a_2 \cdots a_k$" and satisfies (1) and (2). Hence β_1 is a word. Suppose the words $\beta_1 , \cdots , \beta_j$ have already been defined, $1 \leq j < n$, such that $a_1\beta_1 \cdots \beta_j$ is a head of σ, so that σ is $a_1\beta_1 \cdots \beta_j\sigma_j$. Since $\rho(a_1\beta_1 \cdots \beta_j) = n - 1 - j \geq 0$, σ_j is not null. Then there is a unique head β_{j+1} of σ_j satisfying (1) and (2). By T5 for strings of length less than k, β_{j+1} is a word. Thus we can find words $\beta_1 , \cdots , \beta_n$ such that $a_1\beta_1 \cdots \beta_n$ is a head of σ. This string is a word by W1, and consequently satisfies (1) and (2), by T2. Hence σ is $a_1\beta_1 \cdots \beta_n$ by T3.

The criterion of spelling embodied in T1 explains why the syntax of simple languages is simple.

An examination of the rules of sentence formation and the rules of classification of sentences as true in the languages hitherto considered and a comparison with the rules of word formation in these languages reveals such a striking analogy that we are led to seek a theory which unifies these rules with respect to their common features. This may be done by means of Post's concept of production.

EXERCISES

Ex. 1. Formulate the object language of a Boolean algebra with the operations $\cap$ and N ($N\alpha = \alpha'$) as a simple language. State the postulates in the new notation without parentheses.

Ex. 2. Set up a system of postulates for the elementary arithmetic of integers, positive, negative, and 0, using the idea on p. 154.

Ex. 3. Prove that if L is a simple language, then a string σ in L is a word if and only if $\rho(\sigma) = -1$ and the rank of every tail of σ is negative.

SECTION 2 PRODUCTION, CANONICAL LANGUAGES, EXTENSION, AND DEFINITION

Let us examine the language of II2 from a slightly different point of view. The alphabet consists of the letters $p, p_1, p_{11}, \cdots$, the connective $\sim$ of degree 1, and the connective $\supset$ of degree 2. The rules of word formation are W1 and W2. The rule of sentence formation is simply that all words are sentences and conversely. The rules of truth are stated by means of the symbol "$\vdash$" which indicates that the string which follows is to be classified as true:

A1″. If $\vdash\alpha$, then α is a sentence.
A4″. If α, β, γ are sentences, then $\vdash \supset\supset \alpha \supset \beta\gamma \supset\supset \alpha\beta \supset \alpha\gamma$.
A5″. If α, β are sentences, then $\vdash \supset \alpha \supset \beta\alpha$.

A6″. If α, β are sentences, then $\vdash \supset \supset \sim\alpha \sim\beta \supset \beta\alpha$.
A7″. If $\vdash\alpha$ and $\vdash \supset \alpha\beta$, then $\vdash\beta$.

The whole system can be formulated in a more suggestive way if we adjoin to the alphabet the signs $\mathfrak{W}$ and $\vdash$. Here "$\mathfrak{W}\sigma$" is to be interpreted as meaning that σ is a word. Since we identify words and sentences in this language, we do not need to formulate explicitly any rules for sentence formation. The language now appears in the following form:

P1″. $\vdash\alpha \rightarrow \mathfrak{W}\alpha$.
P2″. $\mathfrak{W}\alpha, \mathfrak{W}\beta \rightarrow \mathfrak{W} \supset \alpha\beta$.
P3″. $\mathfrak{W}\alpha \rightarrow \mathfrak{W} \sim\alpha$.
P4″. $\mathfrak{W}\alpha, \mathfrak{W}\beta, \mathfrak{W}\gamma \rightarrow \vdash \supset \supset \alpha \supset \beta\gamma \supset \supset \alpha\beta \supset \alpha\gamma$.
P5″. $\mathfrak{W}\alpha, \mathfrak{W}\beta \rightarrow \vdash \supset \alpha \supset \beta\alpha$.
P6″. $\mathfrak{W}\alpha, \mathfrak{W}\beta \rightarrow \vdash \supset \supset \sim\alpha \sim\beta \supset \beta\alpha$.
P7″. $\vdash\alpha, \vdash \supset \alpha\beta \rightarrow \vdash\beta$.
P0″. $\mathfrak{W}p, \mathfrak{W}p_1, \mathfrak{W}p_{11}, \cdots$.

We may think of P0″ as an initial supply of strings, and rules P1″–P7″ as instructions for producing new strings from strings which we already have. The rules are understood in the sense that if α, β, γ, etc. are arbitrary strings such that the strings appearing to the left of the arrow in any rule are in our stock, then we may add the string to the right of the arrow to that stock.

We call P1″–P7″ *productions* and the strings in P0″ the *axioms*, and an axiom or a string obtainable from the axioms by repeated applications of the productions is called a *theorem*. (Note that P1″ might have been omitted.)

In this formulation we had an infinite alphabet and infinitely many axioms. We can, as indicated before, reformulate the language so that there are only a finite number of axioms and a finite alphabet. We take the alphabet to consist of the signs p, 1, $\supset$, $\sim$, $\mathfrak{W}$, $\vdash$, and $\mathfrak{L}$. "$\mathfrak{L}$" may be thought of as denoting the class of letters. The productions are P1″–P7″ as above and

P8″. $\mathfrak{L}\alpha \rightarrow \mathfrak{L}\alpha 1$,
P9″. $\mathfrak{L}\alpha \rightarrow \mathfrak{W}\alpha$,

and the only axiom is

P0′. $\mathfrak{L}p$.

It is not obvious, at first sight, how one would formulate the first system of combinatory logic given in III3 in the present manner because there are infinitely many premises in E5 (p. 112). We can, however, approach the system in a different way. If a and b are formulae in A, K, and a finite number of variables and x is a variable which does not occur in either a or b, then E5 is used only where the inference from $ax = bx$ to $a = b$ would be allowed. This idea leads us to the desired formulation.

Our alphabet consists of the signs A, K, $|$, x, a, $\mathfrak{M}$, $\mathfrak{L}$, $\mathfrak{A}$, $\mathfrak{F}$ and $=$. The productions are:

P1. $\mathfrak{L}\alpha \rightarrow \mathfrak{L}\alpha a$.
P2. $\mathfrak{L}\alpha \rightarrow \mathfrak{W}\alpha$.
P3. $\mathfrak{W}\alpha, \mathfrak{W}\beta \rightarrow \mathfrak{W}|\alpha\beta$.
P4. $\mathfrak{W}\alpha \rightarrow \alpha = \alpha$.
P5. $\alpha = \beta \rightarrow \beta = \alpha$.
P6. $\alpha = \beta, \beta = \gamma \rightarrow \alpha = \gamma$.
P7. $\alpha = \beta, \gamma = \delta \rightarrow |\alpha\gamma = |\beta\delta$.
P8. $\mathfrak{F}\alpha\beta, \mathfrak{L}\beta, \mathfrak{A}\alpha \rightarrow \mathfrak{F}\alpha a\beta a$.
P9. $\mathfrak{F}\alpha\beta, \mathfrak{W}\beta, \mathfrak{A}\alpha \rightarrow \mathfrak{F}\alpha a\beta$.
P10. $\mathfrak{F}\alpha\beta, \mathfrak{F}\alpha\gamma, \mathfrak{W}\beta, \mathfrak{W}\gamma, \mathfrak{A}\alpha \rightarrow \mathfrak{F}\alpha|\beta\gamma$.
P11. $\mathfrak{F}\alpha\beta, \mathfrak{F}\alpha\gamma, \mathfrak{W}\beta, \mathfrak{W}\gamma, |\beta x\alpha a = |\gamma x\alpha a, \mathfrak{A}\alpha \rightarrow \beta = \gamma$.
P12. $\mathfrak{W}\alpha, \mathfrak{W}\beta, \mathfrak{W}\gamma \rightarrow |||A\alpha\beta\gamma = ||\alpha\gamma|\beta\gamma$.
P13. $\mathfrak{W}\alpha, \mathfrak{W}\beta \rightarrow ||K\alpha\beta = \alpha$.
P14. $\mathfrak{A}\alpha \rightarrow \mathfrak{A}\alpha a$.

The axioms are:

P0. $\mathfrak{L}xa, \mathfrak{F}axa, \mathfrak{W}A, \mathfrak{W}K, \mathfrak{F}aA, \mathfrak{F}aK, \mathfrak{A}a$.

The interpretation is that the "letters" are "xa", "xaa", $\cdots$, (P1), and that A, K, and all letters are words. If α is a string in a, then a word β is of type α (i.e. $\mathfrak{F}\alpha\beta$) if and only if it is built up from A, K, and letters involving at most the same number of a's as in α. P11, which corresponds to E5, says that if β and γ are such words then we may infer $\beta = \gamma$ from $|\beta x\alpha a = |\gamma x\alpha a$.

But $x\alpha a$ is a letter which does not occur in either β or γ. We have used the sign a to distinguish between the letters of the language instead of "1" as before, since in the development of the system on the basis of P0–14, we should like to be able to use "1" as in III3.

We could have eliminated $\mathfrak{W}$ and taken "$\mathfrak{W}\alpha$" as an abbreviation for "$\alpha = \alpha$". This makes possible certain economies in the system.

Another way of looking at these languages is to consider the productions as instructions to a moron, who can scan a string and recognize it as being of a certain form, for producing theorems starting from the axioms. The happy moron can, by merely following the instructions, generate as many theorems as he pleases, and never feels the need for any intelligence in the process. He might just as well be a robot or a machine. Now a mathematician proceeds in a somewhat different way. He is not satisfied with this mechanical method of producing all theorems. He takes, rather, a string which has some interest for him, and by applying his ingenuity tries to produce it from the axioms or to show that it cannot be so produced. If the string is a theorem, then the moron will produce it sooner or later, but on the way he will produce a lot of irrelevant matter which has nothing to do with the problem. If the string is not a theorem, then the moron will never find it out by means of his purely mechanical method of generating all the theorems, for he will never be sure that he cannot produce it by working longer.

The *decision problem* for the language is that of determining whether a given string is a theorem or not. For the language of P0′, P1″–P9″ the solution is essentially given by T1.2.3 and T4.1.1. For as we see from the statements of P1″–P9″, every theorem is of the form $\vdash\alpha$, $\mathfrak{W}\alpha$, or $\mathfrak{L}\alpha$. By P0′ and P8″ $\mathfrak{L}\alpha$ is a theorem if and only if α consists of "p" alone or "p" followed by a string of 1's. Theorem T4.1.1 takes care of all theorems of the form $\mathfrak{W}\alpha$. Theorem 1.2.3 together with the definition of "$\vdash$" given on p. 38 tells us how to decide whether $\vdash\alpha$ is a theorem.

Note that this decision process can also be carried out by the happy moron. It can also be set up in the form of a set of productions and axioms, so that he could apply it and always arrive at the decision. We need only to adjoin new signs F (for "false") and T (for "true") and give rules for producing the string $T\alpha$ whenever α is a theorem and $F\alpha$ whenever α is not a theorem. The criteria just outlined show us what instructions must be given to the moron in order that he may carry out this decision process. Thus all intelligence and ingenuity is eliminated from this language. There is no blemish on the moron's happiness, for he can solve any problem stated within the language. A rule for producing $F\alpha$ in cases where α is a string in the original alphabet which is not a theorem is called by Carnap [VIII]36 a rule of *refutation*. In the present language we can give a complete set of rules of refutation.

The situation is different for P0–P14. According to a theorem of Church, if we adjoin the signs T and F as before, then it is impossible to add a set of productions and axioms to P0–P14, in such a way that $T\alpha$ is a theorem if and only if α is a theorem in the original system, and $F\alpha$ is a theorem if and only if α is not a theorem in the original system. This is already impossible if one restricts oneself to strings of the form $\beta = \gamma$, where β and γ are words formed from "A", "K", and "|" alone. Thus there is no mechanical process for solving all problems stated in this language. Intelligence and ingenuity cannot be dispensed with in this or any other language adequate for arithmetic. For any given string α, one may perhaps, by exercising ingenuity, be able to decide whether it is a theorem or not, but there is no general procedure for this purpose which could be applied by a moron or a machine.

Church's theorem has sometimes been interpreted pessimistically as a proof that there are absolutely unsolvable problems. It is indeed a fundamental discovery on the limitations of human ingenuity that no machine can be invented which will solve all problems stated in the simple language of P0–P14. But optimistically speaking, it is a rigorous proof that brains are indispensable, and that should be comforting to anyone who hopes that he can solve problems which a moron cannot.

The languages considered in this section illustrate the general class introduced by Post. We consider a language with a finite alphabet $\mathfrak{A}$ consisting of signs $a_1, \cdots, a_m$. By a *production* we mean an operation whereby the strings

$$
(1) \qquad \begin{array}{l}
\sigma_{11}\alpha_{i_{11}}\sigma_{12}\alpha_{i_{12}} \cdots \sigma_{1n_1}, \\
\sigma_{21}\alpha_{i_{21}}\sigma_{22}\alpha_{i_{22}} \cdots \sigma_{2n_2}, \\
\cdot \quad \cdot \quad \cdot \quad \cdot \quad \cdot \quad \cdot \quad \cdot \quad \cdot \quad \cdot \quad \cdot \\
\sigma_{k1}\alpha_{i_{k1}}\sigma_{k2}\alpha_{i_{k2}} \cdots \sigma_{kn_k}
\end{array}
$$

produce the string

$$
(2) \qquad \sigma_1\alpha_{j_1}\sigma_2\alpha_{j_2} \cdots \sigma_r .
$$

Here the σ's are given strings in $\mathfrak{A}$, some of them possibly being null, and the numbers $i_{11}, \cdots, i_{k,nk-1}, j_1, \cdots, j_{r-1}$ are chosen from the integers $1, \cdots, M$, for some M. The rule means that if $\alpha_1, \cdots, \alpha_M$ are arbitrary strings, even possibly null, then the strings in (1) yield the string (2). The strings (1) are called the *data* of the production, and (2) is called the *product*. We make the restriction that each α which occurs in the product must occur in at least one datum, and that each datum and the product contain at least one α. We further assume that the product is not null, no matter how the α's are chosen. This amounts to assuming that at least one of $\sigma_1, \cdots, \sigma_r$ is not null.

A *canonical* language is a language L with a finite alphabet, a finite number of productions, and a finite number of axioms. Every precise language which has ever been constructed, except for those containing rules of the type of $F\Omega$ on p. 142, can be formulated as a canonical language. Of course, the canonical forms of such languages as L_2 and L_3 are rather complex, but this is to be expected since these languages are themselves quite complicated. The point is that by abstracting from the special features of a particular language and studying canonical languages in general we can obtain results which apply to all languages which can be put in canonical form, and this includes practically all languages which are useful in mathematics and logic. We shall consider only canonical languages from now on.

With this tool at our disposal we can explain simply and

elegantly many important mathematical and logical notions. One might also expect that many concepts in linguistics which have resisted all attempts up to now at clear and general formulation may now be treated with the same lucidity and rigor which has made mathematics a model for other sciences. The wealth of detail and the manifold irregularities of natural languages have often obfuscated the simple general principles underlying linguistic phenomena.

We wish to emphasize that canonical languages seem to be the most general languages in which the rules of word and sentence formation and the rules of inference are constructive, i.e. in which one can determine in a finite number of steps whether a given chain of strings constitutes a valid proof. Church's theorem may be considered as a proof that a certain problem cannot be solved by constructive methods. If, as some believe, these are the only methods available to man, then that theorem brings out a profound limitation to what man can accomplish. As we have pointed out, this limitation is essentially that he cannot eliminate the necessity of using his intelligence, no matter how cleverly he tries.

The α's occurring in the statement of a production will be called its *string variables*. A string τ will be called an *immediate consequence* of the strings $\tau_1, \cdots, \tau_k$ by a given production P if strings can be substituted for the string variables in P in such a way that the data become $\tau_1, \cdots, \tau_k$ and the product is τ. A sequence of strings $\tau_1, \cdots, \tau_k$ is called a *proof* by $P_1, \cdots, P_r$ from the hypotheses H, where H is a class of strings, if each τ_i is either in H or an axiom or an immediate consequence of some preceding τ's by one of the productions $P_1, \cdots, P_r$. A string τ is a *consequence* of H by $P_1, \cdots, P_r$ if there is a proof by $P_1, \cdots, P_r$ from the hypotheses H in which τ is the last string. A string τ is a *theorem* if it is a consequence of the axioms.

It should be noted that a moron will prove any theorem if he lives and works long enough, and he can check any proposed sequence of strings to determine whether it is a proof, but unless the decision problem for the language in question is solvable, he will, in general, be unable to *discover* a proof for a given string, even if it is a theorem. That requires intelligence directed toward a goal; mere patience does not suffice.

The language L' is called an *extension* of L if (1) the alphabet $\mathfrak{A}$ of L is contained in the alphabet $\mathfrak{A}'$ of L', and (2) each theorem in L is a theorem in L'. The simplest case is where $\mathfrak{A}$ is contained in $\mathfrak{A}'$, each production of L is a production of L', and each axiom of L is an axiom of L'. In that case L' will be called a *direct* extension of L. If L and L' are extensions of each other, then they will be said to be *equivalent*.

The notion of *variable* can now be explained. A variable over L is simply a sign in an extension of L which is not in the original alphabet. This is a generalization of the concept of variable (or indeterminate) as it is used in modern algebra. The letter x used in defining the concept "formula in x" in III2 and III4 is employed as a variable in the present sense.

In the languages L_2 and L_3 and some similar languages which we have studied the notion of "variable" was modified by means of a technical device in order to have infinitely many variables at our disposal and still have a finite alphabet. It is not easy to see how the concept could be redefined generally so as to take care of such a situation.

An extension L' of a language L is said to be *conservative* if a string τ in the alphabet of L is a theorem in L' if and only if it is a theorem in L. Thus a conservative extension of L is one in which the class of theorems expressible in the alphabet of L is left unchanged.

A class $\mathfrak{C}$ of strings in the alphabet $\mathfrak{A}$ of the language L is said to be *canonical* if there is a conservative extension L' of L and a string σ such that α is in $\mathfrak{C}$ if and only if α is a string in $\mathfrak{A}$ and $\sigma\alpha$ is a theorem in L'. We may consider a canonical class as one whose members may be enumerated by a constructive process. For if we construct a machine which generates the theorems of L' and prints α on a special tape every time a theorem of the form "$\sigma\alpha$" is produced, then the machine will list the members of $\mathfrak{C}$ step by step, and each one will appear on the list sooner or later. In particular, the class of theorems in a canonical language is canonical, for we may take σ to be the null string and L' to be L itself.

The class of all strings in the alphabet $\mathfrak{A}$ of L is also canonical. We may adjoin to $\mathfrak{A}$ two new signs, say "$\mathfrak{S}$" and "$\mathfrak{T}$". To each production P in L, with the data $\pi_1, \cdots, \pi_k$, and product π, we take as the corresponding production in the extension

$$\mathfrak{T}\pi_1, \cdots, \mathfrak{T}\pi_k \rightarrow \mathfrak{T}\pi.$$

We adjoin also the productions

$$\mathfrak{T}a_i\alpha \rightarrow a_i\alpha, \qquad i = 1, \cdots, n,$$
$$\mathfrak{S}\alpha, \mathfrak{S}\beta \rightarrow \mathfrak{S}\alpha\beta,$$

and take as axioms $\mathfrak{S}a_i$, $i = 1, \cdots, n$, and $\mathfrak{T}\sigma_i$, $i = 1, \cdots, m$, where a_i, $i = 1, \cdots, n$, are the signs of $\mathfrak{A}$, and σ_i, $i = 1, \cdots, m$, are the axioms of L. Then we have a conservative extension of L in which $\mathfrak{S}\alpha$ is a theorem if and only if α is a string in $\mathfrak{A}$.

A moron can make a list of the members of a canonical class $\mathfrak{C}$ by mechanically applying the productions of L' and picking out the theorems beginning with a certain fixed string σ. He will, however, be unable to decide, in general, whether a given string α will appear on his list if he works long enough. A class $\mathfrak{C}$ for which this decision problem is solvable by a moron will be called *solvable*. More precisely, the class $\mathfrak{C}$ will be said to be solvable if there is a conservative extension L' of L and there are two distinct strings σ_1 and σ_2 such that for any string α in the alphabet of L the string $\sigma_1\alpha$ is a theorem in L' if and only if α is in $\mathfrak{C}$, and $\sigma_2\alpha$ is a theorem in L' if and only if α is not in $\mathfrak{C}$. The decision problem for a language is solvable constructively if and only if the class of theorems is solvable.

The following language N is adequate for a part of arithmetic. The alphabet consists of the signs 1 and =. The only production is

N1. $\alpha = \beta \rightarrow \alpha 1 = \beta 1$,

and the only axiom is N0."$1 = 1$". The decision problem is solvable. For we may adjoin new letters F (for "false") and S (for "string") to the alphabet, and the productions

N2. $\alpha = \alpha, \beta = \beta \rightarrow F\alpha = \alpha\beta$,
N3. $\alpha = \alpha, \gamma = \gamma \rightarrow F\alpha\gamma = \alpha$,

N4. $\alpha = \alpha \rightarrow F\alpha$,
N5. $\alpha = \alpha \rightarrow S\alpha$,
N6. $S\alpha, S\beta \rightarrow S\alpha\beta$,
N7. $S\alpha \rightarrow F = \alpha$,
N8. $S\alpha \rightarrow F\alpha =$,
N9. $S\alpha, S\beta, S\gamma \rightarrow F\alpha = \beta = \gamma$,

and the axioms

N10. S, and $S =$.

These productions show that if α is a string in 1, then $\alpha = \alpha$ is a theorem and that no other strings are theorems. More explicitly: N2 and N3 show that no equation with more 1's on one side than on the other is a theorem; N4 shows that a string of 1's alone is no theorem; N7–N9 show that only equations can be theorems. A string τ in N is a theorem if and only if it is a theorem in the new language. It is not a theorem in N if and only if Fτ is a theorem in the new language.

We can now explain the process of definition. The simplest type of definition is that in which a new sign is taken as an abbreviation for a given string σ in the alphabet of the language. This amounts to adjoining the new sign, say "s", to the alphabet, and the productions

Ps(1). $\alpha s\beta \rightarrow \alpha\sigma\beta$
Ps(2). $\alpha\sigma\beta \rightarrow \alpha s\beta$

to the list of productions in L. In other words we extend L in such a way that in every context "s" and σ are interchangeable. This extension is conservative, and to each string in the extension there corresponds a string in L such that each is a consequence of the other.

More often a new sign is defined in context. That is, certain strings containing the new sign are taken as abbreviations of strings in L. For this to constitute a definition in the usual sense of the word, the extension of L thus constructed must be conservative, i.e. no new theorems in the old alphabet are provable. Also, there must be a condition of translatability, i.e. that at least to every meaningful string in the extension there corresponds a string in L such that each is a consequence of the other. In order to formulate this condition in a general manner, we must suppose that certain classes of strings are distinguished as meaningful.

Thus in the above language N we may define a *sentence* as a string of the form $\alpha = \beta$ where α and β are numerals, and a numeral is a string of 1's. Formally, this may be done by adjoining the letters $\mathfrak{N}$ and $\mathfrak{S}$ and the productions:

N11. $\alpha = \alpha \rightarrow \mathfrak{N}\alpha$.
N12. $\mathfrak{N}\alpha \rightarrow \alpha = \alpha$.
N13. $\mathfrak{N}\alpha, \mathfrak{N}\beta \rightarrow \mathfrak{S}\alpha = \beta$.

It is convenient to adjoin also the productions

N14. $\alpha = \beta \rightarrow \beta = \alpha$.
N15. $\alpha = \beta, \beta = \gamma \rightarrow \alpha = \gamma$.
N16. $\alpha = \beta, \gamma = \delta \rightarrow \alpha\gamma = \beta\delta$.

We shall use "N" from now on to denote the language of N0–N16.

We may then define addition by adjoining the signs (,), and +, and the production

N17. $\mathfrak{N}\alpha, \mathfrak{N}\beta \rightarrow (\alpha + \beta) = \alpha\beta$.

The language N' thus obtained is a conservative extension of N since N14–N16 are trivially valid in N, for the only equations which are theorems in N are of the form "$\alpha = \alpha$". To every string γ' in N' such that $\mathfrak{S}\gamma'$ is a theorem there corresponds a string γ in N such that $\mathfrak{S}\gamma$ is also a theorem (in N') and each of γ and γ' is a consequence of the other (in N'). This assures the translatability of every *sentence* in N' into an equivalent sentence in N. We do not need to be able to translate such strings as "+((1)=".

A more complicated type of definition is definition by *recursion*, sometimes called definition by induction. Here the new sign is defined in some simple contexts, and then rules are given for translating an occurrence of it in a more complicated context in terms of one or more occurrences in simpler contexts. Thus we may define multiplication in N' as follows:

N18. $\mathfrak{N}\alpha \rightarrow (\alpha \times 1) = \alpha$.
N19. $\mathfrak{N}\alpha, \mathfrak{N}\beta \rightarrow (\alpha \times \beta 1) = ((\alpha \times \beta) + \alpha)$.

This amounts to adjoining the sign $\times$ and the productions N18 and N19. Thus we do not equate $(\alpha \times \beta)$ directly to a string in which "$\times$" does not occur, but we give productions whereby any sentence in the new language N'' may be translated into an equivalent sentence in N'.

For example the sentence

$$\text{"}((111 \times 11) + 1) = (1111 + 11)\text{"}$$

in N'' is equivalent to the sentence

$$\text{"}(111111 + 1) = (1111 + 11)\text{"}$$

in N' (i.e. each is a consequence of the other), and in fact, both are equivalent to the false sentence

$$\text{"}1111111 = 111111\text{"}$$

in N.

Still more complicated is the type of definition where several new signs are defined simultaneously. An example of this is D3.3.21, where "term" and "sentence" are so defined.

We are thus led to the following definition of "*definition*". If L' is an extension of L, and $\mathfrak{S}$ is a canonical class of strings in L', and ω is a sign in the alphabet $\mathfrak{A}'$ of L' but not in the alphabet $\mathfrak{A}$ of L (i.e. ω is a variable in L' over L), then ω is *defined* in L' relative to L and $\mathfrak{S}$ if and only if L' is a conservative extension of L, and to every string γ' in the class $\mathfrak{S}$ and in the alphabet $\mathfrak{A} \cup \{\omega\}$, there corresponds a string γ, in L and in the class $\mathfrak{S}$, such that each is a consequence of the other in L'. Thus the sign ω is defined, essentially, if the definition doesn't change the class of theorems, and if it can be eliminated from any sentence.

In particular, a function g on the class of positive integers is *recursive* if there is an extension N_1 of N and a sign "f" defined in N_1 relative to N and $\mathfrak{S}$ such that

$$f(\alpha) = g(\alpha)$$

is a theorem for each α such that $\mathfrak{N}\alpha$ is a theorem. We may define the notion of a recursive function of several variables in a similar manner.

The above discussion shows how we can analyze rigorously a number of concepts for the whole family of canonical languages, where most previous treatments are either vague or refer to some special language. In the next section we shall derive some non-trivial properties common to all canonical languages.

EXERCISES

Ex. 1. Formulate the postulates for Boolean algebra in Chapter I, section 2, as a canonical language.

Ex. 2. Formulate that language using a rule of substitution as on pp. 40–41.

Ex. 3. Adjoin to the alphabet of the language on pp. 40–41 the signs 0 and F, and adjoin the following axioms and productions:

A11b. $\mathfrak{S}0$.

A12b. $F0$.

R18b. $\mathfrak{S}A \rightarrow (A \supset 0) = (\sim A)$.

R19b. $\mathfrak{S}A \rightarrow (0 \supset A) = (\sim 0)$.

R20b. $\mathfrak{S}A \rightarrow (A \supset (\sim 0)) = (\sim 0)$.

R21b. $\mathfrak{S}A \rightarrow ((\sim 0) \supset A) = A$.

R22b. $FA, A = B \rightarrow FB$.

R23b. $VA, \mathfrak{S}B, FS(0|A|B) \rightarrow FB$.

R24b. $VA, \mathfrak{S}B, F((\sim 0)|A|B) \rightarrow FB$.

Prove that if $\mathfrak{S}A$ is a theorem, then $\vdash A$ is not a theorem if and only if FA is a theorem. Hence the class of true sentences, i.e. the strings A such that $\vdash A$, is solvable.

Ex. 4. Prove that the class of words, i.e. the strings α such that $\mathfrak{W}\alpha$ is a theorem, in the language on p. 159 is solvable.

Ex. 5. Prove that the language L_2' (Chapter III, section 3) is a conservative extension of L_2.

Ex. 6. Discuss the analogy between the notion of a variable as explained above, and that of a transcendental extension of a field, and the analogy between the notion of a definition and that of an algebraic extension of a field. (For readers acquainted with algebra.)

Ex. 7. Give extensions of N' in which the following are defined:

(a). α^{β}.

(b). $\alpha!$.

(c). $\alpha < \beta$.

(d). $\alpha - \beta$ (if $\beta < \alpha$).

(e). α divides β.

(f). the greatest common divisor of α and β.

(g). the number of divisors of α.

(h). α is a prime number.

(i). the α-th prime number.

Ex. 8. Show that the following classes of integers are canonical:

(a). the even integers

(b). the perfect squares

(c). the non-squares

(d). the prime numbers

SECTION 3 NORMAL LANGUAGES THEOREMS OF POST AND GÖDEL

A very special kind of canonical language is one in which the productions all have the simple form

(1) $$\sigma_1\alpha \rightarrow \alpha\sigma_2 \qquad (\sigma_1, \sigma_2 \text{ given strings})$$

and there is only one axiom. A production of the form (1) is called *normal*, and a language, with one axiom, whose productions are all normal, is called a *normal language*. Post proved the remarkable

THEOREM 1. *Every canonical language has a conservative normal extension.*

As a result, every canonical class of strings can be generated in a normal language, and a class is solvable if and only if it is *binormal*, i.e. both it and its complement can be generated in a normal language. This makes it possible for us to focus our attention on normal languages without any loss of generality.

The proof, though completely elementary, is rather long, and cannot be given here. We shall, however, make free use of this theorem in our discussions.

We remark, also, that it is sufficient to consider languages with only two signs. For if "a_1", $\cdots$, "a_n" are the signs of a language L, then we may construct a new language in the signs a and b, and make the strings *aba*, *abba*, $\cdots$, $ab\cdots ba$ correspond to the signs of our original language. This is essentially how we avoided infinite alphabets. This shows that a canonical class of strings in 1 can be obtained as the class of all strings in 1 which are theorems in a certain normal language with "1" in its alphabet. For there is a language L, whose alphabet contains "1", and a string σ in L such that $\mathfrak{C}$ is the class of all strings α in 1 such that $\sigma\alpha$ is a theorem in L.

We adjoin two new signs, say "$\mathfrak{N}$" and "d", to the alphabet of L. If

$$\pi_1, \cdots, \pi_k \rightarrow \pi$$

is a production in L, then we replace it by

$$d\pi_1 d, \cdots, d\pi_k d \rightarrow d\pi d.$$

If π is an axiom of L, then we replace it by $d\pi d$. This process we call *sealing* the language L with the sign d. It is very useful in constructing extensions of languages, since it hermetically seals off processes in L from the new processes which we wish to introduce.

We take the following new productions:

$$\mathfrak{N}\alpha \rightarrow \mathfrak{N}1\alpha,$$
$$d\sigma 1\alpha d, \mathfrak{N}1\alpha \rightarrow 1\alpha,$$

and the following new axiom: $\mathfrak{N}1$. Then every theorem in the new language L' is either of the form "$d\pi d$", where π is a theorem of L, or "$\mathfrak{N}\alpha$", where α is a string in 1, or is a member of the class $\mathfrak{C}$, and furthermore, every member of the class $\mathfrak{C}$ is a theorem. Thus $\mathfrak{C}$ is the class of all theorems of L' which are strings in 1. By Post's theorem, there is a conservative normal extension L'' of L', and consequently $\mathfrak{C}$ is the class of all theorems of L'' which are strings in 1.

Let "1", "a_1", $\cdots$, "a_n" be the signs in the alphabet of L''. We introduce a new sign b, and replace "a_i" by "$b1\cdots 1b$", with i 1's, $(i = 1, \cdots, n)$. If we perform this replacement in all the productions and the one axiom of L'', we obtain a normal language L''' with the two-sign alphabet $\{1, b\}$ such that $\mathfrak{C}$ is precisely the class of theorems of L''' which are strings in 1. We have thus proved

THEOREM 2. *$\mathfrak{C}$ is a canonical class of strings in 1 if and only if there is a normal language L with the alphabet $\{1, b\}$ such that a string α in 1 is a theorem in L when and only when α is in $\mathfrak{C}$.*

If L is a normal language, and $\sigma_i\alpha \rightarrow \alpha\tau_i$ $(i = 1, \cdots, n)$ are its productions, and π is its axiom, then the string $\pi a d \sigma_1 c \tau_1 d \cdots d\sigma_r c\tau_r d$, where "$a$", "$c$", and "$d$" are fixed signs not in the alphabet of L, will be called its *basis*. Thus we have a means of representing each normal language with a given alphabet $\mathfrak{A}$ by means of a single string. The string in $\mathfrak{A}$ preceding "a" is the sole axiom of the corresponding language, a string in $\mathfrak{A}$ flanked by "d" and "c" in that order is the head of the datum of a production of the language, and the string between "c" and the next "d" is the tail of the corresponding product. A basis of a normal language with the alphabet $\mathfrak{A}$ will simply be called a *basis* over $\mathfrak{A}$.

The class of all bases over a given alphabet $\mathfrak{A}$ is canonical. For let $\mathfrak{A}$ be $\{b_1, \cdots, b_n\}$ and let "A", "B", "S", "a", "c", and "d" be signs not in $\mathfrak{A}$. We take the following productions

$$
\begin{aligned}
&S\alpha \rightarrow A\alpha,\\
&A\alpha,\ S\beta \rightarrow S\alpha\beta,\\
&S\alpha,\ A\beta,\ S\gamma \rightarrow B\alpha a d\beta c\gamma d,\\
&B\alpha,\ A\beta,\ S\gamma \rightarrow B\alpha\beta c\gamma d,
\end{aligned}
$$

and the axioms: A, Sb_i, $(i = 1, \cdots, n)$. Then $A\alpha$ is a theorem if and only if α is a string in $\mathfrak{A}$, $S\alpha$ is a theorem if and only if α

is a non-null string in $\mathfrak{A}$, $B\alpha$ is a theorem if and only if α is a basis over $\mathfrak{A}$. This language we shall call $\mathfrak{B}_1$ and its alphabet $\mathfrak{A}_1$. Let "p" be a sign not in $\mathfrak{A}_1$. By a *sentence* we shall mean a string of the form "$\alpha p \beta$" where α is a basis over $\mathfrak{A}$ and β is a string in $\mathfrak{A}$. We may think of this sentence as expressing the proposition that β is a theorem in the language whose basis is α. We shall say that the sentence is *true* if the corresponding proposition is true, and *false* if the corresponding proposition is false.

T3. *The class of true sentences is canonical.*

Proof. Let "$\vdash$" be a sign not in $\mathfrak{A}_1$. We adjoin the following productions to $\mathfrak{B}_1$:

$B\pi\alpha\beta \rightarrow \vdash\pi\alpha\beta p\pi$,

$B\alpha d\sigma c\tau d\beta,\ A\sigma,\ S\tau,\ A\gamma,\ \vdash\alpha d\sigma c\tau d\beta p\sigma\gamma \rightarrow$
$\vdash\alpha d\sigma c\tau d\beta p\gamma\tau$.

Then a string α is a true sentence if and only if $\vdash\alpha$ is a theorem in the language $\mathfrak{B}_2$ just constructed. The alphabet $\mathfrak{A}_2$ of $\mathfrak{B}_2$ consists of the signs $\vdash$, p, and those of $\mathfrak{A}_1$.

The above remarks mean that given the alphabet $\mathfrak{A}$, our happy moron can write down step by step all bases over $\mathfrak{A}$ and produce the corresponding true sentences one by one. This is to be expected, since these acts can be performed purely mechanically. We should expect, however, that there is no mechanical procedure for deciding whether a given sentence is true or false, for non-trivial parts of mathematics can be formulated as canonical, and therefore as normal, languages, and it is reasonable to suppose that non-trivial problems require brains. This hunch can be stated and proved rigorously:

THEOREM 4. *The class of false sentences is not canonical, if $\mathfrak{A}$ contains at least two signs.*

Proof. If the class of false sentences is canonical, then there is a conservative extension $\mathfrak{B}_2'$ and a string σ in the alphabet of $\mathfrak{B}_2'$ such that α is a false sentence if and only if α is a string in $\mathfrak{A}_2$ and $\sigma\alpha$ is a theorem in $\mathfrak{B}_2'$. By sealing $\mathfrak{B}_2'$ with a new sign and by using a device like that of p. 171, we can construct a language $\mathfrak{B}_3$ such that α is a false sentence if and only if α is a string in $\mathfrak{A}_2$ and a theorem of $\mathfrak{B}_3$. Also, we may suppose, without loss of generality, that "1" and "b" are signs in $\mathfrak{A}$.

The idea is to set up a one-to-one correspondence R between strings in a, b, c, d, and 1, and positive integers n, which may be thought of as a "name" relation, i.e. the proposition that α has the relation R to n (denoted by "αRn") can be interpreted as meaning that n is a name of the string α. Let $\mathfrak{C}$ be the class of integers n such that βRn, where β is a basis over $\mathfrak{A}$ and n is not a theorem in the language corresponding to β. Then βpn will be a false sentence whenever βRn and n is in $\mathfrak{C}$. But if the class of false sentences is canonical, then the class $\mathfrak{C}$ is also canonical. By theorem 2, there is a normal language L with the alphabet $\{1, b\}$ such that $\mathfrak{C}$ is precisely the class of theorems of L which are strings in 1. Let β_0 be the basis of L. Consequently $\beta_0 pn$ is a true sentence if and only if n is in $\mathfrak{C}$. That is to say, if $g(\beta)$ denotes the integer n such that βRn, then for any basis β over $\{1, b\}$, $\beta_0 pg(\beta)$ is a true sentence if and only if $\beta pg(\beta)$ is a false sentence. In particular, $\beta_0 pg(\beta_0)$ is a true sentence if and only if it is a false sentence, which is a contradiction. It remains only to carry out this plan of proof in detail.

Let "e", "l", "A_1", "A_2", "$\mathfrak{N}$", "R", "$=$", "(", ")", "$+$", "$\times$", and "$\mathfrak{C}$" be signs not in $\mathfrak{A}_3$, the alphabet of $\mathfrak{B}_3$. We construct a new language $\mathfrak{B}_4$ as follows. Its alphabet $\mathfrak{A}_4$ shall consist of $\mathfrak{A}_3$ together with the above mentioned new signs. We seal $\mathfrak{B}_3$ with the sign e, as on p. 171, so that α is a theorem in $\mathfrak{B}_3$ if and only if $e\alpha e$ is a theorem in $\mathfrak{B}_4$. We take also the axioms

$$A_1 1,\ A_1 a,\ A_1 b,\ A_1 c,\ A_1 d,\ A_2 b_i\ , \qquad (i = 1, \cdots, n),$$
$$A_2 A,\ A_2 B,\ A_2 a,\ A_2 c,\ A_2 d,\ A_2 \vdash,\ A_2 p,\ A_2 S,$$

and the productions

$$A_1\alpha,\ A_1\beta \rightarrow A_1\alpha\beta,$$
$$A_2\alpha,\ A_2\beta \rightarrow A_2\alpha\beta.$$

Thus $A_1\alpha$ is a theorem if and only if α is a string in $\{1, a, b, c, d\}$ and $A_2\alpha$ is a theorem if and only if α is a string in $\mathfrak{A}_2$.

We take the axiom

$$1 = 1$$

and the productions N11, N12, N14–N19 of the last section, which provides us with as much arithmetic as we need for the present proof.

The relation between a string in $\{1, a, b, c, d\}$ and its length is characterized by the following axioms and production:

$$1l1,\ al1,\ bl1,\ cl1,\ dl1;$$
$$\alpha l\beta,\ \gamma l\delta,\ A_1\alpha,\ A_1\gamma,\ \mathfrak{N}\beta,\ \mathfrak{N}\delta \rightarrow \alpha\gamma l\beta\delta.$$

It is now easy to define the desired name-relation R. We wish to use "1" as the name of itself, and "2", "3", "4", and "5" as the names of "a", "b", "c", and "d", respectively, and if α is any string in $\{1, a, b, c, d\}$, then its name shall be the integer represented in the ordinary decimal notation by the string in $\{1, 2, 3, 4, 5\}$ obtained by replacing in α the signs 1, a, b, c, and d by their names. Thus the name of the string $abc1db$ shall be the integer 234153, i.e. in unabbreviated form,

$$(2 \times (10)^5) + (3 \times (10)^4) + (4 \times (10)^3) + (1 \times (10)^2) + (5 \times (10)) + 3.$$

This relation may be defined within our language by the axioms

$$1R1,\ aR11,\ bR111,\ cR1111,\ dR11111,$$

and the productions

$$A_1\alpha,\ A_1\beta,\ \alpha R\nu,\ \beta R\mu,\ \beta l1 \rightarrow \alpha\beta R((\nu \times T) + \mu),$$
$$A_1\alpha,\ \alpha R\mu,\ \mu = \nu \rightarrow \alpha R\nu.$$

(Here "T" is an abbreviation of the string 1111111111, which denotes the integer 10.)

The above discussion shows that to each string α in $\{1, a, b, c, d\}$ there corresponds a unique string ν in 1 such that $\alpha R\nu$ is a theorem, and that to different α's correspond different ν's.

We are now ready to construct the class $\mathfrak{C}$ which packs the wallop in this proof. We adjoin the production

$$e\beta p\nu e,\ \beta R\nu \rightarrow \mathfrak{C}\nu.$$

This completes the definition of the language $\mathfrak{B}_4$.

Now $\mathfrak{C}\nu$ is a theorem in $\mathfrak{B}_4$ if and only if there is a β such that $\beta R\nu$ and $e\beta p\nu e$ are theorems in $\mathfrak{B}_4$. But $e\beta p\nu e$ is a theorem if and only if β is a basis over $\mathfrak{A}$ and ν is not a theorem in the language whose basis is β. Furthermore $\beta R\nu$ is a theorem if and only if β is a string in $\{1, a, b, c, d\}$ and ν is its uniquely determined "name". Hence $\mathfrak{C}\nu$ is a theorem in $\mathfrak{B}_4$ if and only if ν is the name of a basis β over $\{1, b\}$ and is not a theorem in the language corresponding to β.

The class of ν's such that $\mathfrak{C}\nu$ is a theorem in $\mathfrak{B}_4$ is canonical, and consequently, by theorem 2, there is a normal language L with the alphabet $\{1, b\}$ such that $\mathfrak{C}$ is precisely the class of theorems in L which are strings in 1. Let β_0 be the basis of L. Then $\vdash\beta_0 p\nu$ is a theorem in $\mathfrak{B}_2$ if and only if $\mathfrak{C}\nu$ is a theorem in $\mathfrak{B}_4$. Thus if $g(\beta)$ is the unique ν such that $\beta R\nu$ is a theorem in $\mathfrak{B}_4$, then for any basis β over $\{1, b\}$ we have that $\vdash\beta_0 pg(\beta)$ is a theorem in $\mathfrak{B}_2$ if and only if $\mathfrak{C}g(\beta)$ is a theorem in $\mathfrak{B}_4$, which is true if and only if $\vdash\beta pg(\beta)$ is not a theorem in $\mathfrak{B}_2$. In particular $\vdash\beta_0 pg(\beta_0)$ is a theorem in $\mathfrak{B}_2$ if and only if it is not a theorem in $\mathfrak{B}_2$, which is a contradiction.

COROLLARY 4a. *If $\mathfrak{K}$ is any canonical class of false sentences, then there is a false sentence not contained in $\mathfrak{K}$.*

We remark that the proof of the theorem shows how to construct explicitly such a false sentence.

COROLLARY 4b. Let $\mathfrak{B}$ be any canonical language adequate for the expression of $\mathfrak{B}_2$ and for the expression of the notions of "true" and "false" sentence. Suppose that $\mathfrak{B}$ is consistent in the sense that no sentence of $\mathfrak{B}_2$ can be proved in $\mathfrak{B}$ to be both true and false. Then there is a false sentence whose falsity is not provable in $\mathfrak{B}$.

This corollary is formulated vaguely, but it would take too long a digression to state it in more precise terms. It will suffice to remark that L_1, L_2, L_3, and L_z are adequate in the above sense, and can be put in canonical form. (See the appendix.) It follows that if these languages are consistent, then they are not categorical, and furthermore, that their decision problems are unsolvable by constructive methods. For L_1 this is an important theorem of Church, which was originally proved by a somewhat different method.

Proof. Let f be a function such that for each α in language $\mathfrak{B}_2$ $f(\alpha)$ is a string in $\mathfrak{B}$ which expresses the proposition that α is a false sentence of $\mathfrak{B}_2$. Seal $\mathfrak{B}$ by a new sign "e" and adjoin a new sign, say "F", to the alphabet, and the production

$$ef(\alpha)e \rightarrow F\alpha.$$

Since $\mathfrak{B}$ is adequate for $\mathfrak{B}_2$ and the notions of "true" and "false" sentence, then every true sentence in $\mathfrak{B}_2$ is provably true in $\mathfrak{B}$. Since $\mathfrak{B}$ is consistent, no true sentence in $\mathfrak{B}_2$ is provably false in $\mathfrak{B}$. Then $F\alpha$ is a theorem in the language just constructed if and only if α is a false sentence in $\mathfrak{B}_2$ whose falsity is provable in $\mathfrak{B}$. Clearly the class of all such α's is canonical, and therefore cannot contain all false sentences.

If $\mathfrak{B}$ contains a notion of negation, then for a false sentence α such that $f(\alpha)$ is not a theorem in $\mathfrak{B}$ neither $f(\alpha)$ nor its negation can be theorems in $\mathfrak{B}$. Note that the negation of $f(\alpha)$ is a statement in the language $\mathfrak{B}$ which we, observing $\mathfrak{B}$ from the outside, can prove to be true, but which cannot be proved within $\mathfrak{B}$. Thus any consistent language $\mathfrak{B}$ satisfying the above conditions will contain undecidable propositions, and there will be true propositions expressible but not provable in $\mathfrak{B}$.

Thus the decision problem for the language $\mathfrak{B}_2$ is not solvable in any canonical language adequate for the statement of that problem. The problem of inventing a machine for solving the decision problem of $\mathfrak{B}_2$ is absolutely unsolvable. The language $\mathfrak{B}_2$ is a specific one with an alphabet of $n + 8$ signs, 6 productions, and $n + 1$ axioms, where n is the number of signs in $\mathfrak{A}$. For the sake of definiteness we set down the primitive frame of $\mathfrak{B}_2$ for the special case $n = 2$.

Alphabet: 1, a, b, c, d, A, B, S, $\vdash$, p.
Axioms: A, $S1$, Sb.
Productions: $S\alpha \rightarrow A\alpha$.
$A\alpha, S\beta \rightarrow S\alpha\beta$.

$$S\alpha,\ A\beta,\ S\gamma \rightarrow B\alpha a d\beta c\gamma d.$$
$$B\alpha,\ A\beta,\ S\gamma \rightarrow B\alpha\beta c\gamma d.$$
$$B\alpha a\beta \rightarrow \vdash \alpha a\beta p\alpha.$$
$$A\gamma,\ A\sigma,\ S\tau,\ B\alpha d\sigma c\tau d\beta,\ \vdash \alpha d\sigma c\tau d\beta p\sigma\gamma \rightarrow \vdash \alpha d\sigma c\tau d\beta p\gamma\tau.$$

We can "arithmetize" $\mathfrak{B}_2$ by taking as the alphabet the digits 1, 2, 3, · · · , 9, 0, corresponding in order to the above signs, and making this replacement throughout the primitive frame of $\mathfrak{B}_2$, thus:

Alphabet: 1, 2, 3, 4, 5, 6, 7, 8, 9, 0.
Axioms: 6, 81, 83.
Productions: $8\alpha \rightarrow 6\alpha.$
$6\alpha,\ 8\beta \rightarrow 8\alpha\beta.$
$8\alpha,\ 6\beta,\ 8\gamma \rightarrow 7\alpha 25\beta 4\gamma 5.$
$7\alpha,\ 6\beta,\ 8\gamma \rightarrow 7\alpha\beta 4\gamma 5.$
$7\alpha 2\beta \rightarrow 9\alpha 2\beta 0\alpha.$
$6\gamma,\ 6\sigma,\ 8\tau,\ 7\alpha 5\sigma 4\tau 5\beta,\ 9\alpha 5\sigma 4\tau 5\beta 0\sigma\gamma \rightarrow 9\alpha 5\sigma 4\tau 5\beta 0\gamma\tau.$

The productions represent simple arithmetic operations, which could be defined in elementary arithmetic. For example, the first production corresponds to the function f defined by

$$f(n) = \begin{cases} n - (2 \times 10^k), & \text{if there is a } k \text{ such that } 8 \times 10^k \leq n < 9 \times 10^k, \\ 6 & \text{otherwise.} \end{cases}$$

Similarly, to each of the other productions there corresponds a certain elementary arithmetic operation which, if the integers operated upon have certain forms, yields a certain result, and otherwise yields the number 6. Then the decision problem of $\mathfrak{B}_2$ becomes the problem of determining for any given integer n whether it can be obtained from the integers 6, 81, and 83 by a finite number of applications of six elementary arithmetic operations. The problem can also be transformed into one of the following type: for a certain elementary arithmetic function f, to determine for which integers n the equation $f(x) = n$ has an integral solution. (See Skolem [XI]26. Thus any canonical language which is consistent and adequate for arithmetic will contain undecidable sentences expressing elementary arithmetic propositions. There will even be such sentences which we can prove to be true by an argument in the syntax language.

If we like, we may take an alphabet of two signs $\{1, b\}$ and replace the signs of the above alphabet by $b1b$, $b11b$, $\cdots$, $b1111111111b$, respectively. We thus obtain a very simple language in two signs whose decision problem is unsolvable by any machine.

The proof of theorem 4 has a very simple meaning. We may think of a basis as a statement, namely the joint statement of all the theorems in the corresponding language, and the integer μ, such that $\beta R \mu$ is a theorem, as a name of that statement. The sentence $\beta p \nu$ may be interpreted as an expression of the proposition that the statement β asserts that the statement whose name is ν is true. The class $\mathfrak{C}$ is the class of names of statements which do not assert their own truth. If the class of false statements were canonical, then there would be a statement β_0 asserting the truth of all statements and only those statements which do not assert their own truth. The contradiction is simply that if β_0 asserts its own truth, then its name is not in $\mathfrak{C}$, so that β_0 does not assert its own truth; and if β_0 does not assert its own truth, then its name is in $\mathfrak{C}$, so that β_0 does assert its own truth. Thus β_0 is exactly the kind of statement which is made in the Epimenides paradox. The theorem says that a canonical language which gave an exhaustive definition of falsity and which had machinery for expressing names would give rise to this paradox.

These results, anticipated by Post and Finsler, and published with rigorous proofs for the first time by Gödel, show that no consistent canonical language can be adequate for the expression of mathematics and at the same time be capable of proving all true propositions in elementary number theory.

The undecidable proposition which was constructed by Gödel is one whose intuitive meaning is that $\mathfrak{B}$ is consistent. Thus Gödel's proof shows that no consistent canonical language can be adequate for arithmetic and also adequate for the proof of its own consistency. This holds, in particular, for such languages as L_2, L_3, and L_z.

This situation has given rise to a great deal of pessimism, since it seems to indicate that the consistency of arithmetic cannot be proved by constructive methods. One might hope, however, to build a language which is not constructively given as a whole, but such that there is a constructive method for determining whether a given chain of sentences is a proof. For a consistency proof all that would be needed would be to show that any constructively given part of the language is consistent. The methods used in this proof would be inexpressible in this part, but would be expressible in a certain larger part of the language. Whether such a program could be realized is a question for the future. As the matter stands today we must close this book sitting squarely and painfully on the horns of the dilemma: the only known adequate languages are incomplete and not provably consistent by the modes of reasoning which they express, and the only safe (i.e. provably consistent) ones are inadequate.

EXERCISES

Ex. 1. Show that if C_1 and C_2 are canonical classes of strings in 1, then so are $C_1 \cup C_2$ and $C_1 \cap C_2$.

Ex. 2. Show that the solvable classes of strings in 1 form a Boolean algebra.

Ex. 3. (a). Show that if f is a recursive function of one variable and if $f(n_1) \leq f(n_2)$ whenever $n_1 \leq n_2$, then the set of values taken on by f is solvable.

(b). If f is any recursive function, then its range is canonical.

Ex. 4. (a). Prove that the class U of bases of normal languages in a given alphabet $\{1, b_1, \cdots, b_n\}$ in which "1" is a theorem is canonical.

(b). If π is the basis of a normal language L in the alphabet $\{1, b_1, \cdots, b_n\}$ and α_0 is a string in 1, $\alpha_0 \neq 1$, let "2" be a sign not in the given alphabet. In each of the productions and axioms of L replace "1" by "21" and "b_i" by "$2b_i$", $i = 1, \cdots, n$. Adjoin the following productions, where k is the length of α_0 :

$$2121 \cdots 2\alpha \rightarrow \alpha 2 \quad (k \text{ 2's in datum}),$$

$$12\alpha \rightarrow \alpha 1.$$

Prove that "1" is a theorem in this new language if and only if α_0 is a theorem in L.

(c). Prove that the class of normal languages in $\{1, a_1, \cdots, a_n\}$ in which "1" is not a theorem is not canonical.

APPENDIX 1 CANONICAL FORMS OF L_1, L_2', AND L_2

L_1

Alphabet: $o, 1, a, f, (,), \supset, \sim, I, F, S, \mathfrak{S}, =, |, \vdash, \neq, 0, \emptyset, Z, U.$

Axioms:

A1. $Zo.$
A2. $U1.$
A3. $o = o.$
A4. $1 = 1.$
A5. $a = a.$
A6. $f = f.$
A7. $(= (.$
A8. $) =).$
A9. $\supset = \supset.$
A10. $\sim = \sim.$

Productions:

P1. $Z\alpha \rightarrow Z\alpha o.$
P2. $U\alpha \rightarrow U\alpha 1.$
P3. $Z\alpha \rightarrow I a\alpha.$
P4. $U\alpha,\ Z\beta \rightarrow F\alpha f\alpha\beta.$
P5. $F1f\alpha,\ I\beta \rightarrow \mathfrak{S}f\alpha\beta.$
P6. $U\alpha,\ F\alpha 1 f\beta,\ I\gamma \rightarrow F\alpha f\beta\gamma.$
P7. $\mathfrak{S}\alpha \rightarrow \mathfrak{S}\sim\alpha.$
P8. $\mathfrak{S}\alpha,\ \mathfrak{S}\beta \rightarrow \mathfrak{S}(\alpha \supset \beta).$
P9. $\mathfrak{S}\alpha,\ I\beta \rightarrow \mathfrak{S}(\beta)\alpha.$
P10. $\vdash\alpha,\ \vdash(\alpha \supset \beta) \rightarrow \vdash\beta.$
P11. $\vdash\alpha,\ I\beta \rightarrow \vdash(\beta)\alpha.$
P12. $\mathfrak{S}\alpha,\ \mathfrak{S}\beta,\ \mathfrak{S}\gamma \rightarrow \vdash((\alpha \supset (\beta \supset \gamma)) \supset ((\alpha \supset \beta) \supset (\alpha \supset \gamma))).$
P13. $\mathfrak{S}\alpha,\ \mathfrak{S}\beta \rightarrow \vdash(\alpha \supset (\beta \supset \alpha)).$
P14. $\mathfrak{S}\alpha,\ \mathfrak{S}\beta \rightarrow \vdash((\sim\alpha \supset \sim\beta) \supset (\beta \supset \alpha)).$
P15. $\alpha = \beta \rightarrow \beta = \alpha.$
P16. $\alpha = \beta,\ \beta = \gamma \rightarrow \alpha = \gamma.$

P17. $\alpha = \beta, \gamma = \delta \rightarrow \alpha\gamma = \beta\delta$.
P18. $\alpha \neq \beta \rightarrow \beta \neq \alpha$.
P19. $\alpha = \beta, \beta \neq \gamma \rightarrow \alpha \neq \gamma$.
P20. $\alpha = \beta, \gamma \neq \delta \rightarrow \alpha\gamma \neq \beta\delta$.
P21. $\alpha \neq \beta, \gamma = \delta \rightarrow \alpha\gamma \neq \beta\delta$.
P22. $Z\alpha \rightarrow a \neq a\alpha$.
P23. $I\alpha \rightarrow \alpha 0 \alpha$.
P24. $I\alpha, I\beta, \alpha \neq \beta \rightarrow \alpha \emptyset \beta$.
P25. $U\alpha, Z\beta, I\gamma \rightarrow \gamma \emptyset f \alpha\beta$.
P26. $I\alpha, F\beta f\gamma \rightarrow \alpha 0 f \gamma\alpha$.
P27. $I\alpha, I\beta, F\gamma f\delta, \alpha\emptyset f\delta, \alpha \neq \beta \rightarrow \alpha\emptyset f\delta\beta$.
P28. $I\alpha, I\beta, F\gamma f\delta, \alpha 0 f\delta \rightarrow \alpha 0 f \delta\beta$.
P29. $I\alpha, \mathfrak{S}\beta, \alpha 0 \beta \rightarrow \alpha 0 \sim\beta$.
P30. $I\alpha, \mathfrak{S}\beta, \alpha\emptyset\beta \rightarrow \alpha\emptyset\sim\beta$.
P31. $I\alpha, \mathfrak{S}\beta, \mathfrak{S}\gamma, \alpha 0 \beta \rightarrow \alpha 0(\beta \supset \gamma)$.
P32. $I\alpha, \mathfrak{S}\beta, \mathfrak{S}\gamma, \alpha 0 \gamma \rightarrow \alpha 0(\beta \supset \gamma)$.
P33. $I\alpha, \mathfrak{S}\beta, \mathfrak{S}\gamma, \alpha\emptyset\beta, \alpha\emptyset\gamma \rightarrow \alpha\emptyset(\beta \supset \gamma)$.
P34. $I\alpha, \mathfrak{S}\beta \rightarrow \alpha\emptyset(\alpha)\beta$.
P35. $I\alpha, I\beta, \mathfrak{S}\gamma, \alpha 0 \gamma, \alpha \neq \beta \rightarrow \alpha 0(\beta)\gamma$.
P36. $I\alpha, I\beta, \mathfrak{S}\gamma, \alpha\emptyset\gamma \rightarrow \alpha\emptyset(\beta)\gamma$.
P37. $I\alpha, I\beta, \beta\emptyset\gamma \rightarrow S(\alpha|\beta|\gamma) = \gamma$.
P38. $I\alpha, I\beta \rightarrow S(\alpha|\beta|\beta) = \alpha$.
P39. $I\alpha, I\beta, I\gamma, F\delta f\zeta \rightarrow S(\alpha|\beta|f\zeta\gamma) = S(\alpha|\beta|f\zeta)S(\alpha|\beta|\gamma)$.
P40. $I\alpha, I\beta, \mathfrak{S}\gamma \rightarrow S(\alpha|\beta|\sim\gamma) = \sim S(\alpha|\beta|\gamma)$.
P41. $I\alpha, I\beta, \mathfrak{S}\gamma, \mathfrak{S}\delta \rightarrow S(\alpha|\beta|(\gamma \supset \delta)) = (S(\alpha|\beta|\gamma) \supset S(\alpha|\beta|\delta))$.
P42. $I\alpha, I\beta, I\gamma, \mathfrak{S}\delta, \alpha \neq \gamma, \beta \neq \gamma \rightarrow S(\alpha|\beta|(\gamma)\delta) = (\gamma)S(\alpha|\beta|\delta)$.
P43. $\alpha = \beta, \vdash\alpha \rightarrow \vdash\beta$.
P44. $I\alpha, \mathfrak{S}\beta, \mathfrak{S}\gamma, \alpha\emptyset\beta \rightarrow \vdash((\alpha)(\beta \supset \gamma) \supset (\beta \supset (\alpha)\gamma))$.
P45. $I\alpha, I\beta, \mathfrak{S}\gamma \rightarrow \vdash((\beta)\gamma \supset S(\alpha|\beta|\gamma))$.

Interpretation: "$I\alpha$" means "α is an individual".
"$F\alpha f\beta$" means "$f\beta$ is a function of degree α".
"$\mathfrak{S}\alpha$" means "α is a sentence".

"$S(\alpha|\beta|\gamma)$" means "the result of substituting α for β in γ."
"$\alpha 0 \beta$" means "α occurs free in β".
"$\alpha \emptyset \beta$" means "α does not occur free in β".
"$Z\alpha$" means "α is a string in o".
"$U\alpha$" means "α is a string in 1".

L_2'

Alphabet: (,), $\in$, $\ni$, $\sim$, $\supset$, a, b, v, V, $\mathfrak{S}$, T, A, V, $=$, 0, $\neq$, $\emptyset$, S, $|$, $\equiv$, $\exists$, $\wedge$, $\vdash$.

Axioms:
A1. Aa.
A2. Bb.
A3. (= (.
A4.) =).
A5. $\in\ =\ \in$.
A6. $\ni\ =\ \ni$.
A7. $\sim\ =\ \sim$.
A8. $\supset\ =\ \supset$.
A9. $a = a$.
A10. $b = b$.
A11. $v = v$.

Productions:
P1. $A\alpha \rightarrow A\alpha a$.
P2. $B\alpha \rightarrow B\alpha b$.
P3. $A\alpha, B\beta \rightarrow V\beta v\beta\alpha$.
P4. $V\alpha v\beta \rightarrow T\alpha v\beta$.
P5. $T\alpha v\beta, T\alpha b v\gamma, B\alpha \rightarrow \mathfrak{S}(v\beta \in v\gamma)$.
P6. $\mathfrak{S}\alpha, V\beta v\gamma, B\beta \rightarrow T\beta v\gamma \ni \alpha$.
P7. $\mathfrak{S}\alpha \rightarrow \mathfrak{S}{\sim}\alpha$.
P8. $\mathfrak{S}\alpha, \mathfrak{S}\beta \rightarrow \mathfrak{S}(\alpha \supset \beta)$.
P9. $\mathfrak{S}\alpha, V\beta v\gamma, B\beta \rightarrow \mathfrak{S}(v\gamma)\alpha$.
P10. As in L_1.
P11. $\vdash\alpha, V\beta v\gamma, B\beta \rightarrow\ \vdash(v\gamma)\alpha$.
P12–P21. As in L_1.
P22. $A\alpha \rightarrow a \neq a\alpha$.
P23. $B\alpha \rightarrow b \neq b\alpha$.
P24. $A\alpha, A\beta, B\gamma, B\delta, \alpha \neq \beta \rightarrow \alpha\gamma \neq \beta\delta$.

P25. $A\alpha, A\beta, B\gamma, B\delta, \gamma \neq \delta \rightarrow \alpha\gamma \neq \beta\delta$.

P26. $B\alpha, B\beta, V\alpha v\gamma, T\beta v\delta \ni \zeta \rightarrow v\gamma \neq v\delta \ni \zeta$.

P27. $B\alpha, V\alpha v\beta \rightarrow v\beta 0 v\beta$.

P28. $B\alpha, B\beta, V\alpha v\gamma, V\beta v\delta, v\gamma \neq v\delta \rightarrow v\gamma\emptyset v\delta$.

P29. $B\alpha, B\delta, T\alpha v\beta, T\alpha b v\gamma, V\delta v\zeta, v\zeta 0 v\beta \rightarrow v\zeta 0(v\beta \in v\gamma)$.

P30. $B\alpha, B\delta, T\alpha v\beta, T\alpha b v\gamma, V\delta v\zeta, v\zeta 0 v\gamma \rightarrow v\zeta 0(v\beta \in v\gamma)$.

P31. $B\alpha, B\delta, T\alpha v\beta, T\alpha b v\gamma, V\delta v\zeta, v\zeta\emptyset v\beta, v\zeta\emptyset v\gamma \rightarrow v\zeta\emptyset(v\beta \in v\gamma)$.

P32. $\mathfrak{S}\alpha, V\beta v\gamma, B\beta, v\gamma 0\alpha \rightarrow v\gamma 0 \sim\alpha$.

P33. $\mathfrak{S}\alpha, V\beta v\gamma, B\beta, v\gamma\emptyset\alpha \rightarrow v\gamma\emptyset \sim\alpha$.

P34. $\mathfrak{S}\alpha, \mathfrak{S}\beta, V\gamma v\delta, B\gamma, v\delta 0\alpha \rightarrow v\delta 0(\alpha \supset \beta)$.

P35. $\mathfrak{S}\alpha, \mathfrak{S}\beta, V\gamma v\delta, B\gamma, v\delta 0\beta \rightarrow v\delta 0(\alpha \supset \beta)$.

P36. $\mathfrak{S}\alpha, \mathfrak{S}\beta, V\gamma v\delta, B\gamma, v\delta\emptyset\alpha, v\delta\emptyset\beta \rightarrow v\delta\emptyset(\alpha \supset \beta)$.

P37. $\mathfrak{S}\alpha, V\beta v\gamma, B\beta \rightarrow v\gamma\emptyset(v\gamma)\alpha$.

P38. $\mathfrak{S}\alpha, V\beta v\gamma, B\beta \rightarrow v\gamma\emptyset v\gamma \ni \alpha$.

P39. $\mathfrak{S}\alpha, V\beta v\gamma, V\delta v\zeta, B\beta, B\delta, v\gamma \neq v\zeta, v\gamma 0\alpha \rightarrow v\gamma 0(v\zeta)\alpha$.

P40. $\mathfrak{S}\alpha, V\beta v\gamma, V\delta v\zeta, B\beta, B\delta, v\gamma \neq v\zeta, v\gamma\emptyset\alpha \rightarrow v\gamma\emptyset(v\zeta)\alpha$.

P41. $\mathfrak{S}\alpha, V\beta v\gamma, V\delta v\zeta, B\beta, B\delta, v\gamma \neq v\zeta, v\gamma 0\alpha \rightarrow v\gamma 0 v\zeta \ni \alpha$.

P42. $\mathfrak{S}\alpha, V\beta v\gamma, V\delta v\zeta, B\beta, B\delta, v\gamma \neq v\zeta, v\gamma\emptyset\alpha \rightarrow v\gamma\emptyset v\zeta \ni \alpha$.

P43. $T\alpha v\beta, V\gamma v\delta, B\alpha, B\gamma, v\delta\emptyset\zeta \rightarrow S(v\beta|v\delta|\zeta) = \zeta$.

P44. $T\alpha v\beta, V\gamma v\delta, B\alpha, B\gamma \rightarrow S(v\beta|v\delta|v\delta) = v\beta$.

P45. $T\alpha v\beta, T\gamma v\delta, T\gamma b v\zeta, V\eta v\theta, B\alpha, B\gamma, B\eta \rightarrow S(v\beta|v\theta|(v\delta \in v\zeta)) = (S(v\beta|v\theta|v\delta) \in S(v\beta|v\theta|v\zeta))$.

P46. $T\alpha v\beta, V\gamma v\delta, \mathfrak{S}\zeta, B\alpha, B\gamma \rightarrow S(v\beta|v\delta|\sim\zeta) = \sim S(v\beta|v\delta|\zeta))$.

P47. $T\alpha v\beta, V\gamma v\delta, \mathfrak{S}\zeta, \mathfrak{S}\eta, B\alpha, B\gamma \rightarrow S(v\beta|v\delta|(\zeta \supset \eta)) = (S(v\beta|v\delta|\zeta) \supset S(v\beta|v\delta|\eta))$.

P48. $T\alpha v\beta$, $V\gamma v\delta$, $\mathfrak{S}\zeta$, $V\eta v\theta$, $B\alpha$, $B\gamma$, $B\eta$, $v\delta \neq v\theta$, $v\beta \neq v\theta \rightarrow S(v\beta|v\delta|(v\theta)\zeta) = (v\theta)S(v\beta|v\delta|\zeta)$.

P49. Data of P48 $\rightarrow S(v\beta|v\delta|v\theta \ni \zeta) = v\theta \ni S(v\beta|v\delta|\zeta)$.

P50. $\alpha = \beta, \vdash\alpha \rightarrow \vdash\beta$.

P51. $V\alpha v\beta$, $B\alpha$, $\mathfrak{S}\gamma$, $\mathfrak{S}\delta$, $v\beta\emptyset\gamma \rightarrow \vdash((v\beta)(\gamma \supset \delta) \supset (\gamma \supset (v\beta)\delta))$.

P52. $V\alpha v\beta$, $T\alpha v\gamma$, $\mathfrak{S}\delta$, $B\alpha \rightarrow \vdash((v\beta)\delta \supset S(v\gamma|v\beta|\delta))$.

P53. $\mathfrak{S}\alpha, \mathfrak{S}\beta \rightarrow \mathfrak{S}(\alpha \wedge \beta)$.

P54. $\mathfrak{S}\alpha, \mathfrak{S}\beta \rightarrow \vdash((\alpha \wedge \beta) \supset \sim(\alpha \supset \sim\beta))$.

P55. $\mathfrak{S}\alpha, \mathfrak{S}\beta \rightarrow \vdash(\sim(\alpha \supset \sim\beta) \supset (\alpha \wedge \beta))$.

P56. $\mathfrak{S}\alpha, \mathfrak{S}\beta \rightarrow \mathfrak{S}(\alpha \equiv \beta)$.

P57. $\mathfrak{S}\alpha, \mathfrak{S}\beta \rightarrow \vdash((\alpha \equiv \beta) \supset ((\alpha \supset \beta) \wedge (\beta \supset \alpha)))$.

P58. $\mathfrak{S}\alpha, \mathfrak{S}\beta \rightarrow \vdash(((\alpha \supset \beta) \wedge (\beta \supset \alpha)) \supset (\alpha \equiv \beta))$.

P59. $\mathfrak{S}\alpha$, $V\beta v\gamma$, $B\beta \rightarrow \mathfrak{S}(\exists v\gamma)\alpha$.

P60. $\mathfrak{S}\alpha$, $V\beta v\gamma$, $B\beta \rightarrow \vdash((\exists v\gamma)\alpha \equiv \sim(v\gamma)\sim\alpha)$.

P61. $V\alpha v\zeta$, $V\alpha bv\xi$, $V\alpha bv\eta$, $V\alpha bbv\theta$, $B\alpha \rightarrow \vdash((v\zeta)((v\zeta \in v\xi) \equiv (v\zeta \in v\eta)) \supset ((v\xi \in v\theta) \supset (v\eta \in v\theta)))$.

P62. $\mathfrak{S}\alpha$, $V\beta v\eta$, $V\beta bv\xi$, $B\beta$, $v\xi\emptyset\alpha \rightarrow \vdash(\exists v\xi)(v\eta)((v\eta \in v\xi) \equiv \alpha)$.

P63. $\mathfrak{S}\alpha$, $B\beta$, $V\beta v\xi$, $V\beta v\eta$, $V\beta bv\zeta$, $v\zeta\emptyset\alpha \rightarrow \vdash((v\eta \in v\xi \ni \alpha) \equiv (\exists v\zeta)((v\eta \in v\zeta) \wedge (v\xi)((v\xi \in v\zeta) \equiv \alpha)))$.

P64. $\mathfrak{S}\alpha$, $B\beta$, $V\beta v\xi$, $V\beta bv\zeta$, $V\beta bbv\eta$, $v\zeta\emptyset\alpha \rightarrow \vdash((v\xi \ni \alpha \in v\eta) \equiv (\exists v\zeta)((v\zeta \in v\eta) \wedge (v\xi)((v\xi \in v\eta) \equiv \alpha)))$.

Interpretation: "$A\alpha$" means "α is a string in a".
"$B\alpha$" means "α is a string in b".
"$V\alpha v\beta$" means "$v\beta$ is a variable of type α".
"$T\alpha v\beta$" means "$v\beta$ is a term of type α, if α is a string in b".
The other signs are interpreted as before.

L_z .

Alphabet: (,), $\in$, $\ni$, $\sim$, $\supset$, a, v, $\vdash$, V, $\mathfrak{S}$, T, A, $=$, 0, $\neq$, $\emptyset$, S, $|$, $\equiv$, $\exists$, $\wedge$.

Axioms:

A1. Aa.

A2. $(= ($.

A3. $) =)$.

A4. $\in \, = \, \in$.

A5. $\ni \, = \, \ni$.

A6. $\sim \, = \, \sim$.

A7. $\supset \, = \, \supset$.

A8. $a = a$.

A9. $v = v$.

A10. $\vdash((vaaa)((vaaa \in va) \equiv (vaaa \in vaa)) \supset ((vaaaaa \in va) \supset ((va \in vaaaa) \supset (vaa \in vaaaa))))$.

Productions:

P1. $A\alpha \rightarrow A\alpha a$.

P2. $A\alpha \rightarrow Vv\alpha$.

P3. $V\alpha \rightarrow T\alpha$.

P4. $T\alpha,\ T\beta \rightarrow \mathfrak{S}(\alpha \in \beta)$.

P5. $\mathfrak{S}\alpha,\ V\beta \rightarrow T\beta \ni \alpha$.

P6–P7. P7–P8 of L_2' .

P8. $\mathfrak{S}\alpha,\ V\beta \rightarrow \mathfrak{S}(\beta)\alpha$.

P9. P10 of L_2' .

P10. $\vdash\alpha,\ V\beta \rightarrow \vdash(\beta)\alpha$.

P11–P21. P12–P22 of L_2' .

P22. $V\alpha,\ T\beta \ni \gamma \rightarrow \alpha \neq \beta \ni \gamma$.

P23. $V\alpha \rightarrow \alpha 0 \alpha$.

P24. $V\alpha,\ V\beta,\ \alpha \neq \beta \rightarrow \alpha\emptyset\beta$.

P25. $T\alpha,\ T\beta,\ V\gamma,\ \gamma 0 \alpha \rightarrow \gamma 0(\alpha \in \beta)$.

P26. $T\alpha,\ T\beta,\ V\gamma,\ \gamma 0 \beta \rightarrow \gamma 0(\alpha \in \beta)$.

P27. $T\alpha,\ T\beta,\ V\gamma,\ \gamma\emptyset\alpha,\ \gamma\emptyset\beta \rightarrow \gamma\emptyset(\alpha \in \beta)$.

P28. $\mathfrak{S}\alpha,\ V\beta,\ \beta 0 \alpha \rightarrow \beta 0 \sim\alpha$.

P29. $\mathfrak{S}\alpha,\ V\beta,\ \beta\emptyset\alpha \rightarrow \beta\emptyset \sim\alpha$.

P30. $\mathfrak{S}\alpha,\ \mathfrak{S}\beta,\ V\gamma,\ \gamma 0 \alpha \rightarrow \gamma 0(\alpha \supset \beta)$.

P31. $\mathfrak{S}\alpha,\ \mathfrak{S}\beta,\ V\gamma,\ \gamma 0 \beta \rightarrow \gamma 0(\alpha \supset \beta)$.

P32. $\mathfrak{S}\alpha,\ \mathfrak{S}\beta,\ V\gamma,\ \gamma\emptyset\alpha,\ \gamma\emptyset\beta \rightarrow \gamma\emptyset(\alpha \supset \beta)$.

P33. $\mathfrak{S}\alpha,\ V\beta \rightarrow \beta\emptyset(\beta)\alpha$.

P34. $\mathfrak{S}\alpha$, $V\beta$, $V\gamma$, $\beta 0\alpha$, $\beta \neq \gamma \rightarrow \beta 0(\gamma)\alpha$.
P35. $\mathfrak{S}\alpha$, $V\beta$, $V\gamma$, $\beta\emptyset\alpha$, $\beta \neq \gamma \rightarrow \beta\emptyset(\gamma)\alpha$.
P36. $\mathfrak{S}\alpha$, $V\beta \rightarrow \beta\emptyset\beta \ni \alpha$.
P37. Data of P34 $\rightarrow \beta 0\gamma \ni \alpha$.
P38. Data of P35 $\rightarrow \beta\emptyset\gamma \ni \alpha$.
P39. $T\alpha$, $V\beta$, $\beta\emptyset\gamma \rightarrow S(\alpha|\beta|\gamma) = \gamma$.
P40. $T\alpha$, $V\beta \rightarrow S(\alpha|\beta|\beta) = \alpha$.
P41. $T\alpha$, $V\beta$, $T\gamma$, $T\delta \rightarrow S(\alpha|\beta|(\gamma \in \delta)) = (S(\alpha|\beta|\gamma) \in S(\alpha|\beta|\delta))$.
P42. $T\alpha$, $V\beta$, $\mathfrak{S}\gamma \rightarrow S(\alpha|\beta|\sim\gamma) = \sim S(\alpha|\beta|\gamma)$.
P43. $T\alpha$, $V\beta$, $\mathfrak{S}\gamma$, $\mathfrak{S}\delta \rightarrow S(\alpha|\beta|(\gamma \supset \delta)) = (S(\alpha|\beta|\gamma) \supset S(\alpha|\beta|\delta))$.
P44. $T\alpha$, $V\beta$, $V\gamma$, $\mathfrak{S}\delta$, $\alpha \neq \gamma$, $\beta \neq \gamma \rightarrow S(\alpha|\beta|(\gamma)\delta) = (\gamma)S(\alpha|\beta|\delta)$.
P45. $T\alpha$, $V\beta$, $V\gamma$, $\mathfrak{S}\delta$, $\alpha \neq \gamma$, $\beta \neq \gamma \rightarrow S(\alpha|\beta|\gamma \ni \delta) = \gamma \ni S(\alpha|\beta|\delta)$.
P46. $\alpha = \beta$, $\vdash\alpha \rightarrow \vdash\beta$.
P47. $\mathfrak{S}\alpha$, $\mathfrak{S}\beta$, $V\gamma$, $\gamma\emptyset\alpha \rightarrow \vdash((\gamma)(\alpha \supset \beta) \supset (\alpha \supset (\gamma)\beta))$.
P48. $T\alpha$, $V\beta$, $\mathfrak{S}\gamma \rightarrow \vdash((\beta)\gamma \supset S(\alpha|\beta|\gamma))$.
P49–P54. P53–P58 of L_2'.
P55. $\mathfrak{S}\alpha$, $V\beta \rightarrow \mathfrak{S}(\exists\beta)\alpha$.
P56. $\mathfrak{S}\alpha$, $V\beta \rightarrow \vdash((\exists\beta)\alpha \equiv \sim(\beta)\sim\alpha)$.
P57. $\mathfrak{S}\alpha$, $V\beta$, $V\gamma$, $V\delta$, $\beta \neq \gamma$, $\beta \neq \delta$, $\gamma \neq \delta$, $\beta\emptyset\alpha \rightarrow \vdash(\exists\beta)(\gamma)((\gamma \in \beta) \equiv ((\gamma \in \delta) \wedge \alpha))$.
P58. $\mathfrak{S}\alpha$, $V\beta$, $V\gamma$, $V\delta$, $\delta\emptyset\alpha$, $\gamma \neq \delta$, $\beta \neq \delta \rightarrow \vdash((\gamma \in \beta \ni \alpha) \equiv (\exists\delta)((\gamma \in \delta) \wedge (\beta)((\beta \in \delta) \equiv \alpha)))$.
P59. $\mathfrak{S}\alpha$, $V\beta$, $V\gamma$, $V\delta$, $\delta\emptyset\alpha$, $\gamma \neq \delta$, $\beta \neq \delta \rightarrow \vdash((\beta \ni \alpha \in \gamma) \equiv (\exists\delta)((\delta \in \gamma) \wedge (\beta)((\beta \in \delta) \equiv \alpha)))$.

Interpretation: "$V\alpha$" means "α is a variable".
"$T\alpha$" means "α is a term".
The rest as before.

In order to put L_3 into canonical form it would be simplest to use Hailperin's formulation [IX]1.

APPENDIX 2 ALGEBRAIC APPROACH TO LANGUAGE. CHURCH'S THEOREM

Just as the notion of a logic of classes or propositions (and presumably of logic, in general) can be framed as a deductive science, so can the concept of language be profitably studied from that point of view. If we consider strings, including the null string, in a given alphabet, and their behavior with respect to the operation of *concatenation* (the formation of $\alpha\beta$ from α and β), then we are led to the study of a special type of algebra. We shall now formulate this notion as a deductive science.

Undefined terms. A class C, a binary operation, denoted by juxtaposition or a dot, and a binary relation $=$.

Postulates.

P1. If a is in C, then $a = a$.
P2. If $a = b$, then $b = a$.
P3. If $a = b$ and $b = c$, then $a = c$.
P4. If $a = b$ and $c = d$ and a, b, c, d are in C, then $ac = bd$.
P5. If a and b are in C, then ab is a uniquely determined element of C.
P6. If a, b, and c are in C, then $(ab)c = a(bc)$.
P7. If a, b, and c are in C, and $ab = ac$, then $b = c$.
P8. If a, b, and c are in C, and $ba = ca$, then $b = c$.
P9. If a, b, c and d are in C, and $ab = cd$, then either there is an x in C such that $ax = c$ or such that $cx = a$.
D1. A *unit* is an element x of C such that $xx = x$.
D2. A *prime* is an element p of C which is not a unit, and such that if $xy = p$, then either x or y is a unit.
P10. There is a unit in C.
P11. If a is in C and is not a unit then there are primes p and q and elements x and y in C such that $a = px = yq$.

We shall call a triple $(C, ., =)$ satisfying these postulates a *script*. A *language* is a script together with certain relations which define a *syntax*. The alphabet is simply the class of primes, which play the role of the primitive signs. In order to characterize the usual types of language it is convenient to introduce some other algebraic notions.

D3. a is a *part* of b (in symbols "$a \subseteq b$") if there are elements x and y in C such that $xay = b$. We say that a is a *proper part* of b (in symbols "$a \subset b$") if $a \subseteq b$ and $a \neq b$.

D4. The *descending chain condition* is said to hold in C if there is no infinite sequence $\{a_n\}$ of elements of C such that $a_{n+1} \subset a_n$ for all n.

It is easy to show that the descending chain condition holds if and only if each element of C has a factorization into a "product" of a finite number of primes. Such a factorization, if possible, is unique, both as to the prime factors and their order. Thus in a script with descending chain condition, every element can be spelled uniquely in terms of the alphabet. For our present purposes, however, it is unnecessary to assume this condition.

We can formulate the notion of a script within L_1. Let "M" denote the string "$f1110$", "C" denote the string "$f10$", and "E" denote the string "$f110$", so that C, E, and M are functions of degree 1, 11, and 111, respectively. We may interpret "Cx" as meaning that x is in C, "Exy" as meaning that $x = y$, and "$Mxyz$" as meaning that $z = xy$. The postulates are now expressed in L_1 as follows: (We supplement the language L_1 by the usual definitions of "$\wedge$", "$\vee$", "$\equiv$", and "$\exists$" and adopt the use of dots for brackets, and denote the strings "$a0$", "$a00$", $\cdots$ by "a_1", "a_2", $\cdots$.)

P1. $(a_1)(Ca_1 \supset Ea_1a_1)$.

P2. $(a_1)(a_2)(Ea_1a_2 \supset Ea_2a_1)$.

P3. $(a_1)(a_2)(a_3)(Ea_1a_2 \wedge Ea_2a_3 \supset Ea_1a_3)$.

P4. $(a_1)(a_2)(a_3)(a_4)(a_5)(a_6)(Ca_1 \wedge Ca_2 \wedge Ca_3 \wedge Ca_4 \wedge Ea_1a_2 \wedge Ea_3a_4 \wedge Ma_1a_3a_5 \wedge Ma_2a_4a_6 \supset Ea_5a_6)$.

P5a. $(a_1)(a_2)(a_3)(Ca_1 \wedge Ca_2 \wedge Ma_1a_2a_3 \supset Ca_3)$.

P5b. $(a_1)(a_2)(\exists a_3)(Ca_1 \wedge Ca_2 \supset Ma_1a_2a_3)$.

P5c. $(a_1)(a_2)(a_3)(a_4)(Ca_1 \wedge Ca_2 \wedge Ma_1a_2a_3 \wedge Ma_1a_2a_4 \supset Ea_3a_4)$.

P6. $(a_1)(a_2)(a_3)(a_4)(a_5)(a_6)(Ca_1 \wedge Ca_2 \wedge Ca_3 \wedge Ma_1a_2a_4 \wedge Ma_4a_3a_5 \wedge Ma_2a_3a_6 \supset Ma_1a_6a_5)$.

P7. $(a_1)(a_2)(a_3)(a_4)(Ca_1 \wedge Ca_2 \wedge Ca_3 \wedge Ma_1a_2a_4 \wedge Ma_1a_3a_4 \supset Ea_2a_3)$.

P8. $(a_1)(a_2)(a_3)(a_4)(Ca_1 \wedge Ca_2 \wedge Ca_3 \wedge Ma_2a_1a_4 \wedge Ma_3a_1a_4 \supset Ea_2a_3)$.

P9. $(a_1)(a_2)(a_3)(a_4)(a_5)(\exists a_6)(Ca_1 \wedge Ca_2 \wedge Ca_3 \wedge Ca_4 \wedge Ma_1a_2a_5 \wedge Ma_3a_4a_5 .\supset. Ca_6 \wedge .Ma_1a_6a_3 \vee Ma_3a_6a_1)$.

We use "U" to denote the string "$f1000$" and "P" to denote the string "$f10000$".

D1. $(a_1)(Ua_1 \equiv Ma_1a_1a_1)$.

D2. $(a_1)(Pa_1 .\equiv. Ca_1 \wedge \sim Ua_1 \wedge .(a_2)(a_3)(Ma_2a_3a_1 \wedge Ca_2 \wedge Ca_3 \supset Ua_2 \vee Ua_3))$.

P10. $(\exists a_1)(Ua_1 \wedge Ca_1)$.

P11. $(a_1)(\exists a_2)(\exists a_3)(\exists a_4)(\exists a_5)(Ca_1 \wedge \sim Ua_1 \supset Pa_2 \wedge Pa_4 \wedge Ca_3 \wedge Ca_5 \wedge Ma_2a_3a_1 \wedge Ma_5a_4a_1)$.

Let "p" denote the sentence "$P1 \wedge P2 \wedge \cdots \wedge P9 \wedge D1 \wedge D2 \wedge P10 \wedge P11$". We shall now adjoin some further components in order to express the language $\mathfrak{B}_2$ (p. 177). Let "A_0", "A_1", $\cdots$, "A_9", and "T" denote the strings "$f10000$", "$f100000$", $\cdots$, "$f1000 \cdots 0$", where the last has 14 0's.

"A_0x" shall mean "x is "1" ",

"A_1x" shall mean "x is "a" ",

...

"A_9x" shall mean "x is "S" ",

"Tx" shall mean "x is a theorem".

B1a. $(a_1)(A_ia_1 \supset Pa_1)$. $(i = 0, \cdots, 9)$.

B1b. $(a_1)(a_2)(A_ia_1 \wedge A_ia_2 \supset Ea_1a_2)$. $(i = 0, \cdots, 9)$.

B1c. $(a_1)(Pa_1 \supset A_0a_1 \vee A_1a_1 \vee \cdots \vee A_9a_1)$.

B1d. $(a_1)(a_2)(A_ia_1 \wedge A_ja_2 \supset \sim Ea_1a_2)$.
$(i, j = 0, \cdots, 9; i \neq j)$.

B2. $(a_1)(A_5a_1 \supset Ta_1)$.

B3. $(a_1)(a_2)(a_3)(A_9a_1 \wedge A_0a_2 \wedge Ma_1a_2a_3 \supset Ta_3)$.

B4. $(a_1)(a_2)(a_3)(A_9a_1 \wedge A_2a_2 \wedge Ma_1a_2a_3 \supset Ta_3)$.

B5. $(a_1)(a_2)(a_3)(a_4)(a_5)(a_6)(a_7)(a_8)(A_5a_1 \wedge Ca_2 \wedge Ma_1a_2a_3 \wedge Ta_3 \wedge A_9a_4 \wedge Ca_5 \wedge Ma_4a_5a_6 \wedge Ta_6 \wedge Ma_4a_2a_7 \wedge Ma_7a_5a_8 \supset Ta_8)$.

B6. $(a_1)(a_2)(a_3)(a_4)(a_5)(A_9a_1 \wedge Ca_2 \wedge Ma_1a_2a_3 \wedge Ta_3 \wedge A_5a_4 \wedge Ma_4a_2a_5 \supset Ta_5)$.

B7. $(a_1) \cdots (a_{19})(A_9a_1 \wedge Ca_2 \wedge Ma_1a_2a_3 \wedge Ta_3 \wedge A_5a_4 \wedge Ca_5 \wedge Ma_4a_5a_6 \wedge Ta_6 \wedge Ca_7 \wedge Ma_1a_7a_5 \wedge Ta_8 \wedge A_6a_9 \wedge Ma_9a_2a_{10} \wedge A_1a_{11} \wedge Ma_{10}a_{11}a_{12} \wedge A_4a_{13} \wedge Ma_{12}a_{13}a_{14} \wedge Ma_{14}a_5a_{15} \wedge A_3a_{16} \wedge Ma_{15}a_{16}a_{17} \wedge Ma_{11}a_7a_{18} \wedge Ma_{18}a_{13}a_{19} \supset Ta_{19})$.

Here B1a–B1d express that the signs 1, $\cdots$, S form the alphabet of the script C. B2–B4 express the axioms of $\mathfrak{B}_2$. B5–B7 express the first three productions of $\mathfrak{B}_2$. In a similar manner we can write down three more sentences, B8, B9, B10, expressing the last three productions of $\mathfrak{B}_2$. Let "q" denote the sentence B1a $\wedge$ B1b $\wedge$ $\cdots$ $\wedge$ B10. The equation $z = a_{i_1} \cdots a_{i_k}$, where for each j, a_{i_j} is in the alphabet of $\mathfrak{B}_2$, can be expressed in L_1 thus:

$$(\exists a_1)(\exists a_2) \cdots (\exists a_{2k-2})(A_{i_1}a_1 \wedge \cdots \wedge A_{i_k}a_k \wedge Ma_1a_2a_{k+1} \wedge Ma_{k+1}a_3a_{k+2} \wedge \cdots \wedge Ma_{2k-2}a_kz),$$

which we shall denote by "$J_\alpha z$", where α is the corresponding string in $\mathfrak{B}_2$. Then the proposition that the string α is a theorem in $\mathfrak{B}_2$ is expressed by the sentence

$$p \wedge q \;.\!\supset\!.\; (a_{2k-1})(J_\alpha a_{2k-1} \supset Ta_{2k-1}),$$

which we can denote by "$\mathfrak{S}(\alpha)$". Then

$$\vdash \mathfrak{S}(\alpha)$$

is provable in L_1 if and only if α is a theorem in $\mathfrak{B}_2$. Since the class of non-theorems in $\mathfrak{B}_2$ is not canonical, it is impossible to give a mechanical procedure for deciding which of the sentences $\mathfrak{S}(\alpha)$ is provable in L_1 . This proves Church's theorem that the decision problem for L_1 is unsolvable by any mechanical procedure.

By the procedure of Kalmar and Suranyi [IV]1, to each sentence $\mathfrak{S}(\alpha)$ we can construct a sentence of the form

$$(1) \qquad (\exists a_1)(a_2)(\exists a_3)(a_4) \cdots (a_n)\mathfrak{S}_1(\alpha),$$

where $\mathfrak{S}_1(\alpha)$ is a Boolean function of sentences of the form "$f110a_ia_j$", and such that $\vdash\mathfrak{S}(\alpha)$ is a theorem of L_1 if and only if the corresponding sentence of the form (1) is provable in L_1. Thus the decision problem of L_1, even for sentences of the comparatively simple form (1), is unsolvable by any mechanical procedure.

BIBLIOGRAPHICAL AND OTHER REMARKS

I1. The first to attempt to formulate logic as a deductive science with a precisely constructed object language was made by Leibniz [1]. His work, though not very successful, was an important stimulus to others. The first systematic and comparatively successful treatment of logic from this point of view is Boole [19]1. Boole used $+$ (p. 3) as a basic operation, but assigned a meaning to $\alpha + \beta$ only if $\alpha \cap \beta = 0$. For treatments of Boolean algebra with $+$ as basic see Stone [499]3, Bernstein [I]68, Newman [VII]123.

The identity $f(\alpha \cup \beta) \cup f(\alpha \cap \beta) = f(\alpha) \cup f(\beta)$ holds in general Post algebras. (See p. 52). The general proof is similar. This answers a question of MacLane [VII]124.

I2. The postulates used here are due to Byrne [XI]85. Others have been given by Huntington [122]1, 3, Sheffer [196]2, Bernstein [239]1, 2, 24, Whiteman [II]91, Hoberman and McKinsey [II]172. The last authors use T1.1.41 as the sole "formal" law. See, however, Church's review [II]172. Church's criticisms can be met, at the expense of some extra primitives and postulates, by means of a very simple device.

The notion of a deductive science was first brought to the attention of a large public by Hilbert in his work on the Foundations of Geometry. (English translation, 1902, Open Court Publishing Co., Ill.). The germ of the idea, as applied to particular sciences goes back at least as far as algebraists like Peacock, Galois, and Hamilton, and geometers like Gergonne, and was further developed in particular applications by many mathematicians such as Pasch, B. O. Pierce, Peano, and Dedekind. An excellent discussion, with emphasis on the corresponding object languages, will be found in Curry [VI]100.

A great deal of nonsense has been written even by otherwise

competent authors, on the relation between Boolean algebra and the Aristotelian logic of classes. The fact is that the latter is consistent and can be formulated as a perfectly good deductive science; see e.g. Curry [I]114. Many writers interpret Aristotle's "all α's are β's" by "$\alpha \subset \beta$" and his "some α's are β's" by "$\alpha \cap \beta \neq 0$" for *arbitrary* elements in a Boolean algebra, and then find that some of Aristotle's valid moods do not hold. This, they say, shows that his logic is fallacious. There is, however, no reason why this particular interpretation *must* be accepted as the *only* one; rather, the consistency of Aristotle's system and the failure of this interpretation show that this one cannot be accepted. An acceptable Boolean interpretation has been given by Smith [259]8, 24. (See also Miller [IV]121.) A simplification of his interpretation would be to consider the class C_1 of all elements of C except 0 and 1, and to interpret Aristotle's "categorical forms" as above. The whole of Aristotle's logic of classes holds for the elements of C_1. It would be easy to set up a deductive science adequate for the theory of classes on the Aristotelian basis. (The logic of Aristotle is, in itself, not quite adequate for the treatment of such operations as $\cap$.) The advantage of Boolean algebra is its simplicity and just its algebraic form. It is interesting to contrast the theory of Quine [I]45 (no null class), that of Zermelo (L_z in III3) (no universal class), and that of Aristotle (neither null class nor universal class). In the von Neumann-Bernays version of Zermelo's system (von Neumann [299]2, 5, Bernays [II]65, Gödel [VI]112) there is, indeed, a universal class, but there is a distinction between classes and sets, and the universal class is not a set. (See Quine [V]163, p. 165.)

I3. An account of finite Boolean algebras, with references, is given by Bernstein [239]25. The structure and representation of Boolean algebras was first investigated by Stone [I]118 and Tarski [285]18, [I]71, independently and from quite different, but equivalent, points of view. In this section Stone's approach dominates, while in II3 we give an account of some of Tarski's ideas. Many of the results of this section have been generalized by Birkhoff and others to lattices.

Theorem 7 was first proved by Stone [I]118. The proof here is adapted from Frink [VII]39.

We should like to call attention to the very interesting problems which arise when one attempts to set up the logic of relations as a deductive science. See Tarski [VI]73, McKinsey [V]85, Everett and Ulam [XI]85. There is also some recent unpublished work of Lyndon.

II1. The observation that the logic of classes and the logic of propositions are different models of the same deductive science is due to Boole.

The first systematic treatment of the logic of propositions by means of truth tables (i.e. tables for the determinations of the truth values of Boolean functions of propositions) was given by Post [280]1. This method was anticipated by Schröder [42]10, among others.

The distinction between the syntax and the object languages mentioned on p. 31 is sometimes overlooked, even by competent authors. This has led, now and then, to flagrant errors. (See p. 50).

II2. The postulate set A1″–A7″ is Łukasiewicz' modification of Frege's set (see Church [X]19).

There is a widespread superstition that formulations of the logic of propositions *must* be of the type A1″–A7″, that systems of the type A1′–A10′ are appropriate, say, for algebras and other deductive sciences, but that the logic of propositions is unique in that such systems are inappropriate for it. The mystical virtues of using an undefined class (or "predicate") $\mathfrak{T}$ rather than an undefined relation E have been dogmatically asserted without any cogent explanation. The rite of writing "⊢" before a sentence instead of "is in $\mathfrak{T}$" after a sentence has also been attended with almost religious awe.

Assumptions of the type of A2″ and A3″ are called rules of closure. Often a distinction is made between assumptions of the type of A4″–A6″ (called "formal laws") and those of the type of A7″ (called rules of inference). The distinction is rather tenuous. In an exact analysis of the object language, as on

p. 158–159, no obvious general difference appears, unless one regards it as a serious logical matter that the premises of one rule state that certain elements belong to the class C and the premises of another state that certain elements belong to the class 𝔗. Sometimes the situation is disguised by putting assumptions of the type of A2″ and A3″ in the form of preliminary remarks and then omitting an explicit statement of the premises in A4″–A6″. Then these rules are called "axiom schemes", with the convention that the letters "*p*", "*q*", and "*r*" may be replaced by names of arbitrary elements of *C*. The procedure may again be given mystical connotations by the ceremony of using German letters as names of names of arbitrary elements of *C*.

The use of dots as brackets was introduced by Peano [71]1, 21. The simplification used here is due to Curry [II]26. See also Turing [VII]146.

The set A1a–A3a, R1a, R2a, is taken from Church [X]19.

The set A1b–A10b, R1b–R17b, is a canonical form of A1a-A3a, R1a, R2a, in the sense of Post [VIII]50. See also IV2. In such a formulation the role of intuition is reduced to the preliminary instructions and the act of recognizing specific strings as being in the forms of the data in a given rule.

A different method of incorporating the operation of substitution in a more general object language has been given by Chwistek and Hetper [III]1. In [III]120, the reviewer confuses the interpretation of substitution in the syntax language with its meaning as determined by the formal properties within the object language. This error is also committed in [II]170.

II3. The methods of this section and most of the material come from Tarski [285]18, [I]71, supplemented by the ideas of Stone. Concepts of consistency and categoricity essentially equivalent to those discussed here were already introduced by Post [280]1. Related concepts may be found in Carnap [IV]82, [VIII]36, [VIII]81.

A number of notions used by Wittgenstein [281]1, 2 and Carnap are very neatly explained by the algebraic approach. For example, the concept of a state-description arises naturally from the device used by Tarski [285]17 and Stone [III]47 for the construction of atoms in a complete distributive Boolean algebra.

The notion of truth value may be regarded as a special case of that of probability, which is, in turn, essentially equivalent to that of measure. (See Kolmogoroff, Grundbegriffe der Wahrscheinlichkeitsrechnung, Berlin, 1933, Cramér, Methods of Mathematical Statistics, Princeton, 1946, Reichenbach [439]4, Koopman [V]153, [VI]34, [VI]163, Kleene and Evans [IV]120.) In most of the precise treatments of probability the concept is defined on an algebra of classes. Since propositions also form a Boolean algebra, it should be easy and desirable to treat directly the notion of the probability of a proposition.

II4. The fundamental papers on many valued logics are Post [280]1, Łukasiewicz [186]4, Łukasiewicz and Tarski [407]1. Further discussion of Post algebras may be found in Webb [532]1, [I]42, [III]52, and Wade [X]108. A set of postulates and a development as a deductive science occurs in [VII]124. A method for carrying this out is also indicated by Post, op. cit.

Rosser and Turquette [X]61 have presented as deductive sciences many valued logics which are not necessarily functionally complete. Other treatments are given by Wajsberg [437]1, Slupecki [II]46, [XI]92, [XI]128, Bochvar [IV]98, [V]119, [XI]129, and Frink [III]117. For a treatment of quantification in many valued logic see Rosser and Turquette [XIII]117.

In connection with the "paradoxes" of material implication, Russell was once challenged to deduce that 2 = 1 from the proposition that Russell is the Pope. His proof was "If I am the Pope, then the Pope and I are one. Since I am not the Pope, then the Pope and I are two. Hence 2 = 1."

More detailed discussion of material implication and deducibility will be found in Lewis [215]9, Lewis and Langford [456]1, Nelson [411]1, 2, Bennett and Baylis [526]1, [IV]94.

The relations between the intension and extension of classes are discussed by Carnap [XIIII]237, Quine [VIII]45, Church [V]162, [V]163, [VII]100, [VIII]45, Russell [VI]29. The older work of Frege [49]5, 8, 10, 16 and Russell [111]9 is of great importance in this connection.

Expositions of intuitionistic points of view are given by Brouwer [155]7, 10, 20, Weyl [192]2, 9, [XI]103, Heyting [385]2, 3, 10, Dresden [308]1, 3, Lusin [403 1/2]. Interesting interpretations are given by Kolmogorov [314]2, Gödel [418]11, 12. The postulates given here are those of Gentzen [442]2. See also the papers of Heyting, Gödel, Glivenko [381]1, 2, McKinsey [IV]155, Wajsberg [III]169. Fundamentally important contributions to intuitionistic logic have recently been made by Kleene [X]109 and Nelson [XII]93. Examples of proofs of a classical theorem by intuitionistic methods can be found in the American Mathematical Monthly, vol. LII, 1945, p. 562, and the papers cited there.

Huntington [II]91 has given a detailed account of Lewis' system, exhibiting clearly its relations to the Boolean logic. Other papers on connected problems are Becker [351]7, Churchman [III]77, Vredenduin [IV]73, Parry [IV]137, McKinsey [V]110, [VI]177, McKinsey and Tarski [XIII]1, Dugundji [V]150. An important interpretation of Lewis' system has been given by McKinsey [X]83. See also Fitch [XIII]38.

Miss Barcan, [XI]1, 115, [XII]12, has made the first attempt to develop modal logic beyond the propositional logic. Another approach (not yet fully worked out) is due to Carnap [IX]33, [XIIII]237. Some of the difficulties of interpreting such systems are also discussed by Quine [XII]43, Smullyan [XII]139, [XIII]31, and the reviews by Church mentioned above.

Note that the version given here of Fitch's model of Lewis' system is essentially the same as taking the system F_1 of III2 and defining PA, for any A in $\mathfrak{F}_1$, as the element B in $\mathfrak{F}_1$ such that

$$\vdash B\alpha \equiv (\exists y)(Ay)$$

for all α in $\mathfrak{J}$. If $\mathfrak{J}$ has a finite number of elements, then this coincides with the construction on p. 61.

For expositions of Smith's ideas see Smith [259]27, [II]43, Churchman [VIII]53. Mrs. H. C. Doob and the author have, in an unpublished paper, presented Smith's system as a deductive science.

The investigations of Tarski and McKinsey are contained in [VI]117, [IV]26, [IX]96, [XI]83, [XIII]1.

The importance of discussing logical questions on the basis of precisely constructed object languages is very aptly emphasized by Church [V]78.

III1. For an excellent and not too technical exposition of Gödel's and Church's theorems see Rosser [IV]53. More detailed accounts of these and related matters appear in Gödel [418]3, 14, Gentzen [I]75, [IV]32, [IX]70, Hilbert-Bernays [507]1, [V]16, Goodstein [IX]33, [XII]123, Rosser [I]87, [II]129.

III2. A similar approach to the functional logic has been given by Notcutt [503]2.

Formulations of the corresponding object languages are to be found in Hilbert-Ackermann [365]1, Hilbert-Bernays, op. cit., Church [X]19.

The infinite list of postulates can be avoided in several ways. For example, by the aid of devices due to Skolem [II]86, Kalmár [II]48, [III]86, [IV]1, one can formulate the first order theory of polyadic functions in terms of the diadic functional logic. Or else one can combine the notions of this section with those of combinatory logic, as has been hinted at on p. 87.

III3. It is possible to give a general theory of logics based on Boolean algebra and of their description by languages of the type discussed in this section. This involves a combination of the methods of I3, II3, and the last chapter of this book. Such a theory gives a rigorous treatment of the name-relation, logical truth, extension, and intension, thus making precise the somewhat heuristic, but suggestive discussions of Carnap [VIII]36, [VIII]81, [XIIII]237. We hope to publish the detailed development in the near future.

A fundamentally important attack on the problem of defining an interpretation of a language has been published by Kemeny [XIII]16. Although his solution cannot be considered completely satisfactory, it is a valuable point of departure for future work.

It would be easy to modify L_1 so that it would contain also names of individual constants, propositional constants, and function constants of all degrees.

The question as to whether it is legitimate to regard classes and propositions, and other "abstract" entities, as existent in some sense, so that signs purporting to be names of these entities really denote "something", goes back at least to Plato, and has been raised again, in a particularly sharp form, by Goodman and Quine [XII]106. One can, however, consider these entities as "existing in space-time" by identifying them, for example, with certain chemical reactions in men's brains. This is not the only possible interpretation, but the existence of at least one such interpretation shows that we can work with these entities without assuming any metaphysics like Platonic idealism.

The masterpiece of Whitehead and Russell [194]1–7 has been the direct or indirect inspiration of most work on mathematical logic in the last 40 years, even when it is openly condemned or not mentioned explicitly. Some of the steps preliminary to that giant undertaking were influenced by the work of Frege and Peano cited above. One can see its influence very clearly by comparing it, chapter for chapter, with such works as Lewis and Langford [456]1, Quine [458]5, [V]163, Church [X]19, Hilbert-Bernays [507]1. The later parts of the first volume and most of the other two volumes have been unjustly neglected; a number of modern developments in algebra and topology are anticipated and their fundamentals treated quite fully. In charity we do not mention by name some illustrious authors who have exhibited their ignorance of the literature by not citing Principia Mathematica.

The devices of Wiener and Kuratowski appeared in Wiener [238]1, Kuratowski [433]0.1. Quine [X]95 gives a more complicated device, which applies only to special systems but has certain technical advantages.

The present formulation of L_2 is due to Tarski [285]13. The version given here is borrowed from Quine [I]45. Another version will be found in Church [X]19. An elegant formulation of the general theory of types without the Wiener-Kuratowski device, has been given by Church [V]56. Other approaches to the theory of types are given by Quine [III]125, Newman [IX]50, Turing [XIII]80.

FIX is not called an "axiom of reducibility" by Quine, but it plays the same role as that axiom in Principia Mathematica. It avoids many of the philosophical objections to the axiom of reducibility as originally formulated.

L_2' is what we call in Chapter IV a conservative extension of L_2. The analogues of Hailperin's theorems show that FX and FXI constitute a definition of "$\ni$".

Other formulations of Zermelo's system have been given by von Neumann [299]2, 5 and Ackermann [III]85.

III4. The basic works on combinatory logic are Schönfinkel [304]1, Curry [396]1, 2, 3, 5, 7, Rosser [546]1. In the latter paper a proof of the equivalence with Church's system of λ-conversion is given. The basic papers on Church's system are Church [359]4, 6, 8, Kleene [497]1, 2. Excellent expositions of these and related matters may be found in Church [VI]171, Curry [VII]49, and Feys [XII]27. The fundamental rules of combinatory logic have been simplified by Curry [VI]41, 54, and Rosser [VII]18. (Curry has noted an error in the latter in Mathematical Reviews.) A forthcoming book by Curry and Feys will undoubtedly be an important contribution to the literature. We note also the interesting papers of Fitch [I]92, [VII]105, [IX]57, [IX]89.

The device of writing the name of an operation before the names of the operands in order to avoid parentheses is due to Łukasiewicz. The analogous syntactical criteria for word formation in languages using parentheses are given by Kleene [497]1, and Church [VI]171.

The system given here is equivalent to Curry's system of combinatory logic with the postulate $BI = I$. (There is a misprint in the statement of Ax.BW (our T21) on p. 521 of Curry [396]2, but the statement, in abbreviated form, on p. 534 is correct.) The equivalence of this system to the system of λ-conversion defined on p. 123–124 is given by Rosser [VII]18. The system without rule V on p. 124 is called by Church λ-K-conversion, and the one with rules I–IV and the restriction in the rule of word formation that "x" occur free in $\mathfrak{A}$ for $\lambda x\mathfrak{A}$ to be a word is called λ-conversion. In the papers of Rosser postulates are also given for these systems. In fact, Rosser gives a general method for setting up postulates for combinatory logics and proving their completeness. Our version is a slight modification of Rosser's.

The theory of positive integers in combinatory logic is due to Church [359]4, 6 and Kleene [497]2.

Curry proved a consistency theorem for combinatory logic in [396]2. This was strengthened and generalized by Church and Rosser [I]74 and Church [359]8. (See also Church [VI]171). Curry [VI]54 has indicated some simplifications in the proof.

The development of the theory of quantification in Church's calculus of λ-δ-conversion is published only in his rather inaccessible lecture notes [II]39.

The paradox of Kleene and Rosser appeared in [545]1. Its underlying meaning is clarified by Church [359]7 and Curry [XI]136. The derivation of Russell's paradox is taken from Curry [VII]115.

Curry's suggested remedies and announced consistency proofs appear in Curry [VII]41, [VIII]52. We hope that the above mentioned book of Curry and Feys will give full details on these questions.

His discussion of functionality and its use as a primitive notion were published in [396]7, [I]65, [VII]49, and [VIII]52.

III5. The fundamental ideas of this section are due to Frege [49]1, 5, 10, 16 and Peano [71]2, 7, 14, 21, 45. These ideas were amplified, extended and otherwise further developed by Russell [111]4, 6 and Whitehead [99]3, 5. A detailed systematic exposition is given by Whitehead and Russell [194]1, 2, 3, from which most of the definitions in this chapter are borrowed. A somewhat non-technical and enjoyably readable account is given by Russell [111]26. We mention also the excellent exposition of Jørgensen [424]1. Modern treatments with many technical improvements have been given by Quine [458]5, [V]163, [XII]56.

The fact that a relation *can* be defined as a class of ordered pairs does not mean, as some dogmatically assert, that a relation *must* be defined as a class of ordered pairs. It is possible to develop these theories independently, as in Principia Mathematica, or to take either as primitive and to define the other. For example, in Bernays [II]65 a mixed procedure is used. In the systems of Curry, Church, and Robinson [II]29, the notion of function (a special kind of relation)is taken as basic. It is also possible to take the general notion of relation as fundamental, and to adapt the ideas of Tarski [VI]73 to construct a logic in which classes are defined in terms of relations. It is very risky, in general, to make dogmatic assertions, especially when they can be disproved. When, as we show so often in this book, there are many different methods for obtaining certain results, it is stupid to insist that there is only *one* correct method.

If a language adequate for elementary number theory remains consistent when a rule of the type of FΩ is adjoined, then the language is said to be ω-consistent. This concept was introduced by Gödel [418]3. He and Tarski [285]13 have given examples of consistent languages which are not ω-consistent. Rosser [II]129 has investigated the completeness of logics which contain rules of the type of $F\Omega$.

III6. Excellent and not very technical expositions of Gödel's and related theorems have been given by Rosser [IV]53 and Skolem, [XIII]169 (in Norwegian). In Gödel's original proof that such languages as L_3 are not categorical ω-consistency was assumed, but Rosser [I]87 showed how that assumption could be eliminated.

Kleene [II]38 has shown how Richard's paradox leads to theorems of the Gödel type. (See also Church [359]7, Curry [XI]136, and Rosser [IV]53.

For Burali-Forti's paradox see Whitehead and Russell [194]1, Rosser [VII]1.

III7. Zermelo's fundamental paper [125]1 is concerned with the proof of (3) from the axiom of choice. Peano [71]4 observed, apparently for the first time, that a distinct assumption was involved, but dismissed the axiom as obviously false. Levi (Rend. del R. Ist. Lomb. 1902) pointed out the need for such an assumption in order to prove that every infinite class has a denumerable subclass.

It should be mentioned that there are several non-equivalent weaker forms of the axiom of choice, some of which have been declared acceptable by scholars who oppose the general assumption. One would think, however, that once we admit such non-constructive principles, we might as well go the whole way. The implication and independence relations between these propositions have been investigated by Fraenkel [269]2, 20, 27, [II]1, Lindenbaum and Mostowski [IV]30, Mostowski [IV]129, [XIII] 45, Szmielew [XIII]224. An excellent summary of propositions equivalent to the axiom of choice and its consequences is given by Sierpinski [VII]35.

Fraenkel's independence proof is given in [269]2. A much stronger consistency proof is published by Gödel in his important [VI]112.

A detailed discussion of Zorn's lemma and related principles is given by Tukey, Convergence and Uniformity in Topology, Princeton, 1940. The original papers on this principle are R. L. Moore, Foundations of Point Set Theory, Am. Math. Soc. Colloquium Publications, 1932, p. 84, Kuratowski, Fundamenta Math., v. 3, 1922, Zorn [IX]56, Teichmüller [VI]65, and Wallace [IX]55.

The theorem of Banach and Tarski appeared in Fund. Math., vol. 6, p. 244. See also Robinson, Fund. Math., vol. 34, p. 246.

IV1. Łukasiewicz apparently devised the notation on which the concept of a simple language is based. For the case of binary connectives Theorem 4.1.1 was proved by Menger [370]5. (It was also obtained independently by Adjukiewicz, according to a note in one of Łukasiewicz' papers.) The general theorem was proved by Schröter [IX]69, and rediscovered by Gerneth [XIII]224. P. Hall has, in recent unpublished work, developed a new approach to the fundamental problems of algebra, which should have important applications to the theory of language. He has also rediscovered Schröter's theorem.

IV2. The basic concepts of this chapter were introduced by Post [VIII]50.

The theorem of Church appeared in [I]73. Simpler proofs were given by Kleene [II]38, Skolem [IX]21, Kalmár [IX]24, Post [X]18.

The general theory of canonical classes has been developed by Post in his profound and beautiful paper [X]18.

While the idea of recursive definitions goes back at least to Peano [71]2, the first study of "recursive" arithmetic, i.e. arithmetic based on recursive definitions alone, is due to Skolem [247]4. A formalization of this theory as an independent science has been given by Curry [VII]42. The notion of recursive function (in a special case) was first brought to the attention of the mathematical public by Gödel [418]3. The general definition is due to Gödel and Herbrand, but was first published and studied by Kleene [II]38. Other important work was done by Peter [466]1–4, Robinson [XIII]113, and especially Skolem [XI]26, and an excellent exposition of many of these results will be found in Hilbert-Bernays [507]1, [V]16.

Precise definitions of the concept of "effectively computable" functions have been given by Church [I]73, Post [I]103, and Turing [II]153. These definitions are easily proved equivalent to the one given here, which is essentially an adaptation of the definition in Kleene [II]38 to the ideas of Post [X]18. It must be said that we have really begun to understand the significance of recursiveness only after this paper of Post. Many of his results were rediscovered by Mostowski [XIII]112, who was unfortunately cut off from journals during the war.

The role of eliminability in the notion of definition was, perhaps, first noted by Russell [111]9, in a different connection. (There is, however, a famous maxim of Pascal!) It is emphasized very clearly by Hilbert-Bernays, op. cit. The importance of conservativeness was brought out by Leśniewski [202]11, 13, [V]83, 84. There is an interesting analogy between our criterion for definition and Church's criterion for meaningfulness. (See Church [VI]171).

IV3. Normal languages were introduced by Post [VIII]50, where Theorem 4.3.1 appears.

The theorems and proofs of this section are taken either directly, or with slight adaptations, from Post [X]18.

A fairly general definition of the adequacy of a language for arithmetic is given by Kleene [II]38, p. 740. It is rather clear how this definition would have to be modified to take care of the language $\mathfrak{B}_2$.

The proofs that L_1 , L_2' , and L_2 can be put into canonical form are given in Appendix 1. The proof that L_1 is adequate for the expression of $\mathfrak{B}_2$ is given in Appendix 2, using some ideas of Markov [XIII]52, 53, 170.

In an important series of papers, Post [X]18, [XII]55, [XII]90, and Markov [XIII]52, 53, 170 have shown that several significant mathematical problems cannot be solved by mechanical methods.

The language $\mathfrak{B}_2$ is a kind of "universal" language since every canonical language has a conservative normal extension and the latter can always be translated into a two-sign alphabet. Its basis is represented by a certain string β such that $B\beta$ is a theorem in $\mathfrak{B}_2$, and its theorems correspond to the true sentences of the form $\beta p\gamma$. Thus $\mathfrak{B}_2$ is already adequate for practically all of mathematics. Every mathematical problem which can be formulated in some canonical language, say L_3 , is equivalent to the question of whether a particular string of the form $\vdash \beta p\gamma$ is a theorem in $\mathfrak{B}_2$. Thus $\mathfrak{B}_2$ is a minimum calculus in the sense of Fitch [IX]89. There is an obvious analogy between the universal language $\mathfrak{B}_2$ and the universal machine of Turing [II]42.

We remark that some authors have used the word "luck" for what we call brains or ingenuity. With that interpretation, the history of science shows that the ones who have the luck are, in general, the ones who deserve it.

Wiener, in his recent book, Cybernetics, Wiley and Hermann, 1948, has given a beautiful mathematical model of the brain.

This is a fundamental advance and must be considered as the first significant breach of the frontier between mathematics and psychology. It seems, however, that his definition must be supplemented in an essential way, since one can probably prove rigorously that a machine can solve any problem which a brain, according to Wiener's model, can solve. We may consider intelligence as the capacity for introspection, the faculty of thinking about one's own methods of reasoning and what they can accomplish. In mathematical terms this means the capacity of using a syntax language for reasoning about an object language. It is in this way that a brain can make use of such rules as FΩ in III5. It seems altogether feasible to incorporate this idea into a mathematical definition of a brain and to prove that a brain can solve some problems which a machine cannot. Theorem 4.3.4 shows that certain problems cannot be solved by machines, i.e. that brains are necessary. A result of the kind just suggested would establish rigorously that brains are useful.

INDEX